STUDY GUIDE

GENERAL CHEMISTRY
Principles and Structure
Fourth Edition

JAMES E. BRADY
St. John's University
New York

JOHN WILEY & SONS
New York Chichester Brisbane Toronto Singapore

ISBN 0 471 80682 X

Printed in the United States of America

10 9 8 7 6 5 4 3

PREFACE

It has been gratifying that so many students have found the basic approach of this Study Guide useful, and for that reason its overall format remains unchanged in this edition. Because students usually study a chapter one section at a time, the Study Guide is divided into sections that exactly parallel those in the textbook. Each begins with a statement of objectives that prepares the student for what is to be presented and outlines what he or she is to accomplish. Students are recommended to read this before reading the section in the text, so they are aware of the theme of the section as they proceed.

Each section in the Study Guide also includes a brief review. Here the key concepts that are developed in the textbook are summarized to bring them into focus. In some instances, especially in the critical early chapters, additional explanations of major topics are presented, and additional worked examples further complement those that appear in the textbook.

Most sections include a brief Self-Test intended to allow students to test their mastery of the subject matter before going on. Many of these Self-Tests have been expanded. They generally provide questions of graded difficulty to permit students to progress from simple problems in the direction of more complex ones. None of the problems in the Study Guide are very difficult, however, since there is an ample number of difficult problems in the text itself (those marked with asterisks). Answers to the Self-Test questions are located at the end of each chapter. These have been rechecked for accuracy.

Each section concludes with a list of New Terms. At the request of students, these are now defined. Students are urged to be sure of their meanings before moving on. (In the previous edition, a glossary was included in the Study Guide; this has now been incorporated in the textbook itself.)

James E. Brady

CONTENTS

BEFORE YOU BEGIN . . .

Before you begin your general chemistry course, read the next several pages. They're designed to tell you how to use this study guide and to give you a few tips on improving your study habits.

How to Use the Study Guide

This book has been written to parallel the topics covered in your text, General Chemistry: Principles and Structure. For each section in the text you'll find a corresponding section in the study guide. In the study guide the sections are divided into Objectives, Review, Self-Test and New Terms. Before you read a section in the text, read the Objectives in the study guide. This will give you a feeling for what to keep an eye on as you read the text. It should help you understand what you must pay attention to.

After you've read a section, return to the study guide and read the Review. This will point out specific ideas that you should be sure you have learned. Sometimes you will be referred back to the text to review specific items there. Sometimes there will be additional explanations of difficult or important concepts, and in some instances there will be additional worked-out sample problems. Work with the review and the text together to be sure you have mastered the material before going on.

In most sections you will also find a short Self-Test to enable you to test your knowledge and problem-solving ability. The answers to all of the self-test questions are located at the end of the chapters in the study guide. Try to answer the questions without having to look at the answers. A space is left after each question so that you can write in your answers and then check them all after you've finished.

An important aspect of learning chemistry is becoming familiar with the language. There are many cases where a lack of understanding can be traced to a lack of familiarity with some of the terms used in a discussion or a problem. A great deal of effort was made in your textbook to avoid using a term without first adequately defining it. Once it has been defined, however, it's used with the assumption that you've learned its meaning. It's important, therefore, to learn new terms as they appear, and for that reason, most of them are set in boldface type in the text. At the end of each section of the study guide there is a list of New Terms with their definitions. Look them over and check to be sure you know their meaning before proceeding on to the next section. You might find it worthwhile to write out their meanings in your chemistry notebook. This will help you review important terms later when you prepare for quizzes or examinations.

Study Habits

You say you want to get an A in chemistry? That's not as impossible as you may have been led to believe, but it is going to take some work. First, you must realize that chemistry is a subject that builds on itself. If you let yourself fall behind in your studies, you will soon discover that you don't understand what's going on in class. This makes studying the new material even more difficult and discouraging, and it is very likely that you may never catch up. The first and most important piece of advice, therefore, is stay up-to-date in the course. They key to accomplishing this is efficient study, so your precious study time isn't wasted. Efficient study requires a regular routine, not hard study one night and nothing the next. At first it is difficult to train yourself, but after a short time your study routine will indeed become a study habit and your chances of success in chemistry, or any other subject, will be greatly improved.

To help you get more out of class, try to devote a few minutes the evening before to reading, in the text, the topics that you will cover the next day. Read the material quickly just to get a feel for what the topics are about. Don't worry if you don't understand everything; the idea at this stage is to be aware of what your teacher will be talking about.

Your lecture instructor and your textbook serve to complement one another; they provide you with two views of the same subject. Try to attend lecture regularly and take notes during class. These should include not only those things your teacher writes on the blackboard, but also the important points he or she makes verbally. If you pay attention carefully to what your teacher is saying in class, your notes will probably be somewhat sketchy. They should, however, give an indication of the major ideas. After class, when you have a few minutes, look over your notes and try to fill in the bare spots while the lecture is still fresh in your mind. This will save you much time later when you finally get around to studying your notes in detail.

In the evening (or whatever part of the day you close yourself off from the rest of the world to really study intensely) review your class notes once again. Use the text and study guide as directed above and really try to learn the material presented to you that day. If you have prepared before class and briefly reviewed the notes afterward, you'll be surprised at how quickly and how well your concentrated study time will progress. You may even find yourself enjoying chemistry!

As you study, continue to fill in the bare spots in your class notes. Write out the definitions of new terms in your notebook. In this way, when it comes time for an exam you should be able to review for it simply from your notes.

At this point you're probably thinking that there isn't enough time to do all the things described above. Actually, the preparation before class and brief review of the notes shortly after class take very little time and will probably save more time than they consume.

Well, you're on your way to an A. There are a few other things that can help you get there. If you possibly can, spend about 30 minutes to an hour at the end of a week to review the week's work. Psychologists have found that a few brief exposures to a subject are more effective at fixing them in the mind than a "cram" session before an exam. The brief time spent at the end of a week can save you hours just before an exam (efficiency!). Try it (you'll like it); it works.

There are some people (you may be one of them) who still have difficulty with chemistry even though they do follow good study habits. Often this is because of weaknesses in their earlier education. If, after following intensive study, you are still fuzzy about something, speak to your teacher about it. Try to clear up these problems before they get worse. Sometimes, by having study sessions with fellow classmates you can help each other over stumbling blocks.

Problem Solving

A stumbling block for many chemistry students is numerical problems. Both the textbook and this study guide have worked-out examples in which the solutions to problems are given in rather great detail. Your instructor will also be showing you how to solve problems. But this is not enough! Learning to solve chemistry problems is like learning to play a musical instrument or drive a car. You only learn by doing. Even if you "understand" how a problem is worked out, you still have to try others yourself to see if you really understand the material sufficiently to solve them. Keep working out problems until you can do them; then you can stop. All the problems in the study guide have answers given. In the text, the answers to selected review exercises are given in Appendix C. Work on these so that you can see whether you are getting them correct.

One of the goals of both the text and this study guide is to teach you how to solve numerical problems. Perhaps this one aspect of chemistry, more than all others, makes you fearful about your fate in the course - you're afraid of the "math." Actually, though, there is very little mathematics involved in solving most of the chemistry problems you will meet. Most of the difficulty comes in trying to interpret a question so that you know what kind of problem you're supposed to solve. In this section we'll go over some basic approaches to solving problems. If you have difficulty with a problem later on, review the ideas presented here and try to apply them. You'll find that they're useful not only in chemistry, but in other areas as well, including problems you encounter in day-to-day living.

"Word problems" always seem to present students with the most difficulty. "What am I supposed to find?" "Where do I begin?" These are the kinds of questions you've probably asked yourself when faced with a word problem. Many people have found the following to be the most effective way of approaching problems of this type.

Step 1. First, preview the problem to get an overview of the question - the "big picture." At this point, don't get bogged down by details. Don't worry about numbers or specific formulas that may be encountered in the question. Read the entire question without trying to analyze it in detail. Remember, at this point you're only interested in getting a view of the whole problem.

Step 2. After you've looked over the entire problem, the next step is to identify what it is you are asked to compute. Look for key phrases such as "Find...." or "How many...." or "What is...." These allow you to know where you're headed in the solution. You might also try to make an educated guess at the magnitude of the answer, although this isn't essential at this point.

Step 3. Now that you know where you're headed, look over the information provided in the question. Don't worry about the numbers yet; simply examine the nature of the preliminary data. Sometimes it's helpful to extract the data from a word problem and tabulate it so that it isn't cluttered with words.

Step 4. Consider next the kinds of calculations that you must perform on the data. Don't worry about the numbers yet. Simply analyze how you must combine the data in the problem to get the answer you want. Be sure you have everything you need. If you use the factor-label method described in Appendix A of the text, you should be able to write simple equality statements such as:

$$1 \text{ ft} = 12 \text{ in.}$$
$$1 \text{ yd} = 3 \text{ ft}$$

Notice that these two statements have the units "ft" in common and provide sufficient information to convert yards to inches, or vice versa. Be sure your equality statements connect all the units so that you have a path from the starting data to the final answer. If a connection between units is missing, you haven't assembled all the relationships that you need to work out the arithmetic. Look for the missing link, either in the data given in the problem or in the knowledge that you're supposed to bring to bear on that kind of problem.

In this step you also must be sure you have any necessary chemical equations or mathematical formulas. Be sure to write them down on paper - don't try to work with them in your head.

Step 5. Well, now you can finally worry about the numbers! At this point all of the necessary information has been compiled and you've decided how you must solve the problem. Now you should go about inserting numbers into formulas or constructing and applying the conversion factors as described in Appendix A of the text. If you've done your preparation in Steps 1 to 4, obtaining an answer in this step should not be difficult.

Step 6. Take a deep breath, you've done it! The problem is solved. As a final point, look at the answer you obtained. Does it seem reasonable? Are the units correct? If so, you're finished.

Time to Begin

Well, it's hoped that the few suggestions presented in this introduction will help you over the hurdles in chemistry. Move on to the course now, and good luck on getting that A!

1 INTRODUCTION

As its name implies, this chapter is meant to introduce you to the study of chemistry. It begins to lay the foundation for the remainder of the course. If you have had chemistry in high school, perhaps much of the material covered in this chapter will be familiar to you. You can test your knowledge by reviewing the list of new terms at the end of each section in Chapter 1 of the Study Guide and by taking the self-tests below. If you've never taken chemistry before, be sure to begin the course properly by gaining a thorough understanding of the topics treated here.

1.1   THE SCIENTIFIC METHOD

Objectives

To understand how science develops through the process of observation, formation of theories, and the design of new experiments that test these theories. You should know the distinction between a law and a theory; between qualitative and quantitative observations.

Review

The scientific method is the procedure that scientists use, either consciously or unconsciously, in their investigation of nature. Data are collected and condensed into laws. Theories are invented in an attempt to explain the laws. The theories suggest new experiments that produce new data, new laws and ultimately new theories. This cycle repeats itself over and over as our understanding of nature grows.

<u>Self-Test</u> (True or False)

1. A law is based on repeated observation.   _____

2. A law is an explanation of a theory.   _____

3. Theories can always be proven to be correct.   _____

4. Laws are often expressed in the form of a mathe-
    matical equation.   _____

5. A hypothesis is a tentative law.   _____

6. Numbers are usually associated with qualitative
    observations.   _____

New Terms

Scientific method
: Observation, explanation, and the testing of the explanation by further observation.

Qualitative observation
: An observation that does not involve numerical measurements.

Quantitative observation
: An observation involving measurements that result in numerical data.

Data
: The information obtained in an experiment.

Law
: A statement of behavior based on the results of many experiments. Laws are often expressed in equation form.

Hypothesis
: A tentative explanation of the results of a series of experiments.

Theory
: A tested explanation of the results obtained in many experiments.

1.2   MEASUREMENT

Objectives

To understand that the extent of our knowledge of the world about us is limited by the precision of the measurements that we make. You should be able to recognize the number of significant digits in a number, be able to express numbers in scientific notation, and be able to express the result of a computation to the proper number of significant figures.

Review

Remember that in counting significant figures in a number, only zeros that are not required for the sole purpose of locating the decimal point should be included. Some examples are:

number	number of significant figures
302	3
0.012	2
2.012	4
0.0120	3

You should be sure you know how to write numbers in scientific notation. Check Appendix A (Page A-2) if you need review on this. Also be sure you have learned how to enter numbers into your calculator in scientific notation. Consult your instructor if necessary.

In performing computations with numbers that come from measurements, remember these rules:

1. Multiplication or division. The answer has the same number of significant figures as the least precise factor in the calculation; for example,

   3.05   x   1.3   =   3.965 = 4.0

(3 sig. figures) (2 sig. figures) (answer rounded to 2 sig.
                                                        figures)

2.   <u>Addition or subtraction</u>. The number of significant figures in the answer is controlled by the quantity having the largest uncertainty; for example,

this quantity⎤   214.3   (implies uncertainty of ± 0.1)
has largest   ⎬→+ 21   (implies uncertainty of ± 1)
uncertainty ⎦   235   (answer has implied uncertainty of ± 1)

Example 1.1

Perform the following arithmetic and express the answer to the proper number of significant figures. All the numbers come from measurement.

$$\frac{(2.500 + 0.10) \times 12.35}{1.468}$$

Solution

We perform the arithmetic within parentheses first.

$$2.500 + 0.10 = 2.60$$

Now our problem is

$$\frac{2.60 \times 12.35}{1.468} = 21.873297$$

Because 2.60 has only three significant figures, the answer is rounded to 21.9.

Exact numbers come from definitions. For instance, 1 mile is exactly 5280 feet, with no uncertainty. Similarly, 1 foot is exactly equal to 12 inches, no more or less. In calculations, these numbers may be assumed to possess any desired number of significant figures.

Example 1.2

A desk was measured to be 34.3 in. along its smallest length. Will it fit through a door that is known to be 2.75 feet wide?

Solution

Let's convert 34.3 in. to feet. We can use the relation-ship between feet and inches to construct a conversion factor (see Appendix A in the text) that enables us to change the units inches into the units feet.

$$34.3 \text{ in} \left(\frac{1 \text{ ft}}{12 \text{ in}} \right) = 2.86 \text{ ft}$$

Notice that we may assume that both the 1 and the 12 have as many significant figures as we wish. Since there are three significant figures in 34.3, the answer can be expressed to three significant figures. Also note that the desk won't fit through the door!

In Example 1.2 we have cancelled units just as on Page 10 of the text. You should spend some time now to study and review the factor-label method. It is described in detail in Appendix A of the text. Although this method may seem foreign to you now, if you learn to apply it, you will find that setting up the arithmetic of chemistry problems is really not very difficult at all.

Self-Test

7. Give the number of significant figures in each of the following.
   (a) 205.3

   (b) 113

   (c) 200.0

   (d) 0.005

   (e) 0.0000700

8. Without using a calculator, express the following in scientific notation:
   (a) 1,400 = _____ (assume three significant figures)

   (b) 275.3 = _____

(c)   0.00307 = _____

(d)   0.00002 = _____

9. Without using a calculator, write the following in ordinary decimal notation:

(a) 3.0×10^3 =   ___3000___

(b) 2.0×10^6 =   _____

(c) 1.5×10^{-5} =   _____

(d) 34×10^{-7} =   _____

(e) 0.025×10^3 =   _____

10. The following are measured quantities. How many significant figures are represented in each?

(a) 3×10^2 cm   _____

(b) 2.00×10^{-3} km   _____

(c) 4.000×10^2 g   _____

11. Express each of the measurements in Question 10 in ordinary decimal notation.

(a) _____   (b) _____   (c) _____

12. Evaluate the following expressions to the proper number of significant figures (assume all numbers represent measured quantities).

(a)   2.43 x 1.875 =   _____

(b)   0.017 x 5.968 =   _____

(c)   1.43 x 2.584 x 0.008 =   _____

(d)   12.5 ÷ 2.8 =   _____

(e)   14.34 ÷ 4.780 =   _____

(f)   5.146 + 0.002 =   _____

(g)   5.146 + 0.02 =   _____

(h)   8.08 + 80.8 =   _____

(i)   14.45 + 7.521 + 100.3 =   _____

(j)   2.92 – 8.4 =   _____

13. Evaluate the following to the proper number of significant figures (assume all numbers represent measured quantities).

(a) $\dfrac{1.43 \times 2.658}{(2.65 + 0.01)}$ _____

(b) $(6.33 \times 8.415) + 8.02$ _____

14. Without using a calculator, evaluate the following:

(a) $(2 \times 10^4) \times (3 \times 10^7) =$ _____

(b) $(4 \times 10^6) \times (2 \times 10^{-3}) =$ _____

(c) $(9 \times 10^{12}) \div (3 \times 10^5) =$ _____

(d) $(18 \times 10^9) \div (6 \times 10^{-4}) =$ _____

(e) $(2.51 \times 10^6) + (3.2 \times 10^5) =$ _____

New Terms

Significant figures
Digits obtained in a measurement such that only the right-most digit in the measured value contains any uncertainty.

Precision
How closely repeated measurements of the same quantity come to each other.

Accuracy
How closely an experimental observation lies to the true value.

Scientific notation
Numbers expressed as the product of a decimal number between 1 and 10 multiplied by 10 raised to an appropriate power, for example, $0.035 = 3.5 \times 10^{-2}$.

Exact numbers
Numbers that come from definitions or a direct count of objects. They contain an infinite number of significant figures because they contain no uncertainty.

Factor-label method
The use of the cancellation of units that are associated with numbers in the solving of numerical problems.

1.3   UNITS OF MEASUREMENT

Objectives

> To learn the basic SI and metric systems of units and to become familiar with conversions from one unit to another within the metric system.

Review

> You should familiarize yourself with the SI base units and their symbols. Those that you will encounter in this course are:

Physical quantity	Unit	Symbol
mass	kilogram	kg
length	meter	m
time	second	s
electric current	ampere	A
temperature	kelvin	K
quantity of substance	mole	mol

Notice, on Page 12 of the text, how area, which is not one of the base units, is derived from the base unit for length. In general, all SI units can be traced back to the base units in Table 1.1.

It is important to learn the eight SI prefixes printed in color in Table 1.2. Remember that when one of these prefixes is used, it modifies the basic unit by the corresponding factor in the first column of the table. For example, nano is a prefix meaning "x 10^{-9}." Therefore, 1 nanogram = 1 x 10^{-9} gram (or, 1 ng = 1 x 10^{-9} g, using the symbols for the prefixes and units). Study Table 1.3 to be sure you understand how to apply the SI prefixes.

Be sure you are well familiar with the units most used for measurements in the laboratory.

Measurement	Unit
length	meter, centimeter, millimeter
mass	gram
volume	liter, milliliter, cubic centimeter

Learn to convert from one unit to another (e.g., liters to milliliters, centimeters to millimeters, etc.). Remember:

1 cm = 10 mm
1 L = 1000 mL = 1000 cm^3 (or cc)

Most conversions that you will encounter between the English system and the metric system can be handled by remembering the following:

length: 1.00 inch = 2.54 cm
weight: 2.20 lb = 1.00 kg
volume: 1.00 quart = 946 mL

These can provide the cross-over between the two systems of units. For example, to convert 4.0 ft into meters, first change ft to in., then in. to cm, and finally cm to meters.

$$4.0 \text{ ft}\left(\frac{12 \text{ in.}}{1 \text{ ft}}\right)\left(\frac{2.54 \text{ cm}}{1 \text{ in.}}\right)\left(\frac{1 \text{ m}}{100 \text{ cm}}\right) = 1.2 \text{ m}$$

Note the cancellation of units. In the Self-Test, practice using units to guide the arithmetic. Remember, if the units don't cancel properly you will obtain the wrong answer, no matter how much you paid for your calculator!

In the lab you will measure temperatures in degrees Celsius. Remember that on this scale water boils at 100°C and freezes at 0°C. Check with your instructor to determine whether you will be expected to convert between °C and °F. If so, the equations are in color on Page 17.

One temperature conversion you will have to make is from °C to K. For most purposes the following equation is satisfactory:

$$K = °C + 273$$

It is often useful to remember that the sizes of the kelvin and the Celsius degree are identical. A temperature <u>change</u> of one Celsius degree is the same as a <u>change</u> of one degree on the Kelvin scale.

<u>Self-Test</u> (fill in the blanks)

15.   Make the following conversions:

(a)   150 m = _____ cm

(b)   27 cm = _____ mm

(c)   1.50 L = _____ mL

(d) 0.002 g =   _____ µg

(e) 100 cm^2 =   _____ mm^2 (If necessary, see Example 1.5 on p 10.)

(f) 253 mL =   _____ L

(g) 0.143 g =   _____ mg

(h) 1 m^3 =   _____ cm^3

(i) 1 km =   _____ cm

(j) 84 mL =   _____ L

16. Make the following conversions:

(a) 12.4 in. =   _____ cm

(b) 18.3 cm =   _____ in.

(c) 1.2 mm =   _____ in.

(d) 18.0 m =   _____ yd

(e) 1.3 ft^2 =   _____ m^2

(f) 1400 cm^3 =   _____ qt (assume three significant figures)

(g) 185 km =   _____ miles

(h) 2.37 lb =   _____ g (to three significant figures)

(i) 84.0 g =   _____ oz

(j) 1.00 ton =   _____ kg

17. Perform the following conversions:

(a) 25°C =   _____ K

(b) -30°C   _____ K

(c) 350 K =   _____ °C

(d) 77 K =   _____ °C

(e) 4.0°C =   _____ °F

(f) 50°F =   _____ °C

New Terms

SI

> Systèm International d'Unités. The International System of Units.

Base units

> The primary reference standards for the SI.

Derived units

> Units for quantities that are derived by appropriately combining the SI base units. For example, the unit for area is m^2, which is derived from the SI base unit for length.

Gram

> 0.001 of the SI base unit of mass, the kilogram. It is about 1/30 of an ounce.

Meter

> The SI base unit for length (approximately 39.37 in.).

Liter

> A unit of volume that is slightly larger than a quart (1 L = 1.057 qt). By definition, 1 L = 1 dm^3.

Temperature

> A quantity that is a measure of the hotness of a body. Temperature determines the direction of spontaneous heat flow (always from hot to cold).

Fahrenheit scale

> A temperature scale defined by the boiling point of water = 212°F and the freezing point of water = 32°F.

Celsius scale

> A temperature scale on which water boils at 100°C and freezes at 0°C.

Kelvin

> The SI unit of temperature, equal in size to the Celsius degree.

1.4   MATTER AND ENERGY

Objectives

To learn the distinction between weight and mass. You should learn the definition of the term, matter. You should also learn the difference between kinetic energy and potential energy, and you should understand how potential energy is related to the distances between objects that attract or repel each other.

Review

Matter has mass and occupies space. The amount of matter in an object is specified by giving its mass. Mass is the object's resistance to a change in velocity and is a measure of the amount of matter in a particular sample; weight is the force with which an object is attracted to the earth. Mass is measured by comparing the weights of objects on a balance. The gram is the common unit of mass used in the laboratory.

Kinetic energy is associated with motion ($KE = \frac{1}{2}mv^2$); potential energy is associated with the distance of separation between particles that either attract or repel one another. Remember that if there is neither an attraction nor repulsion between two objects, there are no potential energy changes when the objects move toward or away from each other. It is very important to understand thoroughly the concepts summarized in Figure 1.9. They will be used frequently later in the book in analyzing energy changes of all sorts. Study this figure and its accompanying explanation carefully!

The law of conservation of energy is also a useful concept that we will use in later chapters. Remember, in any isolated system, whether it be the entire universe or some small portion of it that we happen to be studying in the lab, the total energy remains constant even though other changes (e.g., chemical reactions) may be occurring within it.

The SI unit of energy is the joule (J). The calorie (cal) is another important energy unit. Remember the conversions:

$$1 \text{ cal} = 4.184 \text{ J}$$
$$1 \text{ kcal} = 4.184 \text{ kJ}$$

(Other energy conversion factors are located in a table inside the rear cover of the book.)

Self-Test

18. Perform these conversions:

(a) 254 kJ = _____ kcal

(b) 32.5 kcal = _____ kJ

(c) 375 J = _____ kJ

(d) 495 cal = _____ kJ

(e) 3.4 J = _____ erg

19. Suppose the north pole of one magnet is brought up against the south pole of another. How does the potential energy of the magnets change?

_____

20. Suppose the south pole of one magnet is brought up against the south pole of another. How does the potential energy of the magnets change?

_____

21. How is the joule defined in terms of the SI base units?

_____

22. How is the temperature of the surroundings affected when a system undergoes an exothermic change?

_____

New Terms

Matter
       Anything that has mass and occupies space.

Weight
       The force with which an object having a given mass is attracted to the earth or some other object that it may be near. Often we use the term weight to mean mass, even though they are not the same.

Energy
       The capacity to do work.

Kinetic energy
>   Energy that an object possesses because of its motion.
>   K.E. = $1/2\ mv^2$, where m is the object's mass and v is the
>   object's velocity.

Potential energy
>   Energy that an object possesses because of the attractions
>   or repulsions that it experiences. It is stored energy, and
>   the amount of this stored energy changes when there are
>   changes in the attractions or repulsions.

Endothermic change
>   A change that absorbs energy from the surroundings.

Exothermic change
>   A change that releases energy into the surroundings.

Law of conservation of energy
>   Energy is neither created nor destroyed but, instead, can
>   only be transformed from one kind of energy to another.

Joule
>   The SI unit of energy. $1\ J = 1\ kg\ m^2/s^2$. It is the kinetic
>   energy possessed by an object with a mass of 2 kg moving
>   at a speed of 1 m/s.

Kilojoule
>   1 kJ = 1000 J

Calorie
>   1 cal = 4.184 J (exactly). One calorie will raise the tem-
>   perature of 1 g of water by 1°C.

Kilocalorie
>   1 kcal = 1000 cal

1.5   PROPERTIES OF MATTER

Objectives

>   To distinguish between intensive and extensive properties;
>   you should learn the meaning of density, specific gravity,
>   and specific heat, and how to use them in calculations.
>   You should understand the difference between physical

properties and chemical properties of matter.

Review

Remember, an intensive property is one that is independent of the size of the sample under consideration. For instance, all samples of pure water, regardless of size, freeze at 32°F; freezing point is an example of an intensive property. Volume is an extensive property - one that depends on sample size. The volumes occupied by different samples of water, for example, are different, depending on the amount of water in each sample.

Melting point and volume are also physical properties; that is, they may be specified without referring to another substance. Chemical properties are always described by relating one substance to another.

Density is a very useful intensive property. It relates mass to volume. It can be used to calculate the volume of a given mass of substance, and vice versa. The three quantities, density (d), mass (m), and volume (V) are related by the equation,

$$d = \frac{m}{V} \qquad (1.1)$$

If you know any two quantities in this equation, you can calculate the third.

Example 1.3

What volume would be occupied by 8.53 g of a substance whose density is 2.54 g/mL?

Solution

You can solve this problem either by Equation 1.1 above or by the cancellation of units. Solving Equation 1.1 for the volume,

$$V = \frac{m}{d}$$

and substituting

$$V = \frac{8.53 \text{ g}}{2.54 \text{ g/mL}}$$

gives
$$V = 3.36 \text{ mL}$$

To solve the problem by unit cancellation you must realize that the density is a conversion factor relating mass and volume.

$$d = \frac{2.54 \text{ g}}{1 \text{ mL}} \quad \text{or} \quad \frac{1}{d} = \frac{1 \text{ mL}}{2.54 \text{ g}}$$

Therefore,

$$8.53 \text{ g} \left(\frac{1 \text{ mL}}{2.54 \text{ g}} \right) = 3.36 \text{ mL}$$

Specific gravity is the ratio of the density of a substance to the density of water.

$$\text{sp. gr.} = \frac{d_{\text{substance}}}{d_{\text{water}}}$$

Remember that specific gravity is unitless. It can be used to calculate density in a variety of units if the density of water in those units is known.

$$d_{\text{substance}} = (\text{sp. gr.}) \times d_{\text{water}}$$

Specific heat is the amount of heat energy needed to raise the temperature of one gram of a substance one Celsius degree. Review Example 1.10 on Page 24.

Self-Test

23. Indicate whether each of the following are intensive (I) or extensive (E) properties:

(a) mass _____   (d) boiling point _____

(b) color _____   (e) density _____

(c) volume _____   (f) specific gravity _____

24. Indicate whether each of the following are physical (P) or chemical (C) properties:

(a) nickel chloride is green.   _____

(b) carbon monoxide combines with oxygen to produce carbon dioxide.
_____

(c) grain alcohol boils at 78.5°C.
_____

(d) ozone (produced in smog) is very reactive toward gasoline vapors.
_____

(e) carbohydrates are metabolized in the body to produce carbon dioxide and water.
_____

25. An object with a mass of 14.3 g displaces 5.22 mL of water when placed in a graduated cylinder. Calculate the density of the object.

_____

26. What is the mass of 25.0 mL of an oil if its density is 0.843 g/mL?

_____

27. What volume of alcohol (density = 0.789 g/mL) has a mass of 18.0 g?

_____

28. The density of water is 8.34 lb/gallon, or 62.4 lb/ft^3. The specific gravity of sea water is 1.025. What is the density of sea water in units of

(a) lb/gallon _____

(b) lb/ft^3 _____

(c) g/cm^3 _____

29. A 1.50-g piece of gold absorbed 0.162 cal when its temperature was raised by 3.50°C. Calculate the specific heat of gold in the units

(a) cal/g °C _____

(b) J/g °C _____

30. A sample of water with a mass of 150 g has its temperature raised from 30.0°C to 45.0°C. Calculate the amount of energy absorbed by the water in units of

(a) kcal _____

(b) kJ _____

New Terms

Extensive property
    A property that depends on the size of a sample.

Intensive property
    A property whose value is independent of the size of the
    sample under consideration.

Density
    The ratio of an object's mass to its volume.

Specific gravity
    The ratio of the density of a substance to the density of
    water. It has no units.

Specific heat
    The amount of heat needed to raise the temperature of one
    gram of a substance by one degree Celsius. The units are
    $J g^{-1} °C^{-1}$ or $cal g^{-1} °C^{-1}$.

Physical property
    A property (e.g., color) that can be specified without
    reference to any other chemical substance.

Chemical property
    A statement that describes how a substance reacts chemically
    with another substance.

1.6   ELEMENTS, COMPOUNDS, AND MIXTURES

Objectives

    To understand the distinction between these three classes
    of substances.

Review

    Remember, mixtures may be of variable composition, such
as solutions of salt in water. Compounds and elements are always
of fixed (constant) composition. Chemical reactions alter the
chemical properties of the substances involved; physical changes
do not. Mixtures may be separated by physical means into their
component compounds. Compounds can only be separated into

elements by chemical reaction. In order of decreasing complexity we have: mixtures, compounds, elements. Elements are the simplest substances that are encountered in the chemistry laboratory. Study Figure 1.13 on Page 27 of the text.

Self-Test

31. Why do we classify water as a compound?

_____

32. How many elements are presently known?   _____

33. (a) Sea water is a mixture. What does this statement tell us?

    _____

    _____

    (b) What is the maximum number of phases that can be present in a solution?

    _____

34. When the red powder mercury oxide is heated, oxygen gas and liquid metallic mercury are formed. Is this a chemical or physical change?

    _____

New Terms

Element
    The simplest forms of matter that can exist under conditions normally encountered in a chemistry laboratory. Elements cannot be decomposed into simpler substances by chemical reactions.

Compound
    A substance consisting of two or more elements combined in fixed proportions by mass (and by atoms).

Mixture
    Two or more substances combined in no particular proportions.

Homogeneous mixture
    A mixture that has the same properties and composition throughout. A solution.

Heterogeneous mixture
    A mixture that consists of two or more phases.

Solution
> A homogeneous mixture.

Phase
> Any part of a system that has the same uniform properties and composition.

Phase change
> Transition of a sample from solid to liquid, liquid to gas, solid to gas, or any of the reverse of these changes.

Physical process
> A process or event in which the chemical properties of the substances involved do not change. For example, the chemical properties of sugar and water do not change when they are mixed to form a solution. Formation of a solution is a physical process.

Physical change
> A change that does not alter the chemical properties of the substance involved.

Chemical change
> A chemical reaction. An event that causes the chemical and physical properties of substances to change.

Chemical reaction
> An event that produces changes in the chemical and physical properties of the substances involved.

Distillation
> A means of separating liquid mixtures into their individual components. The method involves boiling the mixture and then condensing the more volatile component, which becomes more concentrated in the vapor.

Chromatography
> A method of separating mixtures that relies on the different tendencies of substances to be adsorbed onto the surfaces of certain solids.

Adsorption
> A process whereby a substance sticks to the surface of some other substance.

Absorption
> The act of being swallowed up, much as a sponge swallows up water.

1.7   CONSERVATION OF MASS AND DEFINITE PROPORTIONS

Objectives

To appreciate the historical significance of these two important chemical laws.

Review

These two basic laws of chemistry govern much of our quantitative thinking about chemical reactions.

Self-Test

35.   State the law of conservation of mass. _____

_____

36.   State the law of definite proportions. _____

_____

37.   Suppose one sample of the compound sodium chloride (table salt) contained 23.0 g of the element sodium and 35.5 g of the element chlorine. In a different sample, how many grams of sodium would be found combined with 71.0 g of chlorine?

_____

New Terms

Law of conservation of mass
   Mass is neither created nor destroyed during a chemical reaction.

Law of definite proportions (Law of definite composition)
   In a pure chemical substance, the elements are always present in the same definite proportions by mass.

1.8   THE ATOMIC THEORY OF DALTON

Objectives

To appreciate the historical significance of the development of the atomic theory. You should understand how Dalton's theory explains the chemical laws in Section 1.7 and how it predicts the law of multiple proportions.

Review

Review the postulates of Dalton's theory and the definition of a molecule. Below is a sample problem dealing with the law of multiple proportions.

Example 1.4

Two compounds are formed between copper and oxygen. In one there is 0.290 g of oxygen combined with 2.30 g of copper; in the other there is 0.466 g of oxygen combined with 1.85 g of copper. Show that these data demonstrate the law of multiple proportions.

Solution

You must calculate the weight of one element (let's say oxygen) combined with the $\underline{same}$ weight of the other element (copper) in the two compounds. The data supplied gives you a chemical equivalence between copper and oxygen in the two compounds.

Compound I   2.30 g copper ~ 0.290 g oxygen
Compound II   1.85 g copper ~ 0.466 g oxygen

The weight of oxygen that would be combined with 1.00 g of copper in each of these compounds is:

Compound I

$$1.00 \ \cancel{\text{g copper}} \left(\frac{0.290 \ \text{g oxygen}}{2.30 \ \cancel{\text{g copper}}} \right) = 0.126 \ \text{g oxygen}$$

Compound II

$$1.00 \text{ g copper} \left(\frac{0.466 \text{ g oxygen}}{1.85 \text{ g copper}} \right) = 0.252 \text{ g oxygen}$$

The law of multiple proportions holds if the ratio of these weights of oxygen is a ratio of small whole numbers. Therefore, you set up the ratio,

$$\frac{0.126 \text{ g oxygen}}{0.252 \text{ g oxygen}} = \frac{1}{2}$$

Self-Test

38. In two compounds, each containing 1.00 g of carbon, there are 0.333 g and 0.167 g of hydrogen, respectively. What is the ratio of weights of hydrogen in the two compounds?

39. Phosphorus and oxygen form two compounds. In compound 1 there are 3.47 g of oxygen combined with 2.68 g of phosphorus; in the other there are 2.82 g of oxygen combined with 3.64 g of phosphorus. What is the ratio of the weights of oxygen that combine with 1.00 g of phosphorus in the two compounds?

40. A 4.00-g sample of cupric bromide was heated, driving off some of the bromine and leaving 2.57 g of cuprous bromide. This cuprous bromide was then decomposed to give bromine and pure copper (1.14 g). Assuming that no copper was lost during these chemical changes, calculate the weights of bromine in the two copper compounds.

    (a) Wt. of bromine in cupric bromide _____

    (b) Wt. of bromine in cuprous bromide _____

    (c) What is the <u>ratio</u> of the weights of bromine
         in the two compounds? _____

New Terms

Molecule

An electrically neutral group of atoms bound tightly enough together that they behave as and can be recognized as a single particle.

Law of multiple proportions
      When two compounds are formed from the same two elements,
      the masses of one element that combine with the same mass
      of the other element are in a ratio of small whole numbers.

Chemical equivalence
      A relationship between the amounts of two chemicals in a
      compound or a reaction. For example, in H_2O,
$$2.0 \text{ g H} \sim 16.0 \text{ g O}$$

1.9   ATOMIC WEIGHTS

Objectives

      To understand how a table of atomic weights can be es-
      tablished by comparing the relative weights of the elements
      that combine to form compounds of known composition.

Review

      The atomic weights that we use are not the weights of
individual atoms, but rather the average relative weights of atoms
compared to one particular isotope of carbon as a standard. The
atomic mass of carbon-12 is <u>exactly</u> 12 amu.

Self-Test

41. If the atomic weight of carbon were assigned a value of
     1.0 amu, what would be the atomic weight of

     (a) magnesium   _____

     (b) titanium   _____

     (c) helium   _____

     (d) molybdenum   _____

New Terms

Atomic mass unit
      A unit of mass equal to one-twelfth of the mass on one atom
      of carbon-12.

Atomic weight
    The relative average atomic mass of the atoms of an element
    expressed in atomic mass units.

Dalton
    1 dalton = 1 atomic mass unit

Isotopes
    Atoms of the same element that has slightly different atomic
    masses.

1.10   SYMBOLS, FORMULAS, AND EQUATIONS

Objectives

    To begin to become familiar with chemical symbols, formu-
    las, and chemical equations.

Review

    Note that in writing the symbol for an element the first
letter is capitalized while the second is not. The subscripts in a
formula denote the relative numbers of each kind of element contained in that compound. For example, $Na_2S_4O_7$ contains two
atoms of sodium (Na), four atoms of sulfur (S) and seven atoms
of oxygen (O). The formula $Ca(NO_3)_2$ shows one calcium atom,
two nitrogen atoms and six oxygen atoms. The formulas for hy-
drates show the numbers of water molecules trapped in crystals.
For example, $CrCl_3 \cdot 6H_2O$ contains six water molecules for each
$CrCl_3$.

    Chemical equations are used to indicate what occurs during
a chemical reaction. An equation is balanced if there is the same
number of atoms of each element on the reactant side (left side)
of the arrow as there are on the product side (right side). The
symbols s = solid, ℓ = liquid, g = gas, and aq = aqueous
solution are used sometimes to indicate the phases of reactants
and products.

Self-Test

    Refer to the alphabetical list of elements on the inside
front cover of the textbook to check your answers to Questions

42 and 43.

42. Write the symbol for each of the following elements.

(a) sodium _____   (f) copper _____

(b) sulfur _____   (g) chlorine _____

(c) oxygen _____   (h) potassium _____

(d) hydrogen_____   (i) magnesium _____

(e) iron _____   (j) carbon _____

43. What are the names of the following elements?

(a) Sn _____   (f) Cr _____

(b) Br _____   (g) Ag _____

(c) Al _____   (h) As _____

(d) Ca _____   (i) I _____

(e) P _____   (j) He _____

44. How many atoms of each kind are represented in the formulas below?

(a) KCl _____

(b) NO_2 _____

(c) N_2O_4 _____

(d) $(NH_4)_3PO_4$ _____

(e) $Al_2(SO_4)_3$ _____

(f) $KAl(SO_4)_2 \cdot 12H_2O$ _____

45. Which of the equations below are not balanced?

(a) $CaO + H_2O \longrightarrow Ca(OH)_2$ _____

(b) $CaCl_2 + H_2SO_4 \longrightarrow HCl + CaSO_4$ _____

(c) $Br_2 + 2NaOH \longrightarrow NaOBr + NaBr + H_2O$ _____

(d) $SO_2 + O_2 \longrightarrow SO_3$ _____

(e) $Al_2(SO_4)_3 + 2BaCl_2 \longrightarrow 2BaSO_4 + AlCl_3$ _____

New Terms

Chemical symbol
  The symbol that represents the name of an element. In formulas and equations it is used to represent an atom of the element.

Chemical formula
  A shorthand way of representing the composition of a substance using chemical symbols.

Chemical equation
  A representation using chemical formulas of the changes that occur during a chemical reaction. It is a sort of before-and-after view of the chemical system.

Hydrate
  A crystal that contains molecules of water in a fixed proportion relative to other substances present.

Reactants
  The substances that react during a chemical reaction. The Substances that appear on the left side of a chemical equation.

Products
  The substances that are formed in a chemical reaction. The substances that appear on the right side of a chemical equation.

Coefficients
  Numbers that precede chemical formulas in a chemical equation.

Balanced equation
  A chemical equation that has the same number of atoms of each kind, and the same net electrical charge on both sides of the arrow.

Answers to Self-Test Questions

1. true   2. false   3. false   4. true   5. false   6. false   7.(a) 4
(b) 3   (c) 4   (d) 1   (e) 3   8.(a) 1.40×10^3 (b) 2.753×10^2
(c) 3.07×10^{-3} (d) 2×10^{-5} 9.(b) 2,000,000   (c) 0.000015
(d) 0.0000034   (e) 25   10.(a) 1   (b) 3   (c) 4   11.(a) 300 cm
(b) 0.00200 km   (c) 400.0 g   12.(a) 4.56   (b) 0.10   (c) 0.03
(d) 4.5   (e) 3.000   (f) 5.148   (g) 5.17   (h) 88.9   (i) 122.3
(j) -5.4   13.(a) 1.43   (b) 61.3   14.(a) 6×10^{11} (b) 8×10^3
(c) 3×10^7 (d) 3×10^{13} (e) 2.83×10^6 15.(a) 15,000 cm
(b) 270 mm   (c) 1500 mL   (d) 2000 μg   (e) 10,000 mm^2
(f) 0.253 L   (g) 143 mg   (h) 1×10^6 cm^3 (i) 1×10^5 cm
(j) 0.084 L   16.(a) 31.5 cm   (b) 7.20 in.   (c) 0.047 in.
(d) 19.7 yd   (e) 0.12 m^2 (f) 1.48 qt   (g) 115 mi   (h) 1080 g
(i) 2.96 oz   (j) 909 kg   17.(a) 298 K   (b) 243 K   (c) 77°C
(d) -196°C   (e) 39.2°F   (f) 10°C   18.(a) 60.7 kcal   (b) 136 kJ
(c) 0.375 kJ   (d) 2.07 kJ   (e) 3.4×10^7 erg   19. The P.E.
decreases.   20. The P.E. increases.   21. 1 J = 1 kg m^2/s^2
22. The temperature rises.   23.(a) E   (b) I   (c) E   (d) I
(e) I   (f) I   24.(a) P   (b) C   (c) P   (d) C   (e) C
25. 2.74 g/mL   26. 21.1 g   27. 22.8 mL   28.(a) 8.55 lb/gallon
(b) 64.0 lb/ft^3 (c) 1.025 g/cm^3 29.(a) 0.0309 cal/g°C
(b) 0.129 J/g°C   30.(a) 2.25 kcal   (b) 9.41 kJ   31. All samples
contain hydrogen and oxygen in the same proportions.   32. 108
33.(a) It can be of variable composition and can be separated
into its components by physical processes.   (b) 1   34. chemical
change   35. Mass is neither created nor destroyed during a
chemical reaction.   36. Any sample of a given compound always
contains the same elements in the same proportions by mass.
37. 46.0 g sodium   38. 2-to-1   39. (g of O in I)/(g of O in II) =
1.29/0.775 = 1.66 = 5/3   40.(a) 2.86 g   (b) 1.43 g   (c) 2-to-1
41.(a) 2.0   (b) 4.0   (c) 0.33   (d) 8.0   42.(a) Na   (b) S
(c) O   (d) H   (e) Fe   (f) Cu   (g) Cl   (h) K   (i) Mg   (j) C
43.(a) tin   (b) bromine   (c) aluminum   (d) calcium
(e) phosphorus   (f) chromium   (g) silver   (h) arsenic
(i) iodine   (j) helium   44.(a) K, 1; Cl, 1   (b) N, 1; O, 2
(c) N, 2; O, 4   (d) N, 3; H, 12; P, 1; O, 4   (e) Al, 2; S, 3;
O, 12   (f) K, 1; Al, 1; S, 2; O, 20; H, 24   45.(a) balanced
(b) unbalanced   (c) balanced   (d) unbalanced   (e) unbalanced

2 STOICHIOMETRY: CHEMICAL ARITHMETIC

This chapter deals with calculations involving quantities of chemical substances, either combined together in a compound or reacting with one another in a chemical reaction. It is very important that you thoroughly understand the concepts developed here because they are necessary in future discussions in other chapters. This is particularly true of the mole concept discussed in Section 2.2. Most students who develop difficulties with chemistry have not really acquired a genuine "feel" for the mole. Therefore, this is really a very important chapter for you to master well. A little extra time spent here may save you a lot of grief later.

2.1 CHEMICAL SYMBOLS AND FORMULAS - ANOTHER LOOK

Objectives

To learn how to read chemical symbols and formulas in the context of chemical problems.

Review

Many students have difficulty understanding the true meaning of an expression such as "15.0 g H_2O." You can, of course, read this as "15.0 grams of water." In chemical problems, however, you must realize that it means "15.0 g of H_2O molecules" even though the word molecules is omitted.

35

New Terms

2.2   THE MOLE

Objectives

To learn to think of the mole as the "chemist's dozen."
You should develop the ability to translate between ratios
of numbers of atoms and molecules that combine and ratios
of numbers of moles of these substances that combine.

Review

Like the dozen (12) or the gross (144), the mole represents a fixed number of objects. These can be atoms, molecules,
or anything we wish to consider. One mole of an element or compound contains a large enough quantity of atoms or molecules to
be worked with in a laboratory. The most important feature of
the mole concept, however, is that in a chemical reaction (for instance, the formation of a compound from its elements) the RATIO
in which atoms combine is exactly the same as the RATIO in
which moles of atoms combine. When $CrCl_3$ is formed, three Cl
atoms are required for each Cr atom. In laboratory-sized quantities, three moles of Cl atoms are required for each one mole of
Cr atoms.

A concept that many students find difficult to grasp is
that we obtain one mole of $CrCl_3$ from three moles of Cl and one
mole of Cr.

$$1 \text{ mol Cr} + 3 \text{ mol Cl} \longrightarrow 1 \text{ mol of } CrCl_3$$

If this troubles you, consider this analogy:

$$1 \text{ doz frames} + 3 \text{ doz wheels} \longrightarrow 1 \text{ doz tricycles}$$

Both equations involve precisely the same kind of reasoning.

Self-Test

1. How many moles of F must react with one mole of S to form:

   (a) SF$_2$ _____   (b) SF$_4$ _____   (c) SF$_6$ _____

2. What mole ratio of carbon to hydrogen is found in propane, C$_3$H$_8$?

   _____

3. How many moles of Cl must react with 0.50 mol of P to form PCl$_5$?

   _____

4. How many moles of oxygen atoms are there in 1.20 mol of Fe$_3$O$_4$?

   _____

5. How many moles of iron (Fe) atoms are there in 1.20 mol of Fe$_3$O$_4$?

   _____

6. Oxygen occurs as molecules of O$_2$. How many moles of O atoms are there in 1.40 mol of O$_2$?

   _____

7. How many moles of O$_2$ would be needed to prepare 5.0 mol of N$_2$O$_4$?

   _____

8. How many moles of Cl$_2$ would be needed to prepare 3.0 mol of PCl$_5$?

   _____

New Terms

Mole (mol)
   The SI unit for quantity of substance. 6.022×10^{23} things. An amount of a substance whose mass in grams is numerically equal to the substance's formula weight.

2.3   MEASURING MOLES OF ATOMS

Objectives

   To learn how to use the table of atomic weights to convert between moles and grams of an element. You should also learn to use Avogadro's number where appropriate.

Review

You should learn to convert between laboratory units of grams and chemical units of moles. Remember that one mole of any element has a mass in grams numerically equal to the element's atomic weight. For example, the atomic weight of fluorine is 19.0; 1 mol of F = 19.0 g F.

Avogadro's number (6.022×10^{23} things = 1 mol things) is used only when you must translate sizes (mass, volume, length, etc.) between the large world that we work in (with balances, graduated cylinders, and rulers) to the submicroscopic world of individual atoms and molecules.

Self-Test

9. What is the weight in grams (to three significant figures) of one mole of:

    (a) carbon atoms _____

    (b) potassium atoms _____

    (c) calcium atoms _____

    (d) nickel atoms _____

    (e) bromine atoms _____

10. How many moles of atoms are there in:

    (a) 32.1 g S _____

    (b) 46.0 g Na _____

    (c) 12.5 g Ag _____

    (d) 3.50 g N _____

11. How many grams does each of the following weigh?

    (a) 1.00 mol Mn _____

    (b) 0.455 mol Al _____

    (c) 1.34 mol Ba _____

    (d) 2.14 mol Zn _____

12. How many grams of each element are present in 0.250 mol of Al_2O_3?

    _____

13. How many grams of O are needed to react with 0.300 mol S to form SO_3?

_____

14. How many grams of Cl must react with 10.0 g C to form C_2Cl_4?

_____

15. How many <u>atoms</u> are there in:

(a) 1.00 mol S

_____

(b) 1.00 mol O_2

_____

(c) 0.341 mol P

_____

(d) 1.85 mol Cl_2

_____

16. What is the weight in grams of 1 atom of Si? _____

17. What is the weight in grams of 1 molecule of O_2?

_____

18. How many atoms are there in 5.27 g of Na? _____

19. How many grams do 1.40×10^{21} atoms of silver weigh?

_____

New Terms

Avogadro's number

The number of things (atoms, molecules, or whatever) in one mole. 6.022×10^{23} things = 1 mole of things.

2.4   MEASURING MOLES OF COMPOUNDS: MOLECULAR WEIGHTS AND FORMULA WEIGHTS

Objectives

To learn to calculate molecular weights and formula weights.

Review

The molecular weight, or formula weight, is simply the sum of all of the atomic weights of all of the atoms in the formula of a compound. For example, the molecular weight of glucose, $C_6H_{12}O_6$, is:

$$\begin{array}{lrr}
\text{carbon} & 6 \times 12.01 = & 72.06 \\
\text{hydrogen} & 12 \times 1.008 = & 12.10 \\
\text{oxygen} & 6 \times 16.00 = & 96.00 \\
\hline
\text{formula weight of } C_6H_{12}O_6 = & 180.16
\end{array}$$

Remember that 1 mol of a compound = 6.022×10^{23} formula units and has a weight in grams numerically equal to the formula weight. Thus, 1 mol $C_6H_{12}O_6$ = 180.16 g.

The term formula weight is always used for compounds that are ionic. (At this time, however, you are not expected to know which compounds are ionic.) For molecular compounds, either molecular weight or formula weight is acceptable.

Self-Test

20. Calculate the formula weights of:

    (a) KNO_3 (potassium nitrate)   _____

    (b) $CO(NH_2)_2$ (urea)   _____

    (c) $C_9H_8O_4$ (aspirin)   _____

    (d) CCl_4 (carbon tetrachloride)   _____

    (e) NaOCl (bleach)   _____

21. How many moles are there in each of the following?

    (a) 14.3 g of $NaC_{18}H_{35}O_2$ (soap)   _____

    (b) 142 g of $(CH_3)_2CO$ (acetone - used in nail polish remover)

        _____

22. What is the weight in grams of:

    (a) 1.00 mol of $CaCl_2$ (calcium chloride)   _____

    (b) 0.0250 mol of $CHCl_3$ (chloroform)   _____

    (c) 3.46 mol of Fe_2O_3 (rust)   _____

    (d) 14.2 mol of $KAl(SO_4)_2 \cdot 12H_2O$ (alum)   _____

New Terms

Molecular weight
    The sum of the atomic weights of all the atoms in a molecule.

Formula weight
    The sum of the atomic weights of all the atoms in one formula unit.

Formula unit
    The collection of atoms specified by the chemical formula. For example, a formula unit of $CaCl_2$ contains one calcium atom and two chlorine atoms.

Electron
    A subatomic particle that is found outside the nucleus of an atom. It carries one unit of negative charge.

Ion
    An electrically charged atom or group of atoms.

Ionic compound
    A compound composed of positive and negative ions.

2.5   PERCENTAGE COMPOSITION

Objectives

    To calculate the percentage composition of a compound from its formula. You should be able to calculate the weight of a given element in a compound given its formula.

Review

    The weight percent of an element in a compound is calculated by dividing the weight of that element in the compound by the molecular weight and then multiplying by 100. The percent Cl in CCl_4 is:

$$\% \text{ Cl in CCl}_4 = \left(\frac{\text{wt Cl in CCl}_4}{\text{M.W. CCl}_4}\right) \times 100$$

$$= \left(\frac{(4)(35.5)}{12.0 + (4)(35.5)}\right) \times 100$$

$$= \left(\frac{142}{154}\right) \times 100$$

$$= 92.2\%$$

To calculate the weight of a given element in a sample of a compound you multiply the weight of the sample by the fraction of the compound that is the desired element. For example, to calculate the weight of chlorine in 85.0 g of CCl_4 we multiply the weight of the sample (85.0 g) by the fraction of CCl_4 that is chlorine.

$$\text{fraction that is Cl} = \frac{\text{wt Cl in CCl}_4}{\text{M.W. CCl}_4}$$

$$= \frac{142 \text{ g Cl}}{154 \text{ g CCl}_4}$$

The weight of Cl in the sample, then, is

$$\text{wt Cl in sample} = 85.0 \text{ g CCl}_4 \left(\frac{142 \text{ g Cl}}{154 \text{ g CCl}_4}\right) = 78.4 \text{ g Cl}$$

Self-Test

23. Calculate the percentage compositions of each of the following:
    (a) $NaNO_3$ _____
    (b) $Ca(HCO_3)_2$ _____
    (c) $NiCl_2$ _____

24. Calculate the weight of Ag in 22.0 g of AgCl. _____

25. Calculate the weight of sulfate, SO_4, in 12.3 g of $BaSO_4$.

    _____

26. In a chemical analysis a 3.14-g sample known to contain $CuSO_4$ and $CuCl_2$ was dissolved in water and treated with $Ba(NO_3)_2$. Solid $BaSO_4$ was formed, which was filtered from

the solution, dried and weighed.   The $BaSO_4$ weighed
2.58 g.

(a)   What weight of SO_4 was in the $BaSO_4$?   _____

(b)   What was the weight percent SO_4 in the original sample?

_____

New Terms

Percentage composition
   The percentages by weight of the elements in a compound.

2.6   CHEMICAL FORMULAS

Objectives

To learn what types of information different kinds of
chemical formulas provide.

Review

The simplest formula only gives the relative numbers of
atoms in the compound.   The molecular formula also gives the
actual number of each element in a molecule of the compound.
The structural formula describes the way in which the atoms in a
molecule are linked together.

structural formula
for cyclohexane

C_6H_{12}

molecular formula
for cyclohexane

CH_2

empirical formula
for cyclohexane

27.   What is the molecular formula and the empirical formula for
      the compound whose structural formula is

```
      H  H
      |  |        (ethylene glycol - antifreeze)
   H—C—C—H
      |  |
   H—O  O—H
```

Empirical formula
      The simple whole-number ratio of atoms in a compound.

Simplest formula
      See *Empirical formula.*

Molecular formula
      A chemical formula that specifies the number of atoms of
      each kind that are present in a molecule of the substance.

Structural formula
      A chemical formula that shows which atoms are bonded to-
      gether in a molecule.

2.7   EMPIRICAL FORMULAS

Objectives

      To calculate empirical formulas from percentage composition,
      or from the weights of elements combined together in a
      compound.

Review

      An empirical formula gives the atom ratio of elements in the
compound; it also gives the ratio of the number of moles of each
element.   The atom ratio and mole ratio, of course, have to be
identical, based on the definition of the mole.   If you are unsure
about this, you should review the mole concept.

To determine an empirical formula you must calculate the number of moles of each element combined in a given sample of the compound, as shown in Example 2.12 in the text. The ratio of moles gives the atom ratio. The following is another example:

Example 2.1

A 4.00-g sample of a copper-bromine compound was decomposed, yielding 1.14 g of pure copper. What is the empirical formula of the compound?

Solution

First, we must have the weight of Br combined with the Cu. This can be obtained in this case as the difference between the total weight of compound and the weight of copper in the compound.

$$4.00 \text{ g} - 1.14 \text{ g} = 2.86 \text{ g Br}$$

Thus, there were 2.86 g of Br combined with 1.14 g of Cu in the original sample.

Next, we calculate the number of moles of Cu and Br.

$$1.14 \text{ g Cu}\left(\frac{1 \text{ mol Cu}}{63.5 \text{ g Cu}}\right) = 0.0179 \text{ mol Cu}$$

$$2.86 \text{ g Br}\left(\frac{1 \text{ mol Br}}{79.9 \text{ g Br}}\right) = 0.0358 \text{ mol Br}$$

Finally, set up the formula as $Cu_{0.0179}Br_{0.0358}$ and divide through by the smallest subscript to obtain whole numbers.

$$Cu_{\frac{0.0179}{0.0179}} Br_{\frac{0.0358}{0.0179}} = CuBr_2$$

(The data for this question came from Question 40 in Chapter 1 of the Study Guide.)

When an analysis is presented in the form of percentage composition by weight, you can write the percentages of each element as weights by assuming 100 g of compound in the sample. Thus 100 g of a compound that is 50% sulfur and 50% oxygen would contain 50 g S and 50 g O.

Examples 2.14 and 2.15 illustrate typical examples of chemical analyses applied to the determination of empirical formulas. Notice that by accurately measuring the weight of CO_2 obtained by combustion of the carbon-containing compound, the weight of carbon in the original sample can be calculated. Similarly, by measuring the weight of H_2O formed in the reaction, the weight of hydrogen in the original sample can be calculated. These calculations assume that <u>all</u> the carbon in the sample is captured in the CO_2 and that all the hydrogen is captured in the H_2O. You should be able to apply similar reasoning to Self-Test Question 29 below.

Self-Test

28. Determine the empirical formulas for the following compounds.

    (a) 7.86 g potassium, 7.14 g chlorine   _____

    (b) 37.9 g Na, 17.1 g P   _____

    (c) 31.9% K, 29.0% Cl, 39.2% O   _____

    (d) 69.6% Mn, 30.4% O   _____

29. A 1.500-g sample containing only nickel and bromine was dissolved in water and allowed to react with silver nitrate. The reaction gave 2.578 g of AgBr.

    (a) How many grams of Br were in the AgBr?   _____

    (b) How many grams of Br were in the nickel-bromine compound?   _____

    (c) How many grams of Ni were in the nickel-bromine compound?   _____

    (d) What is the empirical formula of the nickel-bromine compound?   _____

New Terms

2.8   MOLECULAR FORMULAS

Objectives

To determine the molecular formula of a substance, given its empirical formula and its molecular weight.

Review

The molecular formula is always a multiple of the empirical formula. For example, benzene has a molecular formula of C_6H_6; its empirical formula is CH. The empirical formula occurs "six times" in the molecular formula; that is, the subscripts in the empirical formula of benzene must each be multiplied by six to give the molecular formula. The molecular weight of C_6H_6 is 78; the formula weight of CH is 13. The number of times the empirical formula is repeated is obtained by dividing the molecular weight by the empirical formula weight.

$$\frac{78}{13} = 6$$

Self-Test

30. Determine molecular formulas for the following compounds.

empirical formula	molecular weight	molecular formula
CH_2O	180	_____
CH_3	30	_____
P_2O_3	220	_____
HgCl	472.2	_____

New Terms

2.9   BALANCING CHEMICAL EQUATIONS

Objectives

To write balanced chemical equations.

Review

You should keep in mind the advice that writing a balanced equation is a two-step process. First, write the unbalanced equation with correct formulas for each of the reactants and products. Then, balance the equation. At this point in the course you must balance the equation by inspection; that is, you juggle the coefficients (the numbers preceding the formulas) to make the number of atoms of each kind the same on both sides of the equation. Remember, once you have written correct formulas for the reactants and products you do not change the subscripts in the formulas. Also remember that a properly balanced equation has the smallest whole number set of coefficients. Practice balancing the equations in the Self-Test below.

Self-Test

31.   Balance the following equations.

(a) $CuSO_4 + Al \longrightarrow Al_2(SO_4)_3 + Cu$

_____

(b) $KClO_3 \longrightarrow KCl + O_2$ _____

(c) $CO(NH_2)_2 + H_2O \longrightarrow CO_2 + NH_3$

_____

(d) $PCl_5 + H_2O \longrightarrow H_3PO_4 + HCl$

_____

(e) $N_2O_5 + H_2O \longrightarrow HNO_3$

_____

(f) $C_6H_{14} + O_2 \longrightarrow CO_2 + H_2O$

_____

(g) $C_2H_5SH + O_2 \longrightarrow CO_2 + H_2O + SO_2$

New Terms

2.10   CALCULATIONS BASED ON CHEMICAL EQUATIONS

Objectives

To use a balanced chemical equation to perform calculations involving quantities of substances entering into chemical reaction.

Review

A chemical equation such as

$$2H_2 + O_2 \longrightarrow 2H_2O$$

tells us about reacting molecules. It gives information about what happens on a submicroscopic, atomic scale. The mole concept allows us to expand this information up to laboratory-sized quantities. Whatever ratio exists between atoms or molecules of reactants and products, the same ratio exists between moles of reactants and products. For example, the equation above tells us that for every two molecules of H_2 that react, one molecule of O_2 will also react. Scaling this to laboratory-sized quantities, we can say that for every two moles of H_2 that react, one mole of O_2 will react.

In dealing with chemical equations, chemists do their thinking in terms of moles. Let's use the equation above as an example. If a chemist knew that he had 0.40 mol of O_2, he would look at the equation and realize immediately that he would require 0.80 mol of H_2. The equation tells him that twice as many moles of H_2 must react as O_2. Similarly, he would also conclude that he would be able to obtain 0.80 mol of H_2O. The equation tells him that however moles of H_2 are consumed, the same number of moles of H_2O will be formed.

The purpose of doing these calculations is to be able to measure proper quantities of reactants (or products) in the laboratory. However, we cannot measure moles directly; instead we can only measure mass (i.e., grams). We therefore must translate back and forth between laboratory units (grams) and chemical units (moles).

There is a number of worked-out examples presented in the text illustrating the types of calculations you might encounter. Let's look at another.

Example 2.2

How many grams of H_2 are needed to react completely with 4.75 g of Fe_2O_3 according to the equation,

$$Fe_2O_3 + 3H_2 \longrightarrow 2Fe + 3H_2O$$

Solution

All reasoning involving H_2 and Fe_2O_3 must take place in chemical units. The solution of this problem can be diagrammed as shown below.

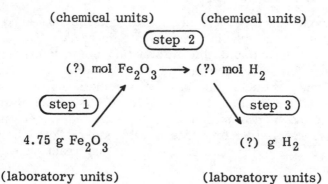

(chemical units)   (chemical units)

(step 2)

(?) mol Fe_2O_3 ⟶ (?) mol H_2

(step 1)   (step 3)

4.75 g Fe_2O_3 (?) g H_2

(laboratory units)   (laboratory units)

Steps 1 and 3 involve translation between grams and moles (this was covered in Sections 2.3 and 2.4).

Step 2 requires the use of the coefficients in the balanced equation.

Step 1 - Translation

$$4.75 \text{ g Fe}_2O_3 \times \left(\frac{1 \text{ mol Fe}_2O_3}{159.6 \text{ g Fe}_2O_3}\right) = 0.0298 \text{ mol Fe}_2O_3$$

Step 2 - The coefficients in the equation allow us to establish the chemical equivalency,

$$1 \text{ mol Fe}_2O_3 \sim 3 \text{ mol H}_2$$

This is then used to construct a conversion factor so that we can calculate the number of moles of H_2 required.

$$0.0298 \text{ mol Fe}_2O_3 \times \left(\frac{3 \text{ mol H}_2}{1 \text{ mol Fe}_2O_3}\right) = 0.0894 \text{ mol H}_2$$

Step 3 - Translation

$$0.0894 \text{ mol H}_2 \times \left(\frac{2.02 \text{ g H}_2}{1 \text{ mol H}_2}\right) = 0.180 \text{ g H}_2$$

Self-Test

32. The reaction between hydrazine, N_2H_4, and hydrogen peroxide, H_2O_2, has been used to power rockets.
$$N_2H_4 + 2H_2O_2 \longrightarrow N_2 + 4H_2O$$

(a) How many moles of N_2H_4 are required to react with 8.00 mol of H_2O_2?

_____

(b) How many moles of N_2 will be formed from 8.00 mol of H_2O_2?

_____

(c) How many moles of water will be formed from 8.00 mol of H_2O_2?

_____

(d) How many grams of water will be formed when 3.00 mol of N_2H_4 react?

_____

(e) How many moles of N_2 will be formed when 500 g of H_2O_2 react?

_____

(f)   How many grams of H_2O_2 are required to react with 1000 g of N_2H_4?

_____

New Terms

2.11   LIMITING REACTANT CALCULATIONS

Objectives

To calculate the amount of products formed when arbitrary amounts of reactants are mixed.

Review

These calculations deal with chemical reactions in which substances are simply mixed together without prior regard for maintaining the proper mole ratios between reactants. In these cases, all reactants usually are not consumed completely; one or more of them remains in excess. The amount of product formed in these situations is controlled by the reactant that is completely used up (the limiting reactant), since once it is gone no more product is able to form. In this type of problem, you first determine the limiting reactant and then base your calculation of the amount of product formed on the amount of the limiting reactant available.

_____

Example 2.3

Zinc and oxygen combine to produce zinc oxide according to the equation,

$$2Zn + O_2 \longrightarrow 2ZnO$$

How much ZnO will be formed if 14.3 g of Zn are mixed with 3.72 g of O_2?

Solution

First, we calculate how many moles of Zn and O_2 are in the mixture.

$$14.3 \text{ g Zn} \times \left(\frac{1 \text{ mol Zn}}{65.4 \text{ g Zn}} \right) = 0.219 \text{ mol Zn}$$

$$3.72 \text{ g O}_2 \times \left(\frac{1 \text{ mol O}_2}{32.0 \text{ g O}_2} \right) = 0.116 \text{ mol O}_2$$

Next, we determine the limiting reactant by choosing one reactant and calculating the amount of the other required to give complete reaction. It doesn't matter which we choose, so let's work with the Zn.

$$0.290 \text{ mol Zn} \times \left(\frac{1 \text{ mol O}_2}{2 \text{ mol Zn}} \right) \sim 0.109 \text{ mol O}_2 \text{ required to react with all the Zn}$$

Notice that we have more O_2 than we need. This means that some O_2 will be left over and all of the Zn will react; zinc is the limiting reactant.

Once the limiting reactant is established we use it to calculate the amount of product that will be formed.

$$0.219 \text{ mol Zn} \times \left(\frac{1 \text{ mol ZnO}}{1 \text{ mol Zn}} \right) \times \left(\frac{81.4 \text{ g ZnO}}{1 \text{ mol ZnO}} \right) \sim 17.8 \text{ g ZnO}$$

The weight of ZnO formed is 17.8 g.

Self-Test

33. Based on the equation,
$$N_2H_4 + 2H_2O_2 \longrightarrow N_2 + 4H_2O$$

(a) How many moles of H_2O will be formed if 2.50 mol N_2H_4 are allowed to react with 4.80 mol H_2O_2?

(b) How many moles of N_2 will be formed if 600 g of N_2H_4 are mixed with 1200 g of H_2O_2?

(c) How many grams of H_2O will be produced if 83.5 g of N_2H_4 are mixed with 180 g of H_2O_2?

(d) In the mixture described in Part (c), how many grams of which reactant will be left over after the reaction has stopped?

_____

New Terms

Limiting reactant
   The reactant that is completely consumed in a chemical reaction. It is the reactant that limits the amount of products that can be formed in a particular experiment.

2.12   THEORETICAL YIELD AND PERCENTAGE YIELD

Objectives

   To see that not all reactions produce the theoretical maximum amount of product. You should learn the definitions of theoretical yield and percentage yield.

Review

   The theoretical yield is the amount of product that would be produced if the reactants were to combine to the maximum extent possible. We calculate the theoretical yield from the limiting reactant by following the procedure described in the last section. In simpler cases we calculate it as the maximum amount of product formed from a particular reactant as in Section 2.10. The percentage yield is calculated as shown on Page 63 of the text.

Self-Test

34. Glucose, $C_6H_{12}O_6$, is converted to ethyl alcohol, C_2H_5OH, and CO_2 by fermentation,

$$C_6H_{12}O_6 \longrightarrow 2C_2H_5OH + 2CO_2$$

Starting with 200 g of glucose,

(a) What is the theoretical yield of ethyl alcohol? _____

(b) If 97.3 g of C_2H_5OH was obtained, what was the percentage yield?

_____

New Terms

Actual yield

The actual amount of products obtained in a particular chemical reaction when the experiment is performed in the laboratory.

Theoretical yield

The maximum amount of product(s) that could be formed from a particular mixture of reactants.

Percentage yield

$$\% \text{ yield} = \frac{\text{actual yield}}{\text{theoretical yield}} \times 100$$

2.13   MOLAR CONCENTRATION

Objectives

To learn the meanings of some terms used in discussing solutions. You should learn the meaning of molar concentration and how to use it as a conversion factor relating amounts of solute and volumes of solutions.

Review

In general, in a solution the solvent is the substance whose physical state doesn't change. If two liquids are mixed, the one present in largest amount is the solvent. When one of the components of a solution is water, then H_2O is taken to be the solvent. All other components of the solution are solutes. Learn the definitions of concentrated and dilute.

The proportions of solute and solvent are specified by giving the solution's concentration. Molar concentration, or molarity, is a convenient concentration unit for dispensing measured amounts of solute dissolved in a solution. Remember the units of molarity:

$$\text{molarity} = \frac{\text{moles of solute}}{\text{liter of solution}}$$

To calculate molarity we need to know the number of moles of the solute and the total volume of the <u>solution</u> in which it is dissolved.

If you know the molarity of a solution you can use it to calculate the number of moles of solute in a specified volume of the solution, or to calculate the volume of solution needed to contain a specified number of moles of solute. Think of molarity as a conversion factor. You should be able to translate a label such as 2.50 M H_2SO_4 into these factors.

$$\frac{2.50 \text{ mol } H_2SO_4}{1 \text{ L solution}} \qquad \frac{1 \text{ L solution}}{2.50 \text{ mol } H_2SO_4}$$

Examples 2.26 and 2.27 illustrate how to use this kind of conversion factor.

In preparing a solution of a known molarity, remember that the solvent (water, for example) is added to the solute until the desired final volume of solution is reached. To prepare 500 mL of solution, for example, we do <u>not</u> just add 500 mL of water to the solute. First the solute is dissolved in a small amount of water, and then more water is added until the final volume is 500 mL. Study Figure 2.2.

<u>Self-Test</u>

35. What is the molarity of the following solutions?

   (a) 0.350 mol $NaHCO_3$ in 0.400 L of solution _____

   (b) 0.250 mol KCl in 200 mL of solution _____

   (c) 15.6 g of $MgCl_2$ in 300 mL of solution _____

   (d) 1.85 g of $AgNO_3$ in 75.0 mL of solution _____

36. How many moles of $CaCl_2$ are in

   (a) 1.15 L of 0.840 M $CaCl_2$ solution? _____

   (b) 325 mL of 0.150 M $CaCl_2$ solution? _____

37. What volume (in milliliters) of 3.00 M NH_3 solution contains

   (a) 1.35 mol of NH_3? _____

   (b) 21.4 g of NH_3? _____

38. How many grams of KNO_3 are needed to prepare 750 mL of 0.200 M KNO_3 solution?

_____

New Terms

Solute
A substance dissolved in a solvent.

Solvent
Generally the substance in a solution that is present in largest amount. If one substance is a liquid, it is normally considered to be the solvent. When water is present, it is taken to be the solvent.

Concentrated
A large proportion of solute to solvent in a solution.

Dilute
Very little solute dissolved in a solution. A low ratio of solute to solvent.

Concentration
A quantitative statement of the proportion of solute to solvent, or of solute to the total amount of solution.

Molar concentration
A ratio of moles of solute to liters of solution. It is the number of moles of solute per liter of solution.

Molarity
See *Molar concentration*.

Molar
A term that describes the molar concentration of a solute in a solution. It means *moles of solute per liter of solution*.

2.14   PREPARING SOLUTIONS BY DILUTION

Objectives
To learn how to perform calculations that are necessary when dilute solutions are to be prepared from concentrated solutions.

Review

Because the amount of solute in a solution remains constant as the solution is diluted, we can use the simple relationship (in blue on Page 68)

$$M_iV_i = M_fV_f$$

Study Examples 2.29, 2.30 and 2.31. It is important to remember that when diluting concentrated laboratory reagents with water, always add the concentrated reagent to the water!

Self-Test

39. If 300 mL of H_2O is added to 600 mL of 0.960 M H_2SO_4, what is the final molarity of the H_2SO_4?   _____

40. How many mL of 3.00 M HCl must be used to prepare 500 mL of 0.100 M HCl?   _____

41. How much water must be added to 50.0 mL of 1.00 M NaOH to produce 0.100 M NaOH?   _____

New Terms

Reagent
    A term often used to refer to common chemicals that are stocked in the laboratory.

2.15 THE STOICHIOMETRY OF REACTIONS IN SOLUTIONS

Objectives

To learn how to use molarity in dealing with the stoichiometry of reactions that take place in solutions.

Review

In most ways, reactions in solution are no different than those that occur elsewhere. The stoichiometric relationships among reactants and products are determined by the mole ratios specified by the coefficients in the balanced chemical equation.

Therefore, the first step in working problems involving reactions in solution is writing a properly balanced equation.

The principal way "solution stoichiometry" problems differ from others that you've done so far is that amounts of reactants or products can be specified as volumes of solutions of known concentrations. In this case, molarity is used as a conversion factor to calculate moles. If an answer to a problem is to be a volume of solution, then molarity is used as a conversion factor to convert moles to volume. Study Examples 2.32 to 2.34 carefully; then work the problems in the Self-Test below.

Self-Test

42. Consider the following reaction that takes place in solution:

$$CaCl_2(aq) + 2AgNO_3(aq) \longrightarrow Ca(NO_3)_2(aq) + 2AgCl(s)$$

Suppose that we began with 200 mL of a 0.200 M solution of $CaCl_2$.

(a) How many moles of $CaCl_2$ are in this solution?

_____

(b) How many moles of $AgNO_3$ would be required to react completely with this amount of $CaCl_2$?

_____

(c) How many milliliters of 0.500 M $AgNO_3$ solution would be needed to contain this number of moles of $AgNO_3$?

_____

43. Consider the reaction described in Question 42 above. Suppose that 200 mL of 0.150 M $CaCl_2$ solution were mixed with 180 mL of 0.220 M $AgNO_3$ solution.

(a) How many moles of $CaCl_2$ are in the first solution?

_____

(b) How many moles of $AgNO_3$ are in the second solution?

_____

(c) When the solutions are mixed, which is the limiting reactant?

_____

(d) How many moles of AgCl are formed in the reaction?

_____

(e) How many moles of the reactant in excess are left over after the reaction has stopped?

_____

(f) What is the molar concentration of the excess reactant in the reaction mixture after the reaction has stopped?

_____

New Terms

Precipitate
    A solid that forms in a solution, often as the result of a chemical reaction.

Answers to Self-Test Questions

1.(a) 2 (b) 4 (c) 6 2. 3 mol C to 8 mol H 3. 2.5 mol Cl
4. 4.80 mol O 5. 3.60 mol Fe 6. 2.80 mol O 7. 10 mol O_2
8. 7.5 mol Cl_2 9.(a) 12.0 g (b) 39.1 g (c) 40.1 g (d) 58.7 g
(e) 79.9 g 10.(a) 1.00 mol S (b) 2.00 mol Na (c) 0.116 mol Ag
(d) 0.250 mol N 11.(a) 54.9 g Mn (b) 12.3 g Al (c) 184 g Ba
(d) 140 g Zn 12. 13.5 g Al and 12.0 g O 13. 14.4 g O
14. 59.1 g Cl 15.(a) 6.02×10^{23} (b) 1.20×10^{24}
(c) 2.05×10^{23} (d) 2.23×10^{24} 16. 4.67×10^{-23} g
17. 5.32×10^{-23} g 18. 1.38×10^{23} atoms 19. 0.251 g Ag
20.(a) 101.1 (b) 60.0 (c) 180 (d) 154 (e) 74.5
21.(a) 0.0467 mol (b) 2.45 mol 22.(a) 111 g (b) 2.98 g
(c) 553 g (d) 6.74×10^3 g 23.(a) 27.1% Na, 16.5% N, 56.5% O
(b) 24.7% Ca, 1.24% H, 14.8% C, 59.2% O (c) 45.3% Ni, 54.7% Cl
24. 16.6 g Ag 25. 5.06 g SO_4 26.(a) 1.06 g SO_4
(b) (1.06 g/3.14 g) x 100% = 33.8% 27. molecular formula =
$C_2H_6O_2$, empirical formula = CH_3O 28.(a) KCl (b) Na_3P
(c) $KClO_3$ (d) Mn_2O_3 29.(a) 1.097 (b) 1.097 (c) 0.403
(d) $NiBr_2$ 30. $C_6H_{12}O_6$, C_2H_6, P_4O_6, Hg_2Cl_2
31.(a) $3CuSO_4 + 2Al \longrightarrow Al_2(SO_4)_3 + 3Cu$
    (b) $2KClO_3 \longrightarrow 2KCl + 3O_2$
    (c) $CO(NH_2)_2 + H_2O \longrightarrow CO_2 + 2NH_3$

31.(d) $PCl_5 + 4H_2O \longrightarrow H_3PO_4 + 5HCl$

(e) $N_2O_5 + H_2O \longrightarrow 2HNO_3$

(f) $2C_6H_{14} + 19O_2 \longrightarrow 12CO_2 + 14H_2O$

(g) $2C_2H_5SH + 9O_2 \longrightarrow 4CO_2 + 6H_2O + 2SO_2$

32.(a) 4.00 mol N_2H_4 (b) 4.00 mol N_2 (c) 16.0 mol H_2O

(d) 216 g H_2O (e) 7.35 mol N_2 (f) 2.12 x 10^3 g H_2O_2

33.(a) 9.60 mol H_2O (H_2O_2 is limiting)

(b) 17.6 mol N_2 (H_2O_2 is limiting)

(c) 188 g H_2O (N_2H_4 is limiting)

(d) 3 g H_2O_2 left over

34.(a) 102 g   (b) 95.4%

35.(a) 0.875 M   (b) 1.25 M   (c) 0.546 M   (d) 0.145 M

36.(a) 0.966 mol   (b) 0.0488 mol

37.(a) 450 mL   (b) 420 mL

38. 15.2 g

39. 0.640 M

40. 16.7 mL

41. 450 mL (<u>total</u> volume must be 500 mL)

42.(a) 0.0400 mol $CaCl_2$ (b) 0.0800 mol $AgNO_3$ (c) 160 mL

43.(a) 0.0300 mol $CaCl_2$ (b) 0.0396 mol $AgNO_3$

(c) $AgNO_3$ is limiting   (d) 0.0396 mol $AgCl$

(e) 0.0102 mol $CaCl_2$ left over

(f) (0.0102 mol)/(0.380 L) = 0.0268 M $CaCl_2$

3 THE PERIODIC TABLE AND THE MAKEUP OF ATOMS

Chemistry is an experimental science, which means that progress is accomplished by observing facts, searching out correlations among them, and seeking explanations. In this chapter we begin by describing some of the properties of the elements, facts that should become part of your chemical knowledge. The discovery of properties such as these led Dmitri Mendeleev to formulate the first periodic table of the elements. In its modern form, the periodic table is one of the most powerful tools in chemistry, because there are very few properties that cannot be correlated with an element's position in the table.

Among the properties related to an element's position in the periodic table is the internal structure of its atoms. Atoms are not indivisible particles as Dalton had originally envisioned them. Instead, they are composed of simpler particles - neutrons and positively charged protons in the nucleus of the atom, and negatively charged electrons surrounding the nucleus. In this chapter we also follow the historical developments that led to the presently accepted theory about atomic structure.

3.1   SOME PROPERTIES OF THE ELEMENTS

Objectives

To learn some of the properties of metals, nonmetals, and metalloids.

Review

The elements can be divided into three broad categories: metals, nonmetals and metalloids. Metals have a characteristic luster (metallic luster), and are generally malleable and ductile. They are good conductors of both heat and electricity. The chemical reactivity of metals covers a broad range. Sodium is an example of a metal that is extremely reactive - it reacts rapidly with water and oxygen in the air. Gold is typical of very unreactive metals. Chromium and iron are hard; lead and gold are soft. The metal with the highest melting point is tungsten; the lowest melting metal is mercury, which is a liquid at room temperature.

Nonmetals lack the luster of metals. They are not malleable and ductile and are poor conductors of heat and electricity. A number of the elemental nonmetals occur in nature as diatomic molecules. Those that are gases are H_2, O_2, N_2, F_2, and Cl_2. Bromine (Br_2) is a dark red liquid; iodine (I_2) is a dark purple solid. Nonmetals also cover extremes of reactivity. The least reactive nonmetal is helium; the most reactive is fluorine.

Metalloids have properties that lie between those of metals and nonmetals. Their most significant property is their semiconductivity. Many metalloids have something of a metallic luster, but their solids have a distinctly crystalline appearance.

Self-Test

1. Name two metals that are colored. _____

2. Write the formulas of the diatomic nonmetals.

    _____

3. Which metal has the highest melting point? _____

4. What are the two forms of elemental carbon?

    _____

New Terms

Metals

   Elements that are lustrous, have high thermal and electrical conductivity, and that are generally ductile and malleable.

Nonmetals
  Elements that are poor conductors of heat and electricity
  and lack the other properties normally associated with metals.

Metalloids
  Elements with properties that lie between those of metals
  and nonmetals.

Malleability
  A metal's ability to be hammered or rolled into thin sheets.

Ductility
  A metal's ability to be stretched (drawn) into wire.

Diatomic molecule
  A molecule that is composed of only two atoms, for example,
  H_2 and HCl.

3.2   THE FIRST PERIODIC TABLE

Objectives
  To learn about the origin of the periodic table.

Review
  Mendeleev, a Russian chemist and teacher, observed that
when the elements are arranged in order of increasing atomic
weight, similar properties recur at regular intervals. He broke
up the string of elements and stacked them so elements with
similar properties are found in the same column (group). Because he insisted on arranging the elements so those in a given
column had similar properties, he was forced to leave blanks at
various points in his table. He realized these corresponded to
undiscovered elements, and he was even able to predict some of
the properties of these new elements, which aided in their later
discovery.

5. In Mendeleev's table, iodine (I) and tellurium (Te) are not
    in order of increasing atomic weight. What was the main
    reason that Mendeleev reversed the atomic-weight order
    for these elements?

    _____

    _____

New Terms

Group
    A column of elements in the periodic table.

3.3   ATOMIC NUMBERS AND
THE MODERN PERIODIC TABLE

Objectives

To learn the basis of the modern periodic table. You
should learn the nomenclature that applies to the periodic
table and the names applied to different sets of elements.

Review

As noted in the introduction to this Chapter, the periodic
table is one of the most useful devices available to a chemist or
a chemistry student. Your ability to use the periodic table ef-
fectively depends on how well you understand its construction.

Remember that the elements are arranged in horizontal
rows (called periods) in order of increasing atomic number. The
periodic law states that when arranged in this manner the elements exhibit a periodic recurrence of properties. An important
feature of the periodic table, both Mendeleev's and the modern
version, is that elements with similar chemical properties are
arranged in vertical columns called groups.

This section introduces you to a set of nomenclature associated with the periodic table. The important terms are given
in boldface type in the text and are listed on the following page.
You should learn the meanings of these terms. After you've
studied them, take the following self-test.

Self-Test

6. Which of the following are representative elements: Cl, Fe, Cu, Na, Xe?

    _____

7. Which of these are transition elements: As, Hg, Ti, Ge, Sr?

    _____

8. Which of these is a halogen: S, Sn, Br, Na, Mg?

    _____

9. Which of these is a noble gas: O, Ne, Na, Ca, Zn?

    _____

10. Which of these is an alkali metal: Li, B, C, F, Xe?

    _____

11. Which of these is an alkaline earth metal: Zn, C, Cs, Ba, Kr?

    _____

12. Which of these are inner transition elements: Np, Ru, F, As, Pm?

    _____

13. Which of these is a metalloid: S, Ni, Ge, He, Mg?

    _____

14. Which are metals: Sr, Si, Cr, Ce, U, P?

    _____

15. Which are nonmetals: S, Ga, P, Pr, I, K?

    _____

16. What is the more common term that means "family of elements"?

    _____

New Terms

Atomic number
    An element's position number in the periodic table.

Periodic law
    When the elements are arranged in order of increasing atomic number, there is a periodic recurrence of properties.

Group
   A column of elements in the periodic table.

Period
   A horizontal row of elements in the periodic table.

Representative element
   An element in one of the A-groups of the periodic table.

Transition elements
   Elements located between Groups IIA and IIIA in the
   periodic table.

Inner transition element
   A member of the two long rows of elements below the main
   body of the periodic table.   (Z = 58 -71 and 90 - 103)

Lanthanide elements
   Elements with atomic numbers 58 through 71.

Actinide elements
   Elements 90 through 103.

Rare earth metals
   The lanthanide elements (atomic numbers 58 - 71).

Alkali metals
   The elements of Group IA, except hydrogen.

Alkali earth metals
   The elements in Group IIA.

Halogens
   The elements of Group VIIA.

Noble gases
   The elements in Group 0 of the periodic table: helium,
   neon, argon, krypton, zenon, and radon.

3.4   THE STRUCTURES OF ATOMS

Objectives

   To learn about some of the experiments that led to the
   discovery that atoms are not indivisible particles.

Review

Faraday's experiments on electrolysis showed that chemical reactions could be caused by electricity, which suggested that matter is electrical.

Gas discharge tube experiments led to the discovery of cathode rays, which were later shown to be composed of electrons. Thomson's experiments suggested that these particles were part of all matter, and he was able to measure their charge-to-mass ratio.

Self-Test

Answer Questions 17 and 18 as true (T) or false (F).

17. In a gas discharge tube, electrons travel toward the cathode, so they are called cathode rays.

                                   _____

18. In Thomson's experiment, the amount of deflection that the electron experiences as it passes between electrically charged plates is directly proportional to the particle's charge.

                                   _____

19. When a current of one ampere flows past a point in a wire for a period of one second, the amount of electrical charge that passes that point is called a

                            _____

New Terms

Gas discharge tube
A glass tube fitted with metal electrodes at either end and containing a gas at a low pressure. When a high voltage is applied across the electrodes, electric current passes through the tube and the gas glows.

Electrode
A metal plate, which can be given an electrical charge, sealed into the end of a gas discharge tube or in a cathode ray tube.

Cathode
The negative electrode in a gas discharge tube.

Anode
The positive electrode in a gas discharge tube.

Cathode rays
> The stream of electrons that are emitted by the cathode in a gas discharge tube and that move through the tube to the anode.

Charge-to-mass ratio
> The ratio of a particle's charge to its mass, expressed in units of coulombs per gram.

Coulomb
> The SI unit of electrical charge. It is the amount of charge that passes a given point in a wire when a current of 1 ampere flows for 1 second.

Ampere
> The SI unit of electric current. One coulomb per second: $1 A = 1 C/s$

3.5   THE CHARGE ON THE ELECTRON

Objectives

> To understand how the charge on the electron was measured.

Review

R. A. Millikan determined the charge on the electron by measuring the charge on oil drops that had picked up electrons. The charge on the oil drops was always a multiple of -1.60×10^{-19} coulombs, and Millikan reasoned that this value must be equal to the electron's charge. (Your instructor probably doesn't expect you to memorize this number - to be sure, though, you should ask.)

New Terms

3.6   POSITIVE PARTICLES AND THE MASS SPECTROMETER

Objectives

To understand that atoms must also contain positive particles and that these positive particles are much heavier
than the electron. You should learn how charges on particles are expressed in multiples of the charge on the
electron.

Review

The mass spectrometer is a device used to measure the
charge-to-mass ratio of positive particles (positive ions). These
ions always have much smaller e/m ratios than the electron, which
tells us that they are much heavier than the electron. The
largest e/m ratio is observed for the hydrogen ion, which is simply a proton. The proton is a fundamental particle.

All atoms of elements other than hydrogen contain more
than one proton, and all the atoms of a given element have the
same number of protons. This number is called the element's
atomic number.

The electron is assigned a charge of 1-; the proton has a
charge of 1+. This is because charge is gained or lost by atoms
when they gain or lose electrons. A relative charge of 1- really
corresponds to an actual charge of -1.60×10^{-19} coulombs. You
will almost always deal with relative charges.

New Terms

Mass spectrometer
    A device that allows the determination of the charge-to-mass
    ratio of positive particles.

Proton
    A subatomic particle found in the nuclei of all atoms. It
    carries one unit of positive charge ($+1.60 \times 10^{-19}$ C) and
    its mass (1.67×10^{-24} g) is very nearly 1 amu (about the
    same as the mass of a hydrogen atom). It is often symbol-
    ized as H^+ in chemical equations.

Atomic number
    The number of protons in the nucleus of an atom.

3.7   RADIOACTIVITY

Objectives

    To learn the types of radioactivity shown by certain kinds
    of atoms and understand that this phenomenon provides
    additional evidence that there are particles simpler than
    the atom.

Review

    Three basic types of radioactivity are observed:

    α-rays composed of He^{2+} ions (α-particles)
    β-rays composed of electrons (β-particles)
    γ-rays composed of very penetrating radiation similar to
            X rays

    Since these emissions come spontaneously from atoms of
certain elements, these atoms must be composed of smaller,
simpler particles.

New Terms

Alpha particle (α-particle)
    The nucleus of a helium atom, He. One of the types of
    radiation given off by radioactive substances.

Beta particle (β-particle)
    A particle given off by a radioactive nucleus. It is actually
    an electron.

Gamma rays (γ-rays)
    High energy, short wavelength (high frequency) radiation
    similar to X rays that is given off by radioactive substances

Radioactivity
    The spontaneous emission of radiation by certain unstable
    atomic nuclei.

3.8   THE NUCLEAR ATOM

Objectives

To see how experiments led to the idea that the atom has a tiny, very dense positive nucleus.

Review

E. Rutherford concluded that an atom must possess a very tiny nucleus that contains all of the positive charge in the atom and nearly all its mass. This is the only way he could account for the scattering of some α-particles at large angles from thin metal foils, and the fact that most of the α-particles passed through the foil nearly unaffected.

New Terms

Nucleus
The very tiny, massive particle found at the center of the atom. It contains all of the atom's positive charge and nearly all of its mass. Protons and neutrons are found in the nucleus.

3.9   THE NEUTRON

Objectives

To examine the properties of the fundamental particle called the neutron.

Review

Neutrons are particles of zero charge and of mass almost the same as the proton. You should review the properties of the proton, neutron and electron in Table 3.2.

New Terms

Self-Test

The following questions review topics in Sections 3.4 to 3.9. Try to answer them without referring back to the text or to the review material in this book.

20. (True or False)

   (a) Faraday's experiments permitted the determination of the charge-to-mass ratio of the electron.

   (b) The cathode ray tube used by Thomson is similar to a television picture tube.

   (c) Cathode rays have different properties for different samples of matter.

   (d) The charge on the electron was measured by experiments using charged oil droplets.

   (e) From the data obtained from Thomson's cathode ray tube experiments and Millikan's experiments, the mass of the electron could be calculated.

   (f) The charge-to-mass ratio for positive particles is always larger than the charge-to-mass ratio for the electron.

   (g) An alpha particle is the same as an electron.

   (h) Gamma rays are not particles, but instead are high energy light waves.

   (i) In the mass spectrometer the positive particle with the largest e/m ratio is the proton.

   (j) The diameter of the nucleus of an atom is approximately 1/100,000 of the diameter of the atom.

21. (Fill in the blanks)

   (a) An atom that has acquired a charge by the gain or loss of electrons is called

   (b) The relative charge on an α-particle is

   (c) The relative charge on a γ-ray is

3.10 ISOTOPES

Objectives

To learn the meaning of the term isotope. You should learn how to write the symbol for a given isotope of an element and how to calculate the average atomic mass from the actual isotopic masses and their relative abundances.

Review

Isotopes of the same element have the same atomic number (number of protons) but different numbers of neutrons. Remember that when writing the symbol for an isotope, the atomic number, Z, is a left subscript and the mass number, A (the sum of protons plus neutrons), is a left superscript. The number of neutrons is A - Z. For example,

$$^{70}_{32}Ge \qquad \begin{aligned} &Z = 32 \ (32 \text{ protons}) \\ &A = 70 \\ &A - Z = 38 \ (38 \text{ neutrons}) \end{aligned}$$

The relative atomic masses discussed previously are actually average atomic masses. Example 3.1 in the text and the example below illustrate how the average atomic mass can be calculated from fractional abundances and accurate relative isotopic masses. (Remember, the actual mass of an isotope is not the same as its mass number.)

Example 3.1

Naturally occurring chlorine is composed of a mixture of 75.53% ^{35}Cl, and 24.47% ^{37}Cl. These have isotopic masses of 34.969 and 36.966 amu, respectively. Calculate the average atomic mass of chlorine.

Solution

Multiply the mass of a mole of each isotope by its fractional abundance (obtained from percent by dividing by 100). Then add the results to get the average weight of a mole of chlorine. This is the average atomic mass.

^{35}Cl   (34.969 g)(0.7553) = 26.41 g

^{37}Cl   (36.966 g)(0.2447) = $\underline{\quad 9.05 \text{ g}}$

Total   = 35.46 g

The average atomic mass is 35.46 amu.

Self-Test

22. Answer true (T) or false (F).

    (a) The number of protons in the nucleus of an atom is given by the mass number. _____

    (b) Isotopes of a given element have the same number of protons but differ in the number of neutrons. _____

23. How many protons are there in these atoms?

    (a) $^{32}_{16}$S _____   (b) $^{192}_{77}$Ir _____   (c) $^{39}_{19}$K _____

24. How many neutrons are there in these atoms?

    (a) $^{108}_{47}$Ag _____   (b) $^{209}_{83}$Bi _____   (c) $^{19}_{9}$F _____

25. Give the number of protons, neutrons, and electrons in the following.

	No. of protons	No. of neutrons	No. of electrons
$^{126}_{53}$I			
$^{118}_{50}$Sn^{2+}			
$^{79}_{34}$Se^{2-}			

26. Antimony occurs in nature as a mixture of two isotopes, 57.25% ^{121}Sb with a mass of 120.904 amu and 42.75% ^{123}Sb with a mass of 122.904 amu. What is the average atomic mass of Sb? _____

New Terms

Isotopes
> Atoms of the same element that differ slightly in their masses. The nuclei of all isotopes of a given element have the same number of protons, but they differ in the number of neutrons.

Mass number
> The sum of the number of protons and the number of neutrons in a particular nucleus.

Radioactive decay
> The gradual transformation of a collection of unstable nuclei into a collection of stable nuclei by the emission of various forms of radiation (α, β, or γ)

Answers to Self-Test Questions

1. copper and gold   2. H_2, O_2, N_2, F_2, Cl_2, Br_2, I_2
3. tungsten   4. graphite and diamond   5. Elements in the same column had to have similar properties.   6. Cl, Na, Xe   7. Hg, Ti
8. Br   9. Ne   10. Li   11. Ba   12. Np, Pm   13. Ge
14. Sr, Cr, Ce, U   15. S, P, I   16. Group   17. F   18. T
19. coulomb   20.(a) F   (b) T   (c) F   (d) T   (e) T   (f) F
(g) F   (h) T   (i) T   (j) T   21.(a) an ion   (b) 2+   (c) 0
22.(a) F   (b) T   23.(a) 16   (b) 77   (c) 19   24.(a) 61   (b) 126
(c) 10   25. 53 protons, 73 neutrons, 53 electrons; 50 protons, 68 neutrons, 48 electrons; 34 protons, 45 neutrons, 36 electrons
26. 121.8 amu

4 ELECTRONIC STRUCTURE AND THE PERIODIC TABLE

The chemical properties of an element are determined by the number and arrangement of the electrons in its atoms. This distribution of electrons is called the atom's electronic structure, and that is the central focus of this chapter. We begin with a discussion of the properties of light because it is an analysis of the light emitted by atoms when they are heated or when an electric current is passed through them that gives the clues to electronic structure. Later in the chapter we examine some properties whose variations within the periodic table can be understood in terms of the electronic structures of the elements.

4.1 ELECTROMAGNETIC RADIATION AND ATOMIC SPECTRA

Objectives

To learn some interrelated properties of light waves and to understand that the light emitted by an atom that has been "energized" is composed of only a relatively few colors, rather than an entire rainbow.

Review

Light (electromagnetic radiation) travels as waves through space. In a vacuum it travels at a constant speed (c) equal to 3.00×10^8 m/s. An even more precise value of c can be found on the inside rear cover of the text. The intensity of the wave is its amplitude. The product of the wave's frequency (ν) and its wavelength (λ) is equal to c.

$$\lambda \cdot \nu = c$$

The SI unit of frequency is the hertz: $1\ Hz = 1\ s^{-1}$

A white-hot object like the sun or an incandescent lamp emits light of all colors to give a continuous spectrum. Excited atoms emit only certain wavelengths (colors) and produce a line spectrum. For hydrogen, it is possible to find an equation that allows the calculation of the wavelengths of the lines. An important aspect of this equation is that it involves the difference between the reciprocals of squares of integers. The occurrence of these integers provides the clue to the electronic structure of the atom.

Self-Test

1.   A typical radar transmitter emits microwaves with a frequency of 9300 MHz (megahertz). What is the wavelength of these waves expressed in meters?

_____

2.   Sodium emits yellow light at a wavelength of 589 nm. What is its frequency?

_____

3.   The frequency of a green light wave is 5.49×10^{14} Hz. What is its wavelength in

(a)   centimeters   _____

(b)   nanometers   _____

4.   What is the wavelength, in nanometers, of the second line of the Lyman series in the atomic spectrum of hydrogen?

_____

5.   How can an atom be excited so that it emits its characteristic atomic spectrum?

_____

6.   In the Rydberg equation, if $n_1 = 5$, what values can n_2 have?

_____

7.   Each element has its own characteristic x-ray spectrum that can be related to the element's atomic number (True or False?)

_____

New Terms

Electronic structure

The distribution of electrons in the volume around an atom's nucleus.

Electromagnetic radiation

General term used to describe light waves in all their various forms - e.g., X rays, ultraviolet and infrared radiation, visible light, TV waves, microwaves, and radio waves.

Amplitude

The intensity of a wave. The maximum height of a wave as measured from the average height of peak and trough.

Wavelength

The distance between successive peaks in a wave.

Frequency

The number of peaks in a wave that pass a given point per second. The SI unit of frequency is the hertz. $1 \text{ Hz} = 1 \text{ s}^{-1}$

Hertz

The SI unit of frequency: $1 \text{ Hz} = 1 \text{ s}^{-1}$

Continuous spectrum

An electromagnetic spectrum that contains all wavelengths.

Atomic emission spectrum

The spectrum emitted by atoms that have been energized (*excited*). This kind of spectrum consists of a relatively small number of different wavelengths of light. See also, *Line spectrum*.

Line spectrum

A spectrum that consists of only a relatively few wavelengths that is produced when the light emitted by energized or excited atoms is passed first through a thin slit, then through a prism, and then allowed to fall on a screen or piece of photographic film. It is also called an atomic spectrum.

Rydberg equation

An empirical equation that allows the computation of the wavelengths of the lines in the emission spectrum of hydrogen.

4.2   THE BOHR THEORY OF THE HYDROGEN ATOM

Objectives

To show that the introduction of the idea of quantized energy levels in the atom permitted the explanation of atomic spectra. You should learn the relationship between frequency of light and energy.

Review

Planck had shown that the energy in a beam of light is proportional to the frequency of the light wave. Remember that $E = h\nu$.

The significance of Bohr's theory was that it introduced for the first time the idea that in an atom the electron is only permitted to have certain energies; intermediate energies are forbidden. Electrons change energy by going from one energy level to another. Energy is absorbed by an atom when one of its electrons is raised from one energy level to a higher one, and energy is released when the electron falls from one energy level to a lower one. Energy levels can be identified by the value of a quantum number.

This section also illustrates how complex theories are tested. From the postulates of the theory an equation is derived, in this case an equation that can be used to calculate the wavelengths of lines in the atomic spectrum. This theoretical equation is compared to an equation based solely on the experimental data. If the equations match, it is taken as evidence for the validity of the theory; if they don't, the theory must be wrong. Bohr's success with hydrogen indicated he was on the right trail. The failure of his theory to predict the wavelengths of spectral lines of atoms more complicated than hydrogen demonstrated that there was a basic flaw somewhere in the theory.

Self-Test

8. What is the energy, in joules, of a photon having

   (a) a frequency of 4.50×10^{15} Hz?   _____

   (b) a wavelength of 589 nm?   _____

9. (Multiple choice).   The existence of line spectra demonstrates that
   (a) only certain electrons in atoms can be excited
   (b) the electrons in an atom can have only certain specific energies
   (c) Planck's equation doesn't always hold true
   (d) white light is composed of many wavelengths
   (e) none of these is correct   _____

10. (Multiple choice).   Bohr's theory

   (a) proved that the electron travels in circular orbits about the nucleus
   (b) concluded that the radius of an orbit was inversely proportional to the quantum number, n
   (c) was successful in explaining the Rydberg equation for hydrogen
   (d) states that an electron gains energy when it moves from an orbit with a given value of n to an orbit with a smaller value of n
   (e) none of the above apply to Bohr's theory   _____

New Terms

Photon
   A tiny packet of electromagnetic energy (light energy) whose energy is given by the equation $E = h\nu$.

Quantum
   A tiny packet of light energy having energy $E = h\nu$. Also called a photon.

Planck's constant
   A constant, h, that permits us to calculate the energy of a photon of frequency ν by the equation $E = h\nu$.
   $h = 6.6262 \times 10^{-34}$ J s

Energy level
   A particular energy that an electron can have in an atom or molecule.

Quantum number
   A number related to the energy of an electron.

4.3   THE WAVE NATURE OF MATTER: WAVE MECHANICS

Objectives

To understand that matter, like light waves, has wavelike properties. You should understand the phenomenon of diffraction and the meanings of the terms, wave function and orbital. You should also learn the names and permissible values of the quantum numbers used to identify electron orbitals.

Review

As predicted by de Broglie, it has been shown experimentally that matter has wave properties. Proof lies in the diffraction of particles. Diffraction results from constructive and destructive interference of waves.

In an atom, electrons behave as standing waves. The theory that describes these waves is called wave mechanics, or quantum mechanics. Solution of a wave equation gives a set of wave functions, ψ. Each wave function describes an electron standing wave (atomic orbital) that has a characteristic energy and that describes a particular region around the nucleus where the electron is likely to be found.

Standing waves give rise naturally to integer quantum numbers, and to describe a three-dimensional wave three quantum numbers are required. Therefore, each orbital is identified by a set of three quantum numbers: n, ℓ, and m_ℓ. Review the values permitted for these quantum numbers on Pages 118 and 119 of the text.

$$n = 1, 2, \ldots,$$

$$\ell = 0, 1, 2, \ldots, n-1$$

$$m_\ell = 0, \pm 1, \pm 2, \ldots, \pm \ell$$

Remember that subshells are identified by their value of ℓ.

ℓ	0	1	2	3
letter designation	s	p	d	f

Before moving on, examine the energy level diagram in Figure 4.12. Note that within a shell the energy of the sub-shells vary as: s< p< d< f. Also note that an s subshell consists of one orbital; a p subshell, three orbitals; a d subshell, five orbitals; and an f subshell, seven.

Self-Test

11. What are the values of n, ℓ and m_ℓ for each orbital in a 2p subshell?

_____

12. What values of m_ℓ are allowed in the following?

(a) 2s subshell   _____

(b) 3d subshell   _____

(c) 5f subshell   _____

(d) 4p subshell   _____

13. Give the proper subshell designation corresponding to the following sets of quantum numbers.

(a) n = 3, ℓ = 1   _____

(b) n = 4, ℓ = 3   _____

(c) n = 4, ℓ = 2   _____

(d) n = 2, ℓ = 0   _____

14. Why don't we see wave properties for large particles like cars and baseballs?

_____

New Terms

Wave mechanics
    A theory of atomic structure based on the wave properties of matter.

Quantum mechanics
    See *Wave mechanics*.

Diffraction
    The scattering of light as it passes through a tiny pinhole or through a very narrow slit.

Diffraction pattern
    The pattern that is produced by constructive and destructive
    interference of diffracted waves.

Standing wave
    A wave whose peaks and nodes do not change position with
    time.

Node
    In a wave, a place where the amplitude or intensity is zero.

Wave function
    A mathematical function represented by the symbol ψ and
    obtained by solution of a wave equation. It describes the
    shape and size of an orbital and can be used to calculate
    the energy of an electron in that orbital.

Orbital
    A particular electron waveform with a particular energy. In
    an atom, each orbital has a specific set of values of its
    quantum numbers, n, ℓ, and m_ℓ.

Shell
    A term used to describe all the electrons (or orbitals) in an
    atom that have a given value of the principal quantum num-
    ber, n.

Principal quantum number
    The quantum number n, which can have values of $1, 2, 3...$,
    ∞. The value of n specifies the electron's shell and de-
    termines the size of the orbital.

Azimuthal quantum number
    The secondary quantum number whose values can be
    $0, 1, 2, ...(n - 1)$ where n is the principal quantum num-
    ber.

Magnetic quantum number
    The quantum number m_ℓ which can have values from $-\ell$ to
    $+\ell$.

Ground state
    The lowest-energy electron configuration for an atom or a
    molecule.

4.4   ELECTRON SPIN AND THE PAULI EXCLUSION PRINCIPLE

Objectives

To see that the electron behaves as if it were spinning about its axis like a top. You should learn that the Pauli exclusion principle limits the number of electrons per orbital to two. You should learn how electron spin influences the magnetic properties of substances.

Review

The electron behaves like a tiny electromagnet, implying that it is spinning about its axis. There are two values of the spin quantum number, m_s, $+\frac{1}{2}$ and $-\frac{1}{2}$, corresponding to two directions of rotation.

The Pauli exclusion principle requires that any two electrons in an atom have different sets of values for their quantum numbers: n, ℓ, m_ℓ and m_s. If the first three are identical for two electrons, the electrons must spin in opposite directions.

The maximum number of electrons that can be placed in a given orbital is two, and they must have opposite spins. The maximum electron population per subshell is:

subshell	max population
s	2
p	6
d	10
f	14

It sometimes helps to remember this if you realize that the numbers 2, 6, 10, 14 form an arithmetic progression, each successive number being four larger than the one before it.

You should review the magnetic properties of substances as they are determined by the electron's spin.

Self-Test

15. (Multiple choice). One electron in an atom has the quantum numbers: $n = 3$, $\ell = 2$, $m_\ell = -1$, $m_s = \frac{1}{2}$. Which of the following is <u>not</u> a possible set of quantum numbers for a second electron in this same atom?

(a) $n = 1$, $\ell = 0$, $m_\ell = 0$, $m_s = -\frac{1}{2}$

(b) $n = 2$, $\ell = 1$, $m_\ell = -1$, $m_s = \frac{1}{2}$

(c) $n = 3$, $\ell = 2$, $m_\ell = -1$, $m_s = \frac{1}{2}$

(d) $n = 3$, $\ell = 1$, $m_\ell = -1$, $m_s = \frac{1}{2}$

(e) $n = 3$, $\ell = 2$, $m_\ell = 0$, $m_s = \frac{1}{2}$

16. (Fill in the blanks). The maximum number of electrons in

   (a)   the 2s subshell is   _____

   (b)   the 3p subshell is   _____

   (c)   the 6g subshell is   _____

17. A neutral potassium atom must be paramagnetic. Why?

_____

New Terms

Spin quantum number
   The quantum number m_s, which determines the direction in
   which the electron appears to be spinning. Its values are
   $+\frac{1}{2}$ and $-\frac{1}{2}$.

Pauli exclusion principle
   No two electrons in the same atom can have all four of their
   quantum numbers the same.

Diamagnetism
   A magnetic property associated with the absence of unpaired
   electrons in a substance. It gives rise to a very slight
   repulsion away from a magnetic field.

Paramagnetism
   A weak attraction toward a magnetic field. It is a property
   possessed by substances having unpaired electrons.

Ferromagnetism
   The strong magnetism associated with iron, cobalt, and
   nickel, which results from the alignment of the magnetic
   poles (in the solid state) of large numbers of paramagnetic
   atoms.

4.5   THE ELECTRON CONFIGURATIONS OF THE ELEMENTS

Objectives

To write electron configurations for the elements. You should learn both the conventional notation (e.g., $1s^2$...) as well as how to construct an orbital diagram.

Review

The number of electrons in a given subshell is specified by writing the subshell designation with the number of electrons indicated as an exponent. Thus $3p^4$ indicates four electrons in a 3p subshell.

Subshells in an atom become populated starting with the lowest energy level first. The sequence in which subshells become filled is determined by the energy level diagram in Figure 4.12 (Page 120 of the text).

When writing orbital diagrams, arrows are used to indicate electrons (head up for one direction of spin, and head down for the other). For example, the orbital diagram for boron (Z = 5) is

$$\text{B} \quad \underset{1s}{\uparrow\downarrow} \quad \underset{2s}{\uparrow\downarrow} \quad \underset{}{\uparrow} \; \underline{} \; \underline{}_{\displaystyle 2p}$$

$$\text{or} \quad \text{B} \; [\text{He}] \; \underset{2s}{\uparrow\downarrow} \quad \underset{}{\uparrow} \; \underline{} \; \underline{}_{\displaystyle 2p}$$

Notice that all the orbitals of the 2p subshell are shown, even though only one of them is populated by an electron. Remember that [He] stands for the filled noble gas core. In a similar fashion we would write the orbital diagram for Ca as

$$\text{Ca} \; [\text{Ar}] \; \underset{4s}{\uparrow\downarrow}$$

When more than one electron occupies a p, d or f subshell, Hund's rule applies, which tells us that for an atom in its ground state the electrons are spread out over the orbitals as much as possible with their spins in the same direction. For example, the orbital diagram for phosphorus is

$$P \quad [Ne] \quad \underset{3s}{\underline{\uparrow\downarrow}} \quad \underset{3p}{\underline{\uparrow} \quad \underline{\uparrow} \quad \underline{\uparrow}}$$

A phenomenon that has some important consequences in terms of chemical properties is that half-filled and filled subshells are extra stable. This causes Cr and Cu to have unexpected electron configurations.

New Terms

Electronic structure
    The distribution of an atom's electrons among the atom's orbitals.

Electron configuration
    The distribution of electrons in an atom's orbitals.

Orbital diagram
    A diagram that represents an atom's orbitals by dashes (or some other suitable device) and that represents electrons that populate the orbitals by arrows. For example, the orbital diagram of carbon is

$$C \quad \underset{1s}{\underline{\uparrow\downarrow}} \quad \underset{2s}{\underline{\uparrow\downarrow}} \quad \underset{2p}{\underline{\uparrow} \quad \underline{\uparrow} \quad \underline{}}$$

Paired electrons
    Two electrons, one with $m_s = +\frac{1}{2}$ and the other with $m_s = -\frac{1}{2}$. Two electrons with opposite spins.

Core electrons
    The electrons in shells below an atom's outer shell.

Hund's rule
    The lowest-energy electron configuration results when electrons that occupy orbitals of equal energy are spread out over the orbitals as much as possible with spins unpaired.

4.6   THE PERIODIC TABLE AND ELECTRON CONFIGURATIONS

Objectives

To learn to use the periodic table to deduce the electron configuration of an element.

Review

The structure of the periodic table is a direct consequence of the order in which subshells are filled and, as described in the text, you can use the periodic table to help you write electron configurations.

Example 3.2

Write the electron configuration of germanium (Z = 32).

Solution

There are 32 electrons in the atom. Moving from left to right across successive periods we fill:

$1s^2$ (period 1)
$2s^2$ (period 2 - Groups IA and IIA)
$2p^6$ (period 2 - Groups IIIA through the noble gases)
$3s^2$ (period 3 - Groups IA and IIA)
$3p^6$ (period 3 - Groups IIIA through the noble gases)
$4s^2$ (period 4 - Group IA and IIA)
$3d^{10}$ (period 4 - first row of transition elements)
$4p^2$ (period 4 - Groups IIIA and IVA)

Writing all this together:

$$Ge\quad 1s^22s^22p^63s^23p^64s^23d^{10}4p^2$$

Some people prefer to write all subshells of a given shell together.

$$Ge\quad 1s^22s^22p^63s^23p^63d^{10}4s^24p^2$$

Showing the noble gas core and those electrons outside it, we can also write

$$Ge\quad [Ar]\ 3d^{10}4s^24p^2$$

If we only wished to know the configuration of the outer shell
(the valence shell), we could write

$$\text{Ge} \quad 4s^2 4p^2$$

This can be obtained without having to write the entire configuration, as described in Example 4.10.

Self-Test (Sections 4.5 and 4.6)

18. Give the complete electron configuration of

    (a) Mg   _____

    (b) Cl   _____

    (c) Tc   _____

    (d) Ni   _____

19. Give the abbreviated electron configuration (showing the
noble gas core) of

    (a) Si   _____

    (b) V   _____

20. Give the electron configuration of the outer shell of

    (a) Arsenic   _____

    (b) Iodine   _____

21. Construct orbital diagrams for the following:

    (a) Si

    (b) Ca

    (c) Fe

    (d) S

New Terms

Valence shell
    The shell with highest n that is occupied by electrons.

4.7   THE SPATIAL DISTRIBUTION OF ELECTRONS

Objectives

To understand how wave mechanics describes the spatial distribution of electrons (i.e., where the electrons are likely to be found).

Review

Because of the Heisenberg uncertainty principle, wave mechanics describes the probability of finding the electron at points around the nucleus. The electron is viewed as being smeared out throughout the volume of the atom. Regions where the probability of finding the electron is high are said to have a high electron density.

The shapes of the probability distributions for different types of orbitals will be important in discussion of bonding in Chapter 6. Remember that s orbitals are spherical; p orbitals are dumbbell shaped. You should also know that the three orbitals in a p subshell are oriented at 90° to each other. Note also the shapes and orientations of the d orbitals.

Notice that 2s and higher s orbitals contain nodes (where the electron density drops to zero), as do 3p and higher p orbitals. The important point, however, is that s orbitals have an overall spherical shape while the p orbitals tend to "point" in specific directions. Also notice that as the value of n increases, the size of the orbital increases.

New Terms

Uncertainty principle

There are limits to our ability to simultaneously measure a particle's speed (or momentum) and its position.

Probability distribution

How the probability of finding a particular electron varies from place to place around the nucleus of an atom, or around the nuclei of a molecule or polyatomic ion.

Electron density
   The concentration of the electronic charge within a given
   volume.

Electron cloud
   Because of its wave properties, an electron is spread out
   like a cloud around the nucleus.

Charge cloud
   Electron cloud.

4.8   THE VARIATION OF PROPERTIES WITH ATOMIC STRUCTURE

Objectives

   To be able to predict trends in atomic and ionic size,
   ionization energy, and electron affinity.

Review

   Atomic and ionic sizes have tradiationally been specified in
units of angstroms (Å):   1 Å = 10^{-8} cm = 10^{-10} m.   Learn the
conversions in the middle of Page 132 which relate the angstrom
to the preferred SI units nonometers and picometers.

   Atomic size increases going down a group in the periodic
table because the outer shell orbitals become larger and the effective nuclear charge that they experience remains nearly the
same.   Atomic size decreases from left to right in a period because the effective nuclear charge felt by the outer electrons
increases.

   Remember that the lanthanide contraction causes atoms of
the elements immediately following lanthanum in the main body of
the periodic table to be nearly the same size as those above
them.   This makes these elements very dense.

   Ionization energy is the energy needed to remove an electron from an isolated atom or ion.

   Electron affinity is the energy released (or absorbed) when
an electron is added to a gaseous atom.   Students often find this
term confusing.   Perhaps a better name for it would have been
"electron attachment energy."   Unfortunately, however, scientists

choose to call this energy the electron affinity, so you have to become accustomed to the name.

As mentioned earlier, within the periodic table, atomic size generally decreases from left to right in a period and increases from top to bottom within a group. Variations in ionization energy and electron affinity generally parallel variations in size. Large atoms have low ionization energies and low electron affinities while small atoms have high ionization energies and high electron affinities. The variation of properties within the periodic table is summarized below.

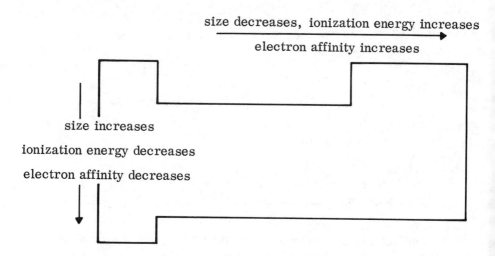

size decreases, ionization energy increases

electron affinity increases

size increases

ionization energy decreases

electron affinity decreases

Remember that the second ionization energy is always larger than the first, the third larger than the second, and so forth. Also remember that the second electron affinity is always an endothermic quantity.

Remember that positive ions are always smaller than the neutral atoms from which they are formed and that an atom gets larger when it becomes a negative ion.

Self-Test

22. The atomic radius of a bromine atom is 1.14 Å. What is this radius expressed in

   (a) nanometers _____   (b) picometers _____ ?

23. Which is the largest atom: C, N, Si, P?   _____

24. Which atom has the largest ionization energy: B, C, Al, Si?

    _____

25. Which atom has the least exothermic electron affinity:
    Si, Al, Ga, Ge?   _____

26. In Each pair, choose the one with the larger radius.

    (a) Na or Na$^+$ _____

    (b) Cl or Cl$^-$ _____

    (c) Mn^{2+} or Mn^{3+} _____

New Terms

Angstrom
   1 Å = 10^{-8} cm = 10^{-10} m. 1 Å = 0.1 nm = 100 pm

Atomic radius
   The effective radius of an atom.

Ionic radius
   The effective radius of an ion, which is nearly constant
   from one compound to another.

Effective nuclear charge
   The effective charge experienced by a particular electron
   in an atom, which is a composite of the positive charge on
   the nucleus and the offsetting negative charge of the electrons in nner shells (and to some extent, by other electrons
   in the same shell).

Lanthanide contraction
   The gradual decrease in size that occurs from element 58 to
   71 which causes the elements that follow the lanthanides to
   have unusually small sizes and large ionization energies.

Ionization energy
   The energy needed to remove an electron from an isolated
   gaseous atom, ion, or molecule (usually expressed in kJ/mol).

Electron affinity (EA)
   The energy change that occurs when an electron is added to
   an isolated gaseous atom or ion (usually expressed in kJ/mol).

Answers to Self-Test Questions

1. 3.2×10^{-2} m   2. 5.09×10^{14} Hz   3.(a) 5.46×10^{-5} cm
(b) 546 nm   4. 103 nm   5. with an electric discharge or by
heating it in a flame   6. $n_2 = 6,7,8,\ldots,\infty$ 7. True
8. 2.98×10^{-18} J   (b) 3.38×10^{-19} J   9. b   10. c
11. $n=2$, $\ell=1$, $m_\ell=-1$; $n=2$, $\ell=1$, $m_\ell=0$; $n=2$, $\ell=1$, $m_\ell=1$
12.(a) 0   (b) 0, ±1, ±2   (c) 0, ±1, ±2, ±3   (d) 0, ±1
13.(a) 3p   (b) 4f   (c) 4d   (d) 2s   14. Their large masses give
them extremely small wavelengths.   15. c   16.(a) 2   (b) 6
(c) 18   17. It has an odd number of electrons, so they all
cannot be paired.   18.(a) Mg $1s^2 2s^2 2p^6 3s^2$
(b) Cl $1s^2 2s^2 2p^6 3s^2 3p^5$ (c) Tc $1s^2 2s^2 2p^6 3s^2 3p^6 3d^{10} 4s^2 4p^6 4d^5 5s^2$
(d) Ni $1s^2 2s^2 2p^6 3s^2 3p^6 3d^8 4s^2$ 19.(a) Si [Ne] $3s^2 3p^2$
(b) V [Ar] $3d^3 4s^2$ 20.(a) As $4s^2 4p^3$ (b) I $5s^2 5p^5$
21.(a) Si [Ne] $\underset{3s}{\underline{\uparrow\downarrow}}$ $\underset{3p}{\underline{\uparrow}\ \underline{\uparrow}\ \underline{\ \ }}$ (b) Ca [Ar] $\underset{4s}{\underline{\uparrow\downarrow}}$

(c) Fe [Ar] $\underset{4s}{\underline{\uparrow\downarrow}}$ $\underset{3d}{\underline{\uparrow\downarrow}\ \underline{\uparrow}\ \underline{\uparrow}\ \underline{\uparrow}\ \underline{\uparrow}}$

(d) S [Ne] $\underset{3s}{\underline{\uparrow\downarrow}}$ $\underset{3p}{\underline{\uparrow\downarrow}\ \underline{\uparrow}\ \underline{\uparrow}}$ 22.(a) 0.114 nm   (b) 114 pm
23. Si   24. Ga   25. Ga   26.(a) Na   (b) Cl$^-$ (c) Mn^{2+}

5 CHEMICAL BONDING: GENERAL CONCEPTS

Chemical bonds are what hold atoms to each other in compounds. The discussion of chemical bonding in your text is divided between two chapters. This first chapter examines some general concepts and provides a simplified treatment of the subject. Here you should learn the types of chemical bonding and how they relate to the electronic structures of the atoms that are bonded together. Once you have mastered these topics, you are ready to learn how to name simple chemical compounds, and this is discussed in the last section of the chapter.

5.1 PROPERTIES OF IONIC AND MOLECULAR COMPOUNDS

Objectives

To learn some of the properties that are characteristic of these kinds of compounds, and to learn how they differ.

Review

Theories of chemical bonding were developed to explain why certain elements form the kinds of compounds that they do. Before you can appreciate these theories, you should know some of the properties that they attempt to explain.

The properties of ionic and molecular compounds reflect the kinds of particles that are within them. Ionic compounds are formed when atoms transfer electrons from one to the other.

This produces electrically charged particles called ions that attract each other. The strong attractive forces between ions cause ionic compounds to be brittle and to have generally high melting points. Ionic compounds do not conduct electricity in the solid state, but they do conduct when melted.

Molecular compounds are formed when atoms combine to form electrically neutral particles called molecules. These substances often are soft and have low melting points. Because their particles are uncharged, molecular compounds do not conduct electricity in either the solid or liquid state.

Self-Test

1.   The compound magnesium chloride, $MgCl_2$, is relatively hard, brittle, and melts at a temperature of 708°C to give a liquid that conducts electricity. From this information, would you conclude that $MgCl_2$ is ionic or molecular?

   _____

2.   The compound titanium tetrachloride, $TiCl_4$, forms soft crystals that melt at a temperature of -25°C. Liquid $TiCl_4$ does not conduct electricity. Is $TiCl_4$ ionic or molecular?

   _____

New Terms

Chemical bond
   Forces of attraction that link atoms together in compounds.

Molecule
   An electrically neutral group of atoms bound tightly enough together that they behave as and can be recognized as a single particle.

Molecular compound
   A compound whose particles are molecules.

Ionic compound
   A compound composed of positive and negative ions.

5.2   LEWIS SYMBOLS

Objectives

To learn how to write the Lewis symbol, or dot symbol, for atoms of the representative elements.

Review

Remember that it is the outer shell (valence shell) elec-trons that are involved in the formation of chemical bonds. Lewis symbols are simply a bookkeeping device that is used to keep track of the valence electrons during bond formation. Dots (or some other symbol such as an x or a circle) are used to represent valence electrons. Review Table 5.1 in the text before working on the following Self-Test.

Self-Test

3.   Write Lewis symbols for:

(a) Si _____   (c) Sr _____

(b) Cl _____   (d) As _____

New Terms

Valence shell
The shell with highest n that is occupied by electrons.

Lewis symbol
The chemical symbol of an element surrounded by dots that represent the valence electrons of an atom of the element.

Lewis structure
Also called Lewis formula or electron-dot formula. A structural formula drawn with Lewis symbols, which repre-sents the valence electrons as dots (or as dashes for pairs of electrons).

Electron-dot formula
See *Lewis structure.*

5.3   THE IONIC BOND

Objectives

To understand what an ionic bond is, how it is formed, and the types of elements that form ionic bonds.

Review

Remember that the ionic bond is formed by electron transfer. This produces ions that attract each other because of their opposite charges. Among the representative elements atoms tend to gain or lose electrons until they achieve an electron configuration that is identical to a noble gas (see Table 5.2). A noble gas atom has eight electrons in its outer shell, hence the octet rule which states that atoms tend to gain or lose electrons until there are eight electrons in the outer shell. You should be able to diagram the formation of an ionic compound using Lewis symbols. The Self-Test at the end of this section provides some practice.

Among the transition elements the octet rule doesn't always hold - other relatively stable electron configurations also exist. Review Table 5.3 in your text.

Ionic compounds also exist that contain polyatomic ions. Learn the formulas, charges, and names of the ions in Table 5.4. When writing the formulas of compounds containing these ions, remember that the ratio of positive to negative ions must be chosen to give a neutral formula. For instance, the compound containing Fe^{3+} and CO_3^{2-} has the formula, $Fe_2(CO_3)_3$. A simple way to get this formula is to use the number of charges on one ion as the subscript on the other.

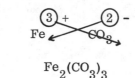

gives $Fe_2(CO_3)_3$

This system works for writing the formula for any ionic compound. Just remember to reduce the subscripts to the smallest set of whole numbers. For example,

$$\overset{\textcircled{2}+}{\text{Mg}} \overset{\textcircled{4}-}{\underset{\text{C}}{\times}} \qquad\qquad \overset{\textcircled{2}+}{\text{Ca}} \overset{\textcircled{2}-}{\underset{\text{SO}_4}{\times}}$$

Mg_4C_2 (subscripts divisible by 2) $Ca_2(SO_4)_2$

Mg_2C (final formula) $CaSO_4$

Self-Test

4. Use Lewis symbols to diagram the formation of an ionic bond between:

   (a) K and Cl _____

   (b) Na and O _____

5. Write the pseudonoble gas configuration for Zn^{2+}.

   _____

6. Write the formulas for the ionic compounds formed from the ions:

   (a) Cr^{2+} and PO_4^{3-} _____

   (b) Cu^{2+} and SO_4^{2-} _____

   (c) Ga^{3+} and ClO_2^{-} _____

   (d) Cr^{3+} and $C_2O_4^{2-}$ _____

   (e) NH_4^{+} and S^{2-} _____

7. What are the names of the polyatomic ions in Question 4?

   (a) _____

   (b) _____

   (c) _____

   (d) _____

   (e) _____

New Terms

Ionic bond
    The electrostatic attraction that holds ions together in an ionic compound.

Electrovalent bond
>An ionic bond.

Cation
>A positive ion.

Anion
>A negative ion.

Octet rule
>An atom tends to gain or lose electrons until its outer shell contains eight electrons.

Post-transition element
>In the periodic table, a representative element in Group IIIA through Group VIIA that occurs after a series of transition elements.

Pseudonoble gas configuration
>For a given n, the configuration $ns^2np^6nd^{10}$.

Polyatomic ion
>An ion composed of two or more atoms.

5.4   FACTORS THAT INFLUENCE THE FORMATION OF IONIC COMPOUNDS

Objectives

>To examine the factors that favor ionic bonding and to learn what gives rise to the stability of ionic compounds.

Review

An ionic compound is stable because of the very large lattice energy that is released when the ions come together to produce the ionic solid. If it were not for this lattice energy, ionic compounds would not exist. Thus, in the gas phase the ions, $Li^+(g)$ and $F^-(g)$, are less stable (i.e., of higher energy) than $Li(g)$ and $F(g)$ and therefore $Li(g)$ and $F(g)$ would not react spontaneously to produce the ions.

Ionic compounds tend to form most readily when metals of low ionization energy and electron affinity react with nonmetals of high ionization energy and electron affinity, and when the lattice energy of the resultant compound is high. Therefore, the metals on the extreme left of the periodic table (Groups IA and IIA) and the nonmetals at the extreme upper right tend to form ionic compounds.

Self-Test

8. What basic principle permits us to analyze the formation of an ionic compound using a Born-Haber cycle?

_____

9. Why isn't LiF composed of Li^{2+} and F^{2-} ions instead of Li^+ and F^- ions?

_____

_____

_____

10. The term stability is generally associated with low _____.

New Terms

Lattice energy
  The amount of energy that would be released by the imaginary process in which isolated particles of a substance (atoms, molecules, or ions) come together to form one mole of a crystal of that substance.

Born-Haber cycle
  A method of examining the contributing energy factors in an overall energy change. It involves constructing an alternative path from reactants to products and analyzing the individual energy changes accompanying each step along the alternative path.

5.5   THE COVALENT BOND

Objectives
  To learn how the covalent bond is formed. You should learn how to draw Lewis structures for covalent molecules. This should include molecules and polyatomic ions that

contain single, double and triple bonds.

Review

Covalent bonding is favored when the difference between the ionization energies and electron affinities of the combining atoms is not large. Sharing a pair of electrons between two atoms lowers their energy, as shown in Figure 5.6. Learn the meanings of the terms bond length and bond energy. A single covalent bond consists of one pair of electrons shared between two atoms. Double and triple bonds consist of two and three shared pairs. A pair of electrons in a bond is usually represented by a dash.

By electron sharing, atoms normally complete their octets. An exception is hydrogen, which never has more than two electrons in its valence shell. Compounds of beryllium and boron are also exceptions. The rules we use to draw Lewis structures often do not apply to them.

Self-Test

11. Using the Lewis symbols for the elements Si, P, S and Cl predict the formulas for the simplest compounds these elements would form with hydrogen and write their Lewis structures.

New Terms

Covalent bond
> A chemical bond formed by the sharing of electrons between two atoms.

Bond energy
> The amount of energy needed to separate two atoms that are joined by a chemical bond and produce electrically neutral particles. It is also the amount of energy released when

such a bond is formed.

Bond length
Also called the bond distance. The distance between the nuclei of two atoms that are joined by a chemical bond.

Single bond
A covalent bond in which a single pair of electrons is shared between two atoms.

Double bond
A covalent bond in which two pairs of electrons are shared.

Triple bond
A covalent bond in which three pairs of electrons are shared between two atoms.

5.6   DRAWING LEWIS STRUCTURES

Objectives

To learn how to draw satisfactory Lewis structures for simple compounds based on their chemical formulas.

Review

To draw a Lewis structure, you must first determine the compound's skeletal structure - that is, you must decide which atoms are attached to each other by covalent bonds. Generally, you will find that the atom written first in a formula is the central atom. It is also helpful to remember that hydrogen forms only one covalent bond, so it cannot be a central atom.

Be sure to learn rules 1 to 5 on Page 158. These tell you how to count and distribute valence electrons among the bonds and atoms in the skeletal structure. Study carefully Examples 5.5 to 5.8 before attempting the following Self-Test.

Self-Test

12. Write electron-dot formulas for the following (the central atom is written first in each formula).

(a) $SiCl_4$ (d) SO_4^{2-}

(b) ClF_3 (e) CO

(c) SCl_2 (f) ClO_2^-

New Terms

Skeletal structure
An arrangement of atoms, used in drawing Lewis structures, showing which atoms are bonded to each other.

5.7   BOND ORDER AND SOME BOND PROPERTIES

Objectives

To learn how three bond properties, bond length, bond energy, and vibrational frequency, are related to the electron density between two atoms.

Review

Bond order is the number of electron pairs shared between two atoms. Remember that as the bond order increases,

(a) bond length decreases
(b) bond energy, which in a sense is the "bond strength," increases
(c) vibration frequency increases

Self-Test

13. The bond length in carbon monoxide, CO, is 113 pm. Judging from the data in Table 5.5 of your text, what can you say about the bond order in CO?

_____

14. Consider these compounds:

```
    H  H                H                   H     H
    |  |                |                   |     |
 H—C—N—H           H—C—C≡N:          H—C=N—N—H
    |   ··              |                  ··    ··
    H                   H

   (I)                 (II)                (III)
```

(a) Which would have the longest carbon-nitrogen bond?

                                        _____

(b) Which would have the largest carbon-nitrogen vibrational frequency?

                                        _____

(c) Which would have the largest carbon-nitrogen bond energy?

                                        _____

(d) What would be the approximate carbon-nitrogen bond length in compound (III)?

_____

15. What kind of information is obtained from the infrared absorption spectrum of a molecule?
_____

New Terms

Bond order
    The net number of pairs of bonding electrons.

Vibrational frequency
    The frequency with which atoms joined by a bond vibrate back and forth, toward and away from each other.

5.8   RESONANCE

Objectives

To learn the meaning of the term resonance and to learn to draw resonance structures where applicable.

Review

Remember that the actual structure of a resonance hybrid never corresponds to any of the resonance forms that you draw for the molecule or ion; it is always something in between. Resonance structures arise when there is more than one reasonable way of distributing electron pairs in a molecule. The NO_3^- ion, for example, is a resonance hybrid of three contributing structures:

When you draw the dot structure for a molecule or ion and find that you must create a double bond to complete the octet of every atom, and when there is a choice of where to form the double bond, resonance structures occur. For instance, in the dot structure for the NO_3^- ion above, the double bond could be placed in any one of three places when you construct the dot formula. Therefore, three resonance structures occur. The actual structure of NO_3^- is a sort of average of these three. Each bond is approximately 1-1/3 bonds.

Self-Test

16. Draw all resonance structures for

(a) SO_3

(b) N_3^- (structure, N······N······N)

(c) HCO_2^- (structure, H······C $\underset{O}{\overset{O}{<}}$)

17. Arrange the following in order of predicted decreasing C—O bond length. Specify the average C—O bond order in each.

(a) $:\ddot{O}=C=\ddot{O}:$

(b) $:C\equiv O:$

(c) $\left[\begin{array}{c} :\overset{..}{O}: \\ \| \\ C \\ \diagup \; \diagdown \\ :\overset{..}{\underset{..}{O}} \quad \overset{..}{\underset{..}{O}}: \end{array}\right]^{2-}$ (one of three resonance structures)

(d) $\left[\begin{array}{c} \overset{..}{O}: \\ \diagup\!\!\diagup \\ H—C \\ \diagdown \\ \overset{..}{\underset{..}{O}}: \end{array}\right]^-$ (one of two resonance structures)

(e)   H
         |
    H—C—$\ddot{O}$—H   Answer _____
         |
         H

New Terms

Resonance

When the actual electronic structure of a molecule or polyatomic ion cannot be adequately represented by a single Lewis structure, it is instead represented as a composite of two or more Lewis structures that are called resonance structures. None of the individual resonance structures describes an actual electronic structure of a molecule or ion.

Resonance hybrid

The actual structure of a molecule or polyatomic ion which is represented by two or more resonance structures.

Resonance structure

One of two or more Lewis structures that can be drawn for a molecule or ion, none of which adequately describes the bonding in the species.

Contributing structure
See *Resonance structure.*

5.9   COORDINATE COVALENT BONDS

Objectives

To see how atoms can use unshared electron pairs to form additional bonds.

Review

The coordinate covalent bond is a bookkeeping device that is sometimes convenient to use in accounting for the bonding in some compounds. Remember that the properties of a covalent bond do not depend on the origin of the electrons shared between the atoms.

Self-Test

18. Draw electron-dot formulas for the following showing how the structure can be explained in terms of coordinate covalent bonding.

(a) H_3O^+ (O is central atom)

(b) BF_4^- (B is central atom)

New Terms

Coordinate covalent bond
A term used to describe a covalent bond in which both of the shared electrons are contributed by the same atom. Once formed, a coordinate covalent bond is no different than any other covalent bond.

Addition compound
   A compound formed by the joining of two molecules with a
   coordinate covalent bond.

5.10   POLAR MOLECULES AND ELECTRONEGATIVITY

Objectives

   To learn that in most molecules electrons are not shared
   equally between atoms because different atoms have different tendencies to attract electrons. You should learn
   the meaning of electronegativity and how this property
   varies within the periodic table.

Review

   Remember that electronegativity refers to the attraction an
atom has for electrons in a bond, and that it is the difference in
electronegativity that determines the polarity of a bond, as well
as which end of a polar bond carries the negative charge. An
important point to remember from this section is that bonds can
vary anywhere between essentially 100% covalent to essentially
100% ionic.

   Molecules having polar bonds can be nonpolar if the effects
of the bond dipoles cancel. This will occur if the molecule has a
symmetrical shape. (In Chapter 6 you will learn how to predict
molecular shapes and the polarity of molecules.)

   You should know how electronegativity varies in the periodic table - increasing from left to right in a period and decreasing from top to bottom in a group. Keep in mind the margin
figure on Page 169.

Self-Test

19. Use Table 5.6 in the text to determine which end of the
     following bonds carries a partial negative charge.

     (a) Sb—H _____   (c) C—O _____

     (b) P—S _____   (d) Br—S _____

20. <u>Without</u> referring to Table 5.6, but using a periodic table, predict which atom in each of the following sets is most electronegative.

(a) Ga, Bi, As, In   _____

(b) Cl, P, Br, Bi   _____

New Terms

Electronegativity
>The relative attraction that an atom has for the electrons in a bond.

Dipole
>A molecule having partial positive and negative charges on opposite ends.

Dipole moment
>The product of the partial charge on either end of a dipole multiplied by the distance between the partial charges. It is a measure of the extent of polarity of a molecule.

Polar bond
>A polar covalent bond.

Electropositive
>Having a low electronegativity.

5.11   THE NAMING OF CHEMICAL COMPOUNDS

Objectives

>To be able to name simple inorganic compounds.

Review

>The rules for naming inorganic compounds are given in this section. If you have had chemistry in high school, you should remember many of them. If you've never had chemistry before, it is important that you learn how to name simple inorganic compounds. Besides increasing your ability to follow what's going on in class, you will probably need to know the names of chemicals if you ever have to get them from the storeroom or

order them from a catalog.

Self-Test

21. Name the following:

(a) $NiCl_2$ _____

(b) $Cr_2(CO_3)_3$ _____

(c) $Sr(NO_3)_2$ _____

(d) K_2SO_4 _____

(e) SF_6 _____

(f) CCl_4 _____

22. Write formulas for the following:

(a) tin(IV) oxide   _____

(b) boron trichloride   _____

(c) calcium bicarbonate   _____

(d) iron(III) oxide   _____

(e) dinitrogen pentoxide   _____

(f) sodium phosphide   _____

23. What is the formula of the sodium salt of periodic acid?

_____

24. What is the name of the acid H_2CrO_4? _____

25. What would be the name for the acid H_2Se?_____

26. Arsenic acid has the formula, H_3AsO_4.

(a) What is the formula of arsenous acid? _____

(b) What is the formula for sodium arsenite?_____

(c) What is the name of KH_2AsO_4? _____

New Terms

Inorganic compound
    A compound whose structure is not primarily determined by
    the linking together of carbon atoms.

Organic compounds
    Compounds whose structures are determined primarily by the linking together of carbon atoms. They are hydrocarbons or can be considered to be derived from hydrocarbons.

Trivial name
    The common name for a compound.

Binary compound
    A compound that consists of two different elements (e.g., HCl, Na_2S, $FeCl_3$).

Stock system
    A system of nomenclature that uses Roman numerals within parentheses to indicate charges.

Binary acid
    A substance with the general formula H_nX which produces acidic aqueous solutions (e.g., HCl, H_2S).

Oxoacid
    An acid that contains hydrogen, oxygen, and one other element (for example, HNO_3, H_3PO_4, H_2SO_4).

Neutralization
    The reaction of an acid with a base. In aqueous solutions, the products are a salt and water.

Salt
    Any ionic compound that does not contain O^{2-} or OH^-. The common name for $NaCl$.

Acid salt
    A salt of a partially neutralized polyprotic acid: for example, $NaHSO_4$ and NaH_2PO_4.

Answers to Self-Test Questions

1. Ionic   2. Molecular
3. (a) ·S̈i·   (b) :C̈l·   (c) ·Sr·   (d) :Äs·

4. (a) K× + ·C̈l: ⟶ K⁺ , [:C̈l:]⁻   (b) Na× + ·Ö: ⟶ 2Na⁺, [:Ö:]²⁻
                                         Na×

5. $3s^2 3p^6 3d^{10}$ 6.(a) $Cr_3(PO_4)_2$ (b) $CuSO_4$ (c) $Ga(ClO_2)_3$
(d) $Cr_2(C_2O_4)_3$ (e) $(NH_4)_2S$ 7. (a) phosphate ion   (b) sulfate
ion   (c) chlorite ion   (d) oxalate ion   (e) ammonium ion
8. law of conservation of energy   9. The lattice energy of $Li^{2+}F^{2-}$
isn't large enough to compensate for the very large endothermic
second ionization energy of Li and the energy needed to place a
second electron into F^-.   10. energy
11.

H
H ⦂ Si ⦂ H

H

H ⦂ P ⦂ H

H ⦂ S ⦂ H

H ⦂ C̈l⦂

12. (a)   :C̈l:
       |
:C̈l — Si — C̈l:
       |
     :C̈l:

(b) :C̈l — F̈:
   /   \
  :F̈.   .F̈:

(c) :C̈l — S̈ — C̈l:

(d) $\left[\begin{array}{c} :Ö: \\ | \\ :Ö — S — Ö: \\ | \\ :Ö: \end{array} \right]^{2-}$

(e) :C≡O:

(f) $\left[:Ö — C̈l — Ö: \right]^-$

13. It must be approximately 3.   14. (a) I   (b) II   (c) II
(d) approximately 132 pm   15. The vibrational frequencies of
bonds.
16. (a)

:O:
‖
S
/ \
.O: .O:

←→

:Ö:
|
S
/ \
.O: .O:

←→

:Ö:
|
S
/ \
:O.   .O:

(b) $[:N≡N—N̈:]^- ⟷ [:N̈—N≡N:]^- ⟷ [:N̈=N=N̈:]^-$

(c) $\left[\begin{array}{c} .O: \\ \parallel \\ H—C \\ \diagdown \\ :O: \end{array} \right]^- ⟷ \left[\begin{array}{c} :O: \\ | \\ H—C \\ \diagdown \\ .O \end{array} \right]^-$

18.(a) $\left[\begin{array}{c} H ⦂ Ö ⦂ H \\ | \\ H \end{array} \right]^+$

(b) $\left[\begin{array}{c} :F̈: \\ | \\ :F ⦂ B ⦂ F: \\ | \\ :F̈: \end{array} \right]^-$

19.(a) H   (b) S   (c) O
                    (d) Br

20.(a) As   (b) Cl   21.(a) nickel(II) chloride
(b) chromium(III) carbonate   (c) strontium nitrate   (d) potassium
sulfate   (e) sulfur hexafluoride   (f) carbon tetrachloride
22.(a) SnO_2 (b) BCl_3 (c) $Ca(HCO_3)_2$ (d) Fe_2O_3 (e) N_2O_5
(f) Na_3P 23. $NaIO_4$ 24. chromic acid   25. hydroselenic acid
26.(a) H_3AsO_3 (b) Na_3AsO_3 (c) potassium dihydrogen arsenate

6 COVALENT BONDING AND MOLECULAR STRUCTURE

This chapter describes the modern theories of chemical bonding and how they can account for (or predict, in some cases) molecular structure. The thing to keep in mind throughout discussions of the different approaches is that each theory is attempting to describe the same thing and each, in its own way, succeeds to a degree. The theories, then, present alternative views of the same phenomenon.

6.1 MOLECULAR SHAPES

Objectives

To learn to recognize the five principle shapes that can be used to describe most molecular structures. You should learn the geometric properties of these five structures.

Review

Study the five basic geometric shapes described in this section. You should know the bond angles characteristic of each molecular shape, and you should be able to sketch the shapes.

Self-Test

1. On a separate sheet of paper, sketch the shapes of a tetra-hedron, a trigonal bipyramid, and an octahedron. Check yourself by comparing your drawings with those in the text

on Pages 181 and 182.   Practice until your drawings are
reasonable accurate.

2.   What are the bond angles in

(a)   a linear molecule?   _____

(b)   a tetrahedral molecule?   _____

(c)   an octahedral molecule?   _____

(d)   a trigonal bipyramidal molecule?   _____

(e)   a planar triangular molecule?   _____

New Terms

Bond angle
When one atom forms a bond to each of two other atoms, that
angle between the two bonds is the bond angle.

Linear molecule
A molecule in which all the atoms lie in a straight line.

Octahedral molecule
A molecule in which the central atom is bonded to six others
that are located at the vertices of an octahedron (a figure
consisting of two square pyramids that share a common base).

Planar triangular molecule
A molecule in which three atoms surround the central atom
at the corners of a triangle.   All four atoms are in the same
plane.

Tetrahedron
A four-sided pyramid with triangular faces.   A tetrahedral
molecule has an atom in the center of the tetrahedron with
other atoms joined to it that are located at the four vertices.

Trigonal bipyramid
A geometrical figure composed of two trigonal pyramids
(pyramids with three-sided faces) sharing a common triangular face.   A trigonal bipyramidal molecule has an atom
in the center of this triangular plane and is joined to five
others that are located at the vertices of the trigonal bipyramid.

6.2   VALENCE SHELL ELECTRON-PAIR REPULSION THEORY

Objectives

> To learn how to predict the shape of a molecule from the molecule's Lewis structure.

Review

The key to success in applying this very simple theory is the ability to construct Lewis structures for molecules and ions. If necessary, review the procedure for drawing Lewis structures on Pages 158 to 161.

The principle behind the VSEPR theory is that electron pairs in the valence shell of an atom tend to get as far apart as possible so that repulsions between them are a minimum. The arrangements of electron pairs that give minimum repulsions are given in Figure 6.1. You should recognize these as the five shapes discussed in the previous section.

When there are lone pairs (unshared pairs) of electrons in the valence shell of the central atom they influence molecular shape. In describing molecular shapes, remember that it is the arrangement of atoms that is specified and not how the electron pairs are arranged about the central atom. In SO_2, for example (Page 184), the electrons are arranged at the corners of a planar triangle. (Note that a multiple bond behaves just like a single bond for the purposes of predicting molecular shapes by the VSEPR theory.) One of these corners is occupied by a lone pair and the other two corners are occupied by oxygen atoms. In describing the shape of SO_2 we state how the two oxygens and the sulfur are arranged, and we ignore the lone pair. Thus SO_2 is said to be nonlinear or bent. It is not said to be planar triangular!

Study the shapes found for differing numbers of electron pairs and differing numbers of lone pairs in Figures 6.2, 6.3, 6.4, and 6.5. Be sure you know the names corresponding to the various structures. Remember that in the trigonal bipyramidal arrangement, the lone pairs are always found in the central triangular plane. The various shapes are summarized in Table 6.1. Although it is best if you can draw the shapes and deduce the structures from your drawings, you can also obtain correct answers if you know the contents of Table 6.1 thoroughly.

<u>Self-Test</u>

3. For each of the following, predict the arrangement of electron pairs and the molecular structure.

	electron arrangement	molecular structure
(a) AsH_3		
(b) $AlCl_4^-$		
(c) BrF_3		
(d) NO_2^-		
(e) ICl_2^-		
(f) H_3O^+		

<u>New Terms</u>

Valence Shell Electron Pair Repulsion Theory
   VSEPR theory. A theory used to predict molecular structure. It is based on the idea that electron pairs in the valence shell of an atom stay as far apart as possible.

Ligand
   An atom or a group of atoms bonded to a central atom in a molecule or polyatomic ion. A molecule or anion that can bind to a metal ion.

Lone pair
   An unshared pair of electrons in the valence shell of an atom.

6.3   POLARITY OF MOLECULES AND MOLECULAR STRUCTURE

<u>Objectives</u>

   To learn how to use molecular structures derived by the VSEPR theory to predict molecular polarity.

Review

A molecule will be nonpolar if its bond dipoles cancel. Each of the molecular structures that we've examined that contain no lone pairs in the valence shell of the central atom, and in which the ligands are all the same, give rise to nonpolar molecules because this cancellation does occur. If one or more lone pairs is in the valence shell, then a polar molecule generally results. Two exceptions are structures with the generalized formula AX_2E_3 and AX_4E_2. These structures, pictured in Figure 6.8, are symmetrical and give complete cancellation of the bond dipoles.

Self-Test

4. Predict whether the following are polar or nonpolar.

   (a) AsF_3 _____

   (b) ClF_3 _____

   (c) SO_3 _____

   (d) CCl_4 _____

   (e) $BeCl_2$ _____

   (f) $POCl_3$ _____

New Terms

Bond dipole
   The dipoles within a molecule caused by the unequal sharing of electrons in the bonds.

6.4   VALENCE BOND THEORY

Objectives

   To describe how this theory views the formation of a chemical bond. You should learn the basic ideas on which the theory is based.

Review

This theory says that a bond is formed by sharing a pair of electrons between overlapping atomic orbitals. Only two electrons can be shared between two orbitals. When orbitals come together, they must each have one electron, or one must be empty if the other orbital supplies two electrons (a coordinate covalent bond). When p orbitals are used in bonding, bond angles tend toward 90°.

Self-Test

5. What would you predict for the structure (shape and bond angles) of:

   (a) H_2S _____

   (b) PH_3 _____

New Terms

Molecular orbital theory

A theory of covalent bonding that views a molecule as a collection of positive nuclei surrounded by a set of orbitals that belong to the molecule as a whole and extend over all the positive centers in the molecule.

Overlap of orbitals

Portions of two orbitals from different atoms share the same space.

Valence bond theory

A theory of covalent bonding that views a bond as being formed by the sharing of one pair of electrons between two overlapping atomic or hybrid orbitals.

6.5   HYBRID ORBITALS

Objectives

To see how the atomic orbitals of an atom can mix to form hybrid orbitals that possess new directional properties. You should learn how molecular shapes can be accounted for by the use of hybrid orbitals. You should learn the directional properties of the different kinds of hybrid orbitals, and how the VSEPR theory can be used to predict which kinds of hybrid orbitals an atom will use to form bonds.

Review

Learn the orientations (summarized in Figure 6.15) of the different hybrid orbital sets in Table 6.2. In applying the information in this table to describing molecular structure, remember that when a central atom enters into bonding with several others, it must supply one unpaired electron for each of the atoms to which it is bonding. Review the descriptions for BeH_2, CH_4 and SF_6. Note that additional electron pairs belonging to the central atom which are not used in bonding can reside in hybrid orbitals, too. This is described for H_2O and NH_3. Remember that when hybrids are formed, s and p orbitals are used first, followed by d orbitals.

For most molecules, the VSEPR theory complements the valence bond theory well because it allows us to predict the orientations of the electron pairs around an atom. This information, in turn, tells us which kind of hybrid orbitals the atom uses.

Remember that when actual data on molecular structure is available, the valence bond description must fit the actual known structure. Review Example 6.10 in the text.

Self-Test

6. What kind of hybrid orbitals are expected to be used by the central atom in each of the following? What molecular structure is expected?

(a) $SiCl_4$ _____ _____

(b) BCl_3 _____ _____

(c) XeF_4 _____ _____

(d) PCl_4 _____ _____

(e) $SnCl_2$ _____ _____

7. In NCl_3, the Cl—N—Cl bond anbles are 106.8°. What kind
    of orbitals does nitrogen probably use in forming bonds
    to the chlorine atoms?

    _____

8. In H_2Te, the bond angle is 89.5°. What kind of orbitals
    does tellurium use in bonding in this molecule?

    _____

9. The ion $SbCl_6^-$ is formed by the attachment of a Cl^- ion to
    an $SbCl_5$ molecule. This involves the creation of a coordinate
    covalent bond. Illustrate the bonding in $SbCl_6^-$ by means of
    an orbital diagram. Use different symbols for the Sb and
    Cl electrons.

New Terms

Hybrid atomic orbitals
    Orbitals formed by mixing the basic atomic orbitals of an
    atom. They are more effective at overlapping with other
    orbitals than are ordinary unhybridized atomic orbitals.

6.6   MULTIPLE BONDS

Objectives

    To see how multiple bonds are described in terms of
    orbital overlap.

Review

    Multiple bonds are usually formed when unpaired electrons
would occur on atoms if the rules in the last section were followed. In ethylene, for example, each carbon atom is bonded to
three other atoms.

This requires three unpaired electrons on the carbon atoms, and if no double bond were formed, we would have the situation,

$$C \quad \underline{\uparrow} \quad \underline{\uparrow x \quad \uparrow x \quad \uparrow x} \qquad \text{(x's are electrons}$$
$$sp^3 \qquad \qquad \text{from other atoms)}$$

This leaves an unpaired electron in an sp^3 hybrid orbital. This tends to displease Mother Nature. As a result, in this kind of situation we only use three hybrid orbitals (sp^2) for σ-bonds. The remaining electron remains in an unhybridized orbital and can then pair with another electron on the neighboring carbon atom to form a π-bond.

Lewis structures are based on the valence bond description of bonding. If a Lewis structure has multiple bonds, you should account for the bonding as described in this section. Be sure you understand the meaning of σ-bond and π-bond. Remember that the basic molecular framework or skeleton of a molecule is accounted for by σ-bonds, which determine the kinds of hybrid orbitals the atoms use. Any unhybridized orbitals containing un-paired electrons then participate in π bonding.

Self-Test

10. Indicate the number of σ- and π-bonds in the bonds of the following molecules:

    (a) CO_2 _____

    (b) CO_3^{2-} _____

    (c) N_2 _____

    (d) C_2^{2-} _____

    (e) GeH_4 _____

11. What kinds of hybrid orbitals are used by the atoms in the molecules below, and what kinds of bonds (σ, π) exist be-tween the atoms?

(a)

H
|
H—C—C≡N:
|
H

(b)

H H   H
| | .. |
H—C—C=N—N—H
| ..
H

New Terms

Pi bond (π bond)

A bond formed by the sideways overlap of a pair of p orbitals. Electron density in the bond is concentrated in two separate regions that lie on opposite sides of an imaginary plane that contains both nuclei.

Sigma bond (σ bond)

A bond formed by the head-to-head overlap of two orbitals. The electron density in the bond is concentrated along an imaginary straight line that connects the two nuclei.

6.7   RESONANCE

Objectives

To relate the Lewis structures for molecules that exhibit resonance to the valence bond description of bonding.

Review

The point that is made here is that Lewis structures are, in effect, simplified versions of valence bond structures.

New Terms

6.8   SINGLE BONDS VERSUS MULTIPLE BONDS: THE MOLECULAR STRUCTURES OF THE ELEMENTAL NONMETALS

Objectives

To look at the effects of chemical bonding on the degrees of complexity of the structures of the elemental nonmetals.

Review

This section illustrates how important chemical bonding is in determining the properties of substances.   In this case, we examine the complexity of the molecular structures of the non-metals.   The key to understanding these structures is the fact that elements in period 2 are able to form strong π-bonds while elements in the following periods form much weaker π-bonds.   As a result, double and triple bonds are observed among period 2 elements, but period 3 elements tend to favor two or three single bonds to separate atoms, rather than π-bonds to just one other atom.

The following are the most important items to review:

(1) allotropism involving oxygen and carbon
(2) the structure of graphite, which accounts for its applications as a dry lubricant
(3) the structure of the S_8 ring in sulfur
(4) the structure of white phosphorus and the existence of the less reactive allotropes, red and black phosphorus

Self-Test

12. How many atoms do the following elements bond to in their elemental forms?

(a)   Cl   _____   (c)   P   _____

(b)   S   _____   (d)   Si   _____

13. How does graphite differ from diamond? _____

_____

14. What is the structure of elemental sulfur? _____

_____

15. What is the structure of white phosphorus? _____

_____

New Terms

Allotropism
   The existence of an element in two or more different forms.

Black phosphorus
   An allotrope of phosphorus having a layer structure, which
   imparts to it some properties similar to graphite.

Diamond
   An allotrope of carbon. The hardest substance known.

Graphite
   The common allotrope of carbon. It is a black slippery solid
   that has a layer structure in which the carbon atoms in each
   layer are arranged in hexagonal rings fused together.
   Graphite is a conductor of electricity.

Red phosphorus
   A relatively unreactive allotrope of phosphorus whose
   molecular structure is presently unknown.

White phosphorus
   A very reactive form of phosphorus that consists of P_4
   molecules.

6.9   MOLECULAR ORBITAL THEORY

Objectives

   To understand how molecular orbitals are created from
   atomic orbitals. You should learn the difference between
   bonding and antibonding molecular orbitals and how the
   electronic structure of a molecule is obtained by filling
   molecular orbitals. You should also learn how molecular
   orbital theory avoids the idea of resonance.

Review

Molecular orbitals appear to be formed by constructive and destructive interference of the electron waves of atomic orbitals. We obtain their descriptions by alternately adding and subtracting atomic orbitals that overlap from different atoms. Bonding orbitals concentrate electron density between nuclei, thereby binding the atoms together. Antibonding orbitals place electron density outside the region between nuclei and, when occupied by electrons, decrease the stability of the molecule.

Molecular orbitals are filled following the same rules for filling atomic orbitals in atoms: (1) electrons go into the lowest energy orbitals first; (2) no more than two electrons may occupy the same orbital; (3) when there are orbitals of the same energy, the electrons spread out as much as possible with spins in the same direction.

Learn how to calculate the net bond order from the number of bonding and antibonding electrons. You should also learn the energy level diagram for diatomic molecules (Figure 6.33).

Notice that molecular orbital theory avoids resonance by permitting molecular orbitals to spread out over more than two atoms.

Self-Test

16. On a separate piece of paper, sketch the molecular orbital energy level diagram for diatomic molecules having the second shell (2s and 2p subshells) as their valence shell. Use this diagram to answer the following questions.

    (a)   Is the molecule Be_2 stable?   _____

    (b)   Which species is more stable, O_2 or O_2^+?   _____

    (c)   Which species is more stable, N_2 or N_2^+?   _____

    (d)   Which has the shorter bond, C_2^- or C_2^{2-}?   _____

New Terms

Molecular orbital
   An orbital in a molecule that is able to extend over all the nuclei of the molecule.

Bonding molecular orbital
   A molecular orbital that gives a buildup of electron density between nuclei and helps stabilize a molecule.

Antibonding orbital
   A molecular orbital that places electron density outside of the region between the nuclei. When filled, an antibonding orbital destabilizes a molecule.

Net bond order
   $$\frac{(\text{no of bonding electrons}) - (\text{no. of antibonding electrons})}{2}$$

Delocalized molecular orbital
   A molecular orbital that spreads over more than two nuclei

Answers to Self-Test Questions

1. See Page 181, 182 of text. 2.(a) 180° (b) 109.5° (c) 90° (d) 120° (in triangular plane), 90° (between triangular plane and vertical bond) (e) 120°

3.

electron arrangement	molecular structure
(a) tetrahedral	trigonal pyramidal
(b) tetrahedral	tetrahedral
(c) trigonal bipyramidal	T-shaped
(d) planar triangular	angular (bent)
(e) trigonal bipyramidal	linear
(f) tetrahedral	trigonal pyramidal

4.(a) trigonal pyramidal - polar (b) T-shaped - polar (c) planar triangular - nonpolar (d) tetrahedral - nonpolar (e) linear - nonpolar (f) tetrahedral - polar because all atoms attached to phosphorus are not alike.

5.(a) angular (bent) molecule, H—S—H angle = 90° (b) trigonal pyramidal molecule, H—P—H angles = 90°

6.(a) sp^3, tetrahedral (b) sp^2, planar triangular (c) sp^3d^2, square planar (d) sp^3d, trigonal bipyramidal (e) sp^2, angular (bent)

7. Based on the bond angles, probably sp^3.

8. Based on the bond angle, probably p.

9. Sb   ↑x ↑x ↑x ↑x ↑x xx   __ __ __   (x = Cl electrons)

sp^3d^2 ↗   unhybridized 5d orbitals

↳coordinate covalent bond

10.(a) two σ-bonds, two π-bonds
   (b) three σ-bonds, one π-bond
   (c) one σ-bond, two π-bonds
   (d) one σ-bond, two π-bonds
   (e) four σ-bonds

11.(a)

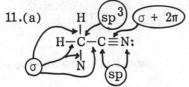

(b)

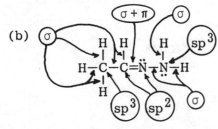

12.(a) one (b) two (c) three (d) four
13. graphite - planar sheets held to each other by weak forces;
diamond - three-dimensional covalent structure
14. Puckered S_8 ring (Figure 6.28)
15. Tetrahedral P_4 molecule (Figure 6.29)
16. (a) no; net bond order = 0
    (b) O_2^+ is more stable since net bond order is greater than
         for O_2.
    (c) N_2, larger net bond order.
    (d) C_2^{2-} (same structure as N_2), larger net bond order.

7 CHEMICAL REACTIONS AND THE PERIODIC TABLE

To make it simpler to learn chemical properties and chemical reactions, they are divided into various types. This chapter introduces you to some of the classes of chemical reactions and how certain chemical properties vary within the periodic table. The topics discussed here are important and should become part of the core of chemical knowledge that you take with you from this course.

7.1   REACTIONS IN SOLUTION

Objectives

To learn about chemical reactions between ions in aqueous solutions. You should learn how to write equations for the dissociation of electrolytes, both strong and weak. You should also learn the terms used to describe reactions between ions and how equations for these reactions can be written.

Review

Be sure you have learned the various terms that apply to solutions which are discussed on Pages 224 and 225. If necessary, refer to the list of new terms at the end of this section.

Compounds that give electrically conducting solutions in water are electrolytes. These include all soluble ionic compounds

(salts) as well as certain molecular compounds such as HCl and
NH_3. Remember that essentially all ionic solids are virtually 100%
dissociated in aqueous solution. A particularly important ion
formed by the ionization of acids is H_3O^+, which is called the
hydronium ion. Compounds that are completely dissociated in
solution are strong electrolytes and those that are incompletely
dissociated are weak electrolytes. You should learn how to write
the equation for the ionization of a weak electrolyte in water.

The concept of dynamic equilibrium introduced in this section is worth studying in detail; it is one of the most important
concepts in chemistry. Remember that chemical reactions are
generally able to proceed in both the forward and reverse directions. When opposing reactions are occurring at the same speed
there is no change in the amount of reactants and products. We
use the term position of equilibrium to describe how far toward
completion a reaction proceeds before equilibrium is reached. In
a reaction

$$A \rightleftharpoons B$$

the position of equilibrium lies far to the right if a lot of B is
produced from A by the time equilibrium is attained.

The kind of ionic reaction described in this section is
called metathesis. Note that in a metathesis reaction, the positive
and negative ions exchange partners.

There are several ways of writing equations for metathesis
reactions. The equation written using full formulas for the compounds is called the molecular equation. For example, consider
the reaction between sodium sulfate and barium nitrate, which
gives a precipitate of barium sulfate.

$$Na_2SO_4(aq) + Ba(NO_3)_2(aq) \longrightarrow BaSO_4(s) + 2NaNO_3(aq)$$

In writing such reactions, be sure you have the correct formulas
for the reactants and products; then proceed to balance the equation.

A better representation of what actually occurs during the
reaction is provided by the ionic equation in which soluble ionic
compounds are written in dissociated form.

$$2Na^+ + SO_4^{2-} + Ba^{2+} + 2NO_3^- \longrightarrow BaSO_4(s) + 2Na^+ + 2NO_3^-$$

Cancelling spectator ions from the ionic equation gives the net ionic equation.

$$SO_4^{2-} + Ba^{2+} \longrightarrow BaSO_4(s)$$

Study Example 7.3 on Page 232 before attempting the Self-Test below.

Self-Test

1. Sugar has a solubility of 211 g per 100 g of water at 25°C. A solution containing 215 g of sugar in 100 g of water at 25°C would be described by which term (or terms)?
   (a) concentrated   (d) supersaturated
   (b) dilute   (e) saturated
   (c) unsaturated

   _____

2. In the solution in Question 1, the solute is _____ and the solvent is _____.

3. In a chemical equation, what symbol do we use to indicate that ions are hydrated in solution?

   _____

4. How do we abbreviate the formula for the hydronium ion?

   _____

5. Sodium carbonate, Na_2CO_3, is a strong electrolyte. Write a chemical equation for its dissociation in water.

   _____

6. Nitrous acid, HNO_2, is a weak acid just like acetic acid is. Write an appropriate chemical equation for the ionization of this compound in water.

   _____

7. What is another term used to describe a metathesis reaction?

   _____

8. What do we call a solid that is formed in a solution as a result of a chemical reaction?

   _____

9. Write the ionic and net ionic equations for the following reactions. All compounds shown are soluble except those having (s) following their formulas.

(a) $NaI + AgNO_3 \longrightarrow AgI(s) + NaNO_3$

(b) $Pb(NO_3)_2 + Ba(OH)_2 \longrightarrow Pb(OH)_2(s) + Ba(NO_3)_2$

(c) $AgCl(s) + NaBr \longrightarrow AgBr(s) + NaCl$

(d) $ZnCl_2 + Na_2CO_3 \longrightarrow 2NaCl + ZnCO_3(s)$

New Terms

Dissociation
    In general, the breaking apart of a substance into simpler substances. For aqueous solutions, the separation of the ions of an ionic compound as it dissolves. The term is also applied to the ionization of molecular compounds in water, which gives ions in solution.

Double replacement reaction
    Metathesis. A reaction between two salts in which cations exchange partners.

Dynamic equilibrium
    An equilibrium in which two opposing processes are occurring at equal rates.

Electrolyte
    A substance that gives ions in an aqueous solution and thereby gives a solution that conducts electricity.

Filtrate
    The liquid that passes through a filter.

Hydrated ion
    An ion that has become surrounded by molecules of water to which it is attracted.

Hydronium ion
    The ion H_3O^+.

Ionic equation
    A chemical equation in which all water-soluble electrolytes are written in ionic form, while solids and weak electrolytes are written in molecular form.

Ionization reaction
> A reaction that produces ions. A reaction of a molecular substance with water in which ions are formed.

Metathesis reaction
> See *Double replacement reaction.*

Molecular equation
> A chemical equation for a reaction in solution in which the formulas of strong electrolytes are written as if the substances were molecular.

Net ionic equation
> A chemical equation obtained by omitting spectator ions from an ionic equation. It shows the net chemical change that occurs.

Nonelectrolyte
> A substance that does not dissociate into ions in an aqueous solution.

Position of equilibrium
> The relative proportions of reactants and products in an equilibrium system.

Precipitate
> A solid that forms in a solution, often as the result of a chemical reaction.

Saturated solution
> A solution that contains as much dissolved solute as it can hold while in equilibrium with undissolved solute.

Solubility
> The amount of solute required to give a saturated solution in a given quantity of solvent or solution.

Spectator ion
> An ion that does not participate in a particular chemical reaction.

Strong electrolyte
> An electrolyte that is 100 percent dissociated in water.

Supersaturated
> A term that describes a solution in which there is more dissolved solute than could normally exist in the solution if the solution were in contact with excess solute. Supersaturated

solutions are unstable with respect to the spontaneous crystallization of excess solute.

Unsaturated

A term applied to a solution that is capable of dissolving more solute.

Weak electrolyte

An electrolyte that is less than 100 percent dissociated in water.

7.2   ACIDS AND BASES IN AQUEOUS SOLUTIONS

Objectives

To learn the definitions of acids and bases in aqueous solutions and how these substances react with each other.

Review

Remember the Arrhenius definitions of acids and bases:

Acids produce H_3O^+ when dissolved in water.

Bases produce OH^- when dissolved in water.

Many acids contain hydrogen atoms that are transferred to water molecules when the acid ionizes in water. In many cases H_3O^+ is simply indicated as H^+ since this is the "active ingredient" in the H_3O^+ ion during chemical reactions. Metal hydroxides, when soluble, dissociate to give OH^- in solution. They are strong bases. You should learn the strong acids and strong bases given in Table 7.2 on Page 236.

Acids and bases react with each other to produce a salt and water. A salt is a general term that is used to refer to any ionic compound except metal hydroxides, which are called bases. An example of an acid-base neutralization reaction is

$$2HCl + Ba(OH)_2 \longrightarrow BaCl_2 + 2H_2O$$

Polyprotic acids (those able to supply more than one H^+ per molecule of acid) can be partially neutralized to give acid

salts; for example, $NaHSO_4$ from the partial neutralization of
H_2SO_4. Bases generally do not undergo partial neutralizations;
instead, all of the OH^- of a base is neutralized in the formation
of salts which can be isolated from solution.

You should also remember that metal oxides are basic and
are called basic anhydrides. When they dissolve in water they
produce hydroxides because of the reaction,

$$O^{2-} + H_2O \longrightarrow 2\ OH^-$$

Even if they are insoluble, metal oxides and hydroxides still react
with acids; for example,

$$Fe_2O_3 + 6H^+ \longrightarrow 2Fe^{3+} + 3H_2O$$
(rust)

Nonmetal oxides are acidic and are called acidic anhydrides.
Many give acids when they dissolve. For example,

$$CO_2 + H_2O \longrightarrow H_2CO_3$$

Self-Test

10. Write the chemical equation for the reaction of the following
with water:
(a) HBr   _____

(b) H_2SO_4 _____

_____

(c) N_2H_4 _____
(d) O^{2-} _____

11. Identify the following as acid (A) or basic (B) anhydrides.

(a) CaO _____   (d) Li_2O _____

(b) SO_2 _____   (e) N_2O_3 _____

(c) CO_2 _____   (f) P_4O_6 _____

12. Write chemical equations showing the reactions of the following with water.
(a) SO_3 _____

(b) P_4O_{10} _____

(c) BaO _____

(d) N_2O_3 _____

13. What is the net neutralization reaction between a strong acid and a strong base in aqueous solution?

_____

14. Write balanced molecular equations for the neutralization reaction between:

(a) $Ca(OH)_2$ and HCl

(b) NH_3 and H_2SO_4 (complete neutralization)

(c) $Al(OH)_3$ and H_2SO_4 (complete neutralization)

(d) NaOH and HNO_3

(e) MgO and H_2SO_4 (complete neutralization)

15. Write formulas for all salts formed between $Ca(OH)_2$ and

(a) $H_2C_2O_4$ _____

(b) H_2CO_3 _____

(c) H_3AsO_4 _____

(d) HBr _____

16. Without referring to Table 7.2, indicate whether the following are strong or weak acids or bases.

(a) HCl _____

(b) HNO_2 _____

(c) HF _____

(d) $HClO_4$ _____

(e) KOH _____

(f) N_2H_4 _____

New Terms

Acid
A substance that gives H_3O^+ in an aqueous solution.

Acid salt
A salt of a partially neutralized polyprotic acid: for example, $NaHSO_4$ and NaH_2PO_4.

Acidic anhydride
A nonmetal oxide that reacts with water to form an acid.

Arrhenius concept of acids and bases
Acids produce H_3O^+ in water and bases produce OH^- in water.

Base
A substance that gives OH^- in aqueous solution.

Basic anhydride
A metal oxide that reacts with water to give a metal hydroxide.

Diprotic acid
An acid that can furnish two H^+ ions per molecule of the acid.

Indicator
A substance whose color in a solution depends on whether the solution is acidic or basic.

Monoprotic acid
An acid that is capable of furnishing only one H^+ per molecule.

Neutralization
The reaction of an acid with a base. In aqueous solutions, the products are a salt and water.

Polyprotic acid
An acid that is capable of furnishing more than one H^+ per molecule of the acid.

Strong acid
An acid that is 100 percent ionized in water.

Strong base
A base that is 100 percent dissociated in water.

Triprotic acid
    An acid that can furnish three H^+ per molecule.

Weak acid
    An acid that is less than 100 percent dissociated in water.

Weak base
    A base that is less than 100 percent dissociated in water.

7.3   BRØNSTED-LOWRY ACIDS AND BASES

Objectives

    To define acids and bases in terms of the transfer of a proton. You should learn to identify acid-base conjugate pairs in an acid-base reaction. You should learn what an amphiprotic (amphoteric) substance is.

Review

    Learn the Brønsted-Lowry definitions of acid and base:

$$\underline{acid} - \text{proton } (H^+) \text{ donor}$$
$$\underline{base} - \text{proton acceptor}$$

Acid-base reactions can be looked upon as reversible.

$$\text{Acid (X)} + \text{Base (Y)} \rightleftharpoons \text{Base (X)} + \text{Acid (Y)}$$

$$HX + Y \rightleftharpoons X^- + HY^+$$

There are two conjugate acid-base pairs in this reaction.

Acid (X) - Base (X) (HX, X^-)
Base (Y) - Acid (Y) (Y, HY^+)

Let's look at a concrete example,

$$HNO_3 + H_2O \rightleftharpoons H_3O^+ + NO_3^-$$

acid   base   acid   base

conjugate pair
conjugate pair

Notice that the only difference between the members of a conjugate pair is a <u>single</u> proton. All other atoms are identical. Also, note that the acid has <u>one</u> more hydrogen than the base.

Example 7.1

From the list below, choose those two which form a conjugate acid-base pair. Which one is the acid?

$$H_2SO_4, \ OH^-, \ HSO_3^-, \ SO_3^{2-}, \ SO_4^{2-}$$

Solution

The only two species that differ from each other by <u>only one hydrogen</u> are

$$HSO_3^- \ \text{and} \ SO_3^{2-}$$

The one with the most hydrogen (HSO_3^-) is the acid.

An amphiprotic (amphoteric) substance can act as either an acid or a base. The most common example is water.

$$\overbrace{\underset{\text{acid}}{H_3O^+} \qquad \underset{\text{base}}{H_2O}}^{} \qquad OH^-$$

$$\underset{\text{acid}}{H_2O} \qquad \underbrace{\qquad \qquad}_{\text{base}} OH^-$$

Review the autoionization reactions on Page 241 of the text. Also, note that the Brønsted-Lowry definition permits acid-base reactions in the absence of a solvent. The reaction between $HCl(g)$ and $NH_3(g)$ is an example.

Some metal ions, especially those with a high charge, produce acidic solutions. An example is the Al^{3+} ion, which exists as $Al(H_2O)_6^{3+}$ in solution.

Self-Test

17. In each of the following, indicate whether the underlined substance is behaving as an acid (A) or a base (B).

   (a) $\underline{H_2O} + HC_2H_3O_2 \rightleftharpoons H_3O^+ + C_2H_3O_2^-$ _____

   (b) $\underline{CN^-} + HCl \rightleftharpoons HCN + Cl^-$ _____

   (c) $\underline{NH_3} + O^{2-} \rightleftharpoons NH_2^- + OH^-$ _____

18. For each pair in Question 17, identify both acid-base conjugate pairs. Underline the acid in each of them.

(a) _____ , _____

(b) _____ , _____

(c) _____ , _____

19. Which of the following <u>could not</u> serve as amphiprotic substances?
(a) NH_3 (b) CN^- (c) O^{2-} (d) HSO_4^- (e) SO_4^{2-}

_____

20. Write a chemical equation to show why solutions containing $Cr(H_2O)_6^{3+}$ are slightly acidic.

_____

New Terms

Amphiprotic
   The ability of a substance to either accept or donate a proton.

Amphoteric
   The ability of a substance to behave as either an acid or a base.

Autoionization reaction
   The reaction of a substance with itself to produce ions.
   For example, $H_2O + H_2O \rightleftharpoons H_3O^+ + OH^-$

Brønsted acid
   A proton (H^+) donor.

Brønsted base
   A proton (H^+) acceptor.

Conjugate acid
   A Brønsted acid, which is formed by the addition of a proton to a base. (NH_4^+ is the conjugate acid of the base NH_3.)

Conjugate base
   A Brønsted base, which is formed by the removal of a proton from a Brønsted acid. (NH_3 is the conjugate base of the acid NH_4^+.)

Conjugate acid–base pair

Two substances related to each other by the gain or loss of a single proton, for example, NH_4^+ and NH_3.

7.4   THE STRENGTHS OF ACIDS AND BASES: PERIODIC TRENDS

Objectives

To compare the relative strengths of acids and bases, and to learn how acid strength varies within the periodic table.

Review

The position of equilibrium in the reaction,

$$HA + B^- \rightleftharpoons HB + A^-$$

allows us to compare the relative strengths of the acids and bases. A strong acid tends to give up its proton more readily than a weak acid. If HA is stronger than HB, the position of equilibrium lies to the right. Similarly, a strong base is able to capture protons more readily than a weak base. If B^- is a stronger base than A^-, the B^- captures more protons than the A^- and the position of equilibrium again lies to the right.

Below are summarized the trends in acidity that we observe among different kinds of acids. You should be aware of these, and the Self-Test provides a way to test your ability to apply the rules. In addition, you should try to understand why these trends occur. If you're not sure about the reasons, reread the explanations provided in the text.

Oxoacids, H_nXO_m

(1) For a given element X the strength of the acid increases as the number of lone oxygens increases.

(2) For acids with the same general formula, the acid strength increases as the atom X becomes more electronegative (going from bottom to top in a group).

(3) As the position of element X goes from left to right across a period, the acid strength increases for acids that have the

same number of oxygens.

Trends (2) and (3) are summarized in Figure 7.7 on Page 246.

Binary acids, H_nX

(1) The strength of the acid increases from left to right across a period.

(2) The strength of the acid increases from top to bottom within a group.

These trends are summarized in Figure 7.8 on Page 247.

Self-Test

21. In each pair below, choose the stronger acid.

(a) H_2SeO_3, H_2SeO_4 _____

(b) $HBrO_3$, $HBrO$ _____

(c) HNO_3, HNO_2 _____

(d) H_3PO_4, H_2SO_4 _____

(e) H_3PO_4, H_3AsO_4 _____

(f) H_3N, H_2O _____

(g) PH_3, NH_3 _____

(h) H_2Se, HBr _____

New Terms

Binary acid
    A substance with the general formula H_nX which produces acidic aqueous solutions (e.g., HCl, H_2S).

7.5   LEWIS ACIDS AND BASES

Objectives

    To provide a still more general definition of an acid and a base. You should learn how the Lewis definition can be used to explain acid-base reactions.

Review

Under the Lewis definition we have:

base - electron pair donor
acid - electron pair acceptor

A Lewis acid and base react with each other by the formation of a coordinate covalent bond. Lewis bases tend to be species that have lone pairs of electrons and completed octets. Lewis acids tend to be substances that can be considered "electron deficient," or which can make themselves electron deficient by rearrangement of their electrons. The latter is illustrated by SO_3 when it reacts with oxide ion.

Lewis acid-base reactions are often viewed as displacement reactions.

$$[:\ddot{S}:]^{2-} \quad + \quad \begin{matrix} acid \\ H \\ :O: \\ H \end{matrix} \longrightarrow [:\ddot{S} - H]^- + [:\ddot{O} - H]^-$$

incoming   outgoing
base   base

$$S^{2-} + H_2O \longrightarrow HS^- + OH^-$$

Self-Test

22. Use electron-dot formulas to show how the reaction of O^{2-} with SO_2 to produce SO_3^{2-} can be considered the reaction between a Lewis acid and base.

23. Diethyl ether (shown below) reacts with boron trichloride to form an addition compound. Use Lewis structures to show how this is a Lewis acid-base reaction.

$$\begin{matrix} & H & H & & H & H \\ & | & | & & | & | \\ H- & C- & C- & \ddot{O}- & C- & C- & H \\ & | & | & & | & | \\ & H & H & & H & H \end{matrix}$$

diethyl ether

New Terms

Lewis acid
   An electron pair acceptor during the formation of a coordinate covalent bond.

Lewis base
   An electron pair donor during the formation of a coordinate covalent bond.

7.6   OXIDATION-REDUCTION REACTIONS; OXIDATION NUMBERS

Objectives

To learn about chemical reactions that occur by the transfer of electrons, either partially or completely, from one atom to another. You should become familiar with, and be able to use <u>oxidation numbers</u> to keep tabs on electrons.

Review

Be sure you know the meaning of the terms oxidation and reduction. You should be able to identify the oxidizing agent and reducing agent in a chemical reaction. The definitions of oxidizing agent and reducing agent are sometimes confusing. Just remember that if a substance is oxidized (i.e., loses electrons), we call it a reducing agent; a substance that is reduced is an oxidizing agent.

It is important to learn the rules for assigning oxidation numbers. Practice on the questions in the Self-Test below.

Self-Test

24. Assign oxidation numbers to the atoms in the following formulas.

   (a) $KClO_3$ _____

   (b) MnO_4^{2-} _____

   (c) $S_2O_3^{2-}$ _____

   (d) $SiCl_4$ _____

(e) BrF_3 _____

(f) P_4O_6 _____

(g) $SbCl_6^-$ _____

(h) $C_{12}H_{22}O_{11}$ _____

(i) S_3^{2-} _____

(j) O_3 _____

25. Identify the oxidizing and reducing agent in the following reactions.

(a) $H_2 + Cl_2 \longrightarrow 2HCl$ _____

(b) $2Na_2S_2O_3 + I_2 \longrightarrow 2NaI + Na_2S_4O_6$ _____

(c) $3O_2 + C_2H_4 \longrightarrow 2CO_2 + 2H_2O$ _____

(d) $K_2Cr_2O_7 + 14HCl \longrightarrow 3Cl_2 + 2KCl + 2CrCl_3 + 7H_2O$

_____

New Terms

Oxidation
   Loss of electrons.   Increase in oxidation number.

Oxidation number
   The charge an atom would have if all the electrons in each of its bonds belonged to the more electronegative atom. Normally, oxidation numbers are assigned following the rules given in the text.

Oxidation-reduction reaction
   A reaction that involves the transfer of electrons from one substance to another.   A reaction that involves a change in oxidation numbers.   Also called a redox reaction.

Oxidation state
   The same as oxidation number.

Oxidizing agent
   In a redox reaction, the substance that is reduced, thereby causing the oxidation.

Redox
> A term meaning *oxidation-reduction*.

Reducing agent
> A substance that causes reduction by supplying electrons.
> It is the substance that is oxidized in a redox reaction.

Reduction
> A gain of electrons, or a decrease in oxidation number.

7.7   BALANCING REDOX EQUATIONS USING OXIDATION NUMBERS

Objectives

> To learn to balance oxidation-reduction reactions by making use of the changes of oxidation numbers.

Review

This section and the next discuss alternative ways of balancing redox reactions. The approach taken by the oxidation-number-change (ONC) method and the ion-electron (IE) method (Section 7.8) are different in several respects. It is only necessary to assign oxidation numbers in the ONC method. The IE method does not employ oxidation numbers even though the same end result is achieved. The key to both methods is making the number of electrons gained equal to the number lost.

In the ONC method, be sure to calculate the number of electrons transferred per formula unit for the reactants. Place coefficients in the equation to make the total electron loss equal to the total electron gain. Balance the remainder of the equation by inspection.

Remember, there is never any reason to be unsure that an equation is balanced correctly. You can always count up the numbers of each kind of atom on each side of the arrow. Also remember that an equation is not balanced unless there is the same net charge on each side.

Self-Test

26. Balance the following by the oxidation-number-change
     method.

   (a) $PH_3 + N_2O \longrightarrow H_3PO_4 + N_2$

   (b) $NaIO_3 + Na_2SO_3 \longrightarrow Na_2SO_4 + NaI$

   (c) $PbO_2 + HCl \longrightarrow PbCl_2 + H_2O + Cl_2$

New Terms

Oxidation-number-change method
   A method for balancing redox equations that makes the total
   increase in oxidation number equal the total decrease.

7.8   BALANCING REDOX EQUATIONS BY THE ION-ELECTRON METHOD

Objectives

   To learn a method of developing balanced net ionic equations for redox reactions in aqueous solution.

Review

   Balancing a redox equation by this method is very simple
if you remember to be sure to follow these steps:

   1. divide the reaction into two half-reactions.

   2. balance atoms other than H and O.

   3. balance O and H (O first, then H) using H_2O and
       H^+, respectively, for reactions in acid solution.

   4. count up the net charge on both sides of each half-
       reaction.

   5. for each half-reaction, add electrons to the most
       positive (least negative) side to make the net charge
       on both sides of the arrow the same.

   6. multiply the half-reactions by appropriate factors to
       make electron gain equal electron loss.

7. add the half-reactions.

8. cancel anything that appears the same on both sides of the equation.

To balance an equation for a reaction taking place in basic solution, first balance it as if it were taking place in acidic solution. Then follow the three-step procedure on Page 259 to convert the equation to basic solution. Remember to add the necessary number of OH^- to <u>both</u> sides of the equation - otherwise you will upset the balance.

When you use the ion-electron method it is extremely important to write the appropriate charges on each formula. If you mean H^+ and write H, without giving the charge, you will almost certainly get the number of electrons wrong. This, of course, will mean that you will multiply the half-reactions by the wrong factors and hence obtain an improperly balanced equation.

<u>Self-Test</u>

27. Balance the following by the ion-electron method. (All reactions in acid solution)

(a) $HNO_2 + I^- \longrightarrow I_2 + NO$

(b) $ClO_3^- + H_2S \longrightarrow Cl^- + S$

(c) $S_2O_8^{2-} + P \longrightarrow SO_4^{2-} + H_3PO_4$

28. Balance the following by the ion-electron method. (All reactions in basic solution)

(a) $CrO_4^{2-} + SO_3^{2-} \longrightarrow CrO_2^- + SO_4^{2-}$

(b) $HO_2^- + ClO_2 \longrightarrow ClO_2^- + O_2$

(c) $MnO_4^- + NO_2^- \longrightarrow MnO_2 + NO_3^-$

(d) $ClO^- + NH_3 \longrightarrow N_2H_4 + Cl^-$ (This reaction between bleach, OCl^-, and ammonia, NH_3, can produce poisonous hydrazine, N_2H_4. Be careful - don't mix household cleansers!)

New Terms

Ion-electron method

A method for balancing redox reactions. It divides the overall reaction into half-reactions that are balanced separately and then combined to give the net ionic equation for the redox reaction.

Half-reaction

An individual oxidation or reduction reaction that includes the correct formulas for all species taking part in the reaction as well as the electrons that are lost or gained. An example is: $2H_2O \longrightarrow O_2(g) + 4H^+(aq) + 4e^-$

7.9   METALS AS REDUCING AGENTS

Objectives

To learn some of the chemical properties of metals. You should learn the periodic trends in the ease of oxidation of metals and what happens to metals when they dissolve in acids. You should also learn how to use the activity series for metals to predict the outcome of single displacement reactions.

Review

When metals react with other elements, they are oxidized and therefore serve as reducing agents. One of the characteristic reactions of metals is with acids. Nonoxidizing acids have H^+ as their only oxidizing agent. Metals that react with these acids liberate H_2 gas. Typical metals that react with such acids are zinc, iron, magnesium, and aluminum. In fact, any metal that lies above hydrogen in the activity series (Table 7.3 on Page 267) liberates H_2 from a nonoxidizing acid.

Metals that are below hydrogen in the activity series will only react with oxidizing acids such as HNO_3, which has the strong oxidizing agent NO_3^-. Note the products in the oxidation of copper by concentrated and dilute HNO_3.

Study Figure 7.10. You should know in a general way how the reactivity of metals varies within the periodic table.

Notice in particular that the metals that are most difficult to oxidize are located in the center of the periodic table in periods 5 and 6. Remember that all the metals in Group IA and Ca, Sr, Ba, and Ra in Group IIA react with cold water to liberate H_2. You should be able to write chemical equations for these reactions.

The activity series allows you to predict the outcome of single displacement reactions. Any metal in Table 7.3 will cause the cation of a metal below it to be reduced. Study Examples 7.12 and 7.13 on Page 266 before attempting the Self-Test below.

Self-Test

29. Based on their positions in the periodic table, which element in each pair below is more easily oxidized?

(a) Rb or Sr   _____

(b) Ti or Ir   _____

(c) Ca or Fe   _____

30. Write a balanced equation for the reaction of hydrochloric acid with each of the following metals. If there is no reaction, write N.R.

(a) magnesium   _____

(b) aluminum   _____

(c) mercury   _____

(d) nickel   _____

(e) tin   _____

31. Write a balanced equation for the reaction of water with

(a) potassium   _____

(b) strontium   _____

32. What is the nitrogen-containing product when copper reacts with

(a) concentrated nitric acid   _____

(b) dilute nitric acid   _____

33. Write a balanced net ionic equation for the reaction of silver with

    (a) concentrated HNO_3

    _____

    (b) dilute HNO_3

    _____

34. What is aqua regia? _____

35. Complete and balance the following equations. If no reaction occurs, write N.R.

    (a) $Ni^{2+}(aq) + Mn(s) \longrightarrow$

    _____

    (b) $Pt(s) + Fe^{2+}(aq) \longrightarrow$

    _____

    (c) $Sn(s) + Pt^{2+}(aq) \longrightarrow$

    _____

    (d) $Zn^{2+}(aq) + Cd(s) \longrightarrow$

    _____

New Terms

Activity series
   A listing of metals in order of decreasing ease of oxidation.

Aqua regia
   One part concentrated HNO_3 and three parts concentrated HCl, by volume. It is a mixture that is able to dissolve the very unreactive metals gold and platinum.

Corrosion
   The oxidation of a metal, which gives products that lack desirable metallic properties.

Noble metal
   A metal that is very unreactive, for example, gold and platinum.

Nonoxidizing acid
    In a solution of a nonoxidizing acid, the strongest oxidizing agent is H_3O^+.

Oxidizing acid
    An acid whose aqueous solutions contain an oxidizing agent that is stronger than H_3O^+. An example is HNO_3, which gives the strong oxidizing agent NO_3^- in aqueous solutions.

Single displacement reaction
    A reaction in which one element displaces another from a compound. For example:
    $$Zn(s) + CuSO_4(aq) \longrightarrow Cu(s) + ZnSO_4(aq)$$

7.10   NONMETALS AS OXIDIZING AGENTS

Objectives

    To learn how the ability of elemental nonmetals to serve as oxidizing agents varies within the periodic table.

Review

    The strength of the nonmetals as oxidizing agents increases from left to right across a period and from bottom to top within a group. Remember specifically the order of oxidizing strength among the halogens:

$$F_2 > Cl_2 > Br_2 > I_2$$

Within this series, a particular elemental halogen will displace one to the right from its compounds. Thus Cl_2 will displace Br^- or I^- from its compounds, but will not displace F^-.

Self-Test

36. Which of the following is expected to be the strongest oxidizing agent: sulfur, bromine, chlorine, selenium?

_____

37. Write balanced chemical equations for any reactions that occur between Br_2 and

   (a) NaF _____

   (b) NaCl _____

   (c) NaI _____

New Terms

7.11   MOLECULAR OXYGEN AS AN OXIDIZING AGENT

Objectives

   To learn how oxygen reacts with metals and with organic compounds.

Review

   Oxygen reacts with many metals to form oxides. When the reaction is rapid and evolves lots of heat and light, it is called combustion.

   Combustion of hydrocarbons gives CO_2 and H_2O as products. If an organic compound also contains oxygen, it is incorporated in the CO_2 and H_2O. When the supply of oxygen is limited, CO and H_2O are formed, and in a severely limited oxygen supply, the carbon can appear as elemental carbon (soot). Sulfur-containing organic compounds give SO_2 as the sulfur-containing product during combustion.

Self-Test

38. Write balanced chemical equations for the following reactions:

   (a) The reaction of calcium with oxygen.

   _____

   (b) The reaction of aluminum with oxygen.

   _____

(c)   The reaction of sulfur with oxygen.

(d)   The combustion of $C_{12}H_{26}$ in an abundant supply of oxygen.

(e)   The combustion of C_9H_{20} in a limited supply of O_2.

(f)   The combustion of C_2H_6 in an extremely limited supply of O_2.

(g)   The combustion of CH_3SH in an abundant supply of oxygen.

(h)   The combustion of $C_2H_4(OH)_2$ in an abundant supply of O_2.

New Terms

Combustion
    A reaction with oxygen that produces heat and light.

Answers to Self-Test Questions

1. (a), (d)   2. sugar, water   3. (aq)   4. H^+

5. $Na_2CO_3(s) \longrightarrow 2Na^+(aq) + CO_3^{2-}(aq)$

6. $HNO_2(aq) + H_2O \rightleftharpoons H_3O^+(aq) + NO_2^-(aq)$

7. double replacement   8. a precipitate

9. (a) $Na^+ + I^- + Ag^+ + NO_3^- \longrightarrow AgI(s) + Na^+ + NO_3^-$

   $Ag^+ + I^- \longrightarrow AgI(s)$

   (b) $Pb^{2+} + 2NO_3^- + Ba^{2+} + 2OH^- \longrightarrow Pb(OH)_2(s) + Ba^{2+} + 2NO_3^-$

   $Pb^{2+} + 2OH^- \longrightarrow Pb(OH)_2(s)$

(c) $AgCl(s) + Na^+ + Br^- \longrightarrow AgBr(s) + Na^+ + Cl^-$

$AgCl(s) + Br^- \longrightarrow AgBr(s) + Cl^-$

(d) $Zn^{2+} + 2Cl^- + 2Na^+ + CO_3^{2-} \longrightarrow 2Na^+ + 2Cl^- + ZnCO_3(s)$

$Zn^{2+} + CO_3^{2-} \longrightarrow ZnCO_3(s)$

10. (a) $HBr + H_2O \longrightarrow H_3O^+ + Br^-$

(b) $H_2SO_4 + H_2O \longrightarrow H_3O^+ + HSO_4^-$

$HSO_4^- + H_2O \longrightarrow H_3O^+ + SO_4^{2-}$

(c) $N_2H_4 + H_2O \longrightarrow N_2H_5^+ + OH^-$

(d) $O^{2-} + H_2O \longrightarrow 2\,OH^-$

11. (a) B (b) A (c) A (d) B (e) A (f) A

12. (a) $SO_3 + H_2O \longrightarrow H_2SO_4$

(b) $P_4O_{10} + 6H_2O \longrightarrow 4H_3PO_4$

(c) $BaO + H_2O \longrightarrow Ba(OH)_2$

(d) $N_2O_3 + H_2O \longrightarrow 2HNO_2$

13. $H_3O^+ + OH^- \longrightarrow 2H_2O$, or simply, $H^+ + OH^- \longrightarrow H_2O$

14. (a) $Ca(OH)_2 + 2HCl \longrightarrow CaCl_2 + 2H_2O$

(b) $2NH_3 + H_2SO_4 \longrightarrow (NH_4)_2SO_4$

(c) $2Al(OH)_3 + 3H_2SO_4 \longrightarrow Al_2(SO_4)_3 + 6H_2O$

(d) $NaOH + HNO_3 \longrightarrow NaNO_3 + H_2O$

(e) $MgO + H_2SO_4 \longrightarrow MgSO_4 + H_2O$

15. (a) CaC_2O_4, $Ca(HC_2O_4)_2$ (b) $CaCO_3$, $Ca(HCO_3)_2$

(c) $Ca_3(AsO_4)_2$, $CaHAsO_4$, $Ca(H_2AsO_4)_2$ (d) $CaBr_2$

16. (a) strong (b) weak (c) weak (d) strong (e) strong
(f) weak   17. (a) acid (b) base (c) acid

18. (a) H_2O, H_3O^+; $HC_2H_3O_2$, $C_2H_3O_2^-$

(b) CN^-, $\overline{HCN}$; $\overline{HCl}$, $\overline{Cl^-}$

(c) NH_3, $\overline{NH_2^-}$; $\overline{O^{2-}}$, $\underline{OH^-}$

19. b, $\overline{c}$ and e. They can't be Brønsted acids because they have
no hydrogen.

20. $Cr(H_2O)_6^{3+} + H_2O \rightleftharpoons Cr(H_2O)_5OH^{2+} + H_3O^+$

21.(a) H_2SeO_4 (b) $HBrO_3$ (c) HNO_3 (d) H_2SO_4 (e) H_3PO_4
(f) H_2O (g) PH_3 (h) HBr

22.

sulfite ion

23.

24.(a) K=+1; Cl=+5, O=-2   (b) Mn=+6, O=-2 (c) S=+2, O=-2
(d) Si=+4, Cl=-1 (e) Br=+3, F=-1 (f) P=+3, O=-2
(g) Sb=+5, Cl=-1 (h) C=0, H=+1, O=-2 (i) S=-2/3
(j) O = zero

25.(a) oxidizing agent = Cl_2, reducing agent = H_2
(b) oxidizing agent = I_2, reducing agent = $Na_2S_2O_3$
(c) oxidizing agent = O_2, reducing agent = C_2H_4
(d) oxidizing agent = $K_2Cr_2O_7$, reducing agent = HCl

26.(a) $PH_3 + 4N_2O \longrightarrow H_3PO_4 + 4N_2$

(b) $NaIO_3 + 3Na_2SO_3 \longrightarrow 3Na_2SO_4 + NaI$

(c) $PbO_2 + 4HCl \longrightarrow PbCl_2 + 2H_2O + Cl_2$

27.(a) $2H^+ + 2HNO_2 + 2I^- \longrightarrow 2NO + I_2 + 2H_2O$

(b) $ClO_3^- + 3H_2S \longrightarrow Cl^- + 3S + 3H_2O$

(c) $8H_2O + 5S_2O_8^{2-} + 2P \longrightarrow 10SO_4^{2-} + 2H_3PO_4 + 10H^+$

28.(a) $H_2O + 2CrO_4^{2-} + 3SO_3^{2-} \longrightarrow 2CrO_2^- + 3SO_4^{2-} + 2OH^-$

(b) $OH^- + HO_2^- + 2ClO_2 \longrightarrow 2ClO_2^- + O_2 + H_2O$

(c) $H_2O + 2MnO_4^- + 3NO_2^- \longrightarrow 2MnO_2 + 3NO_3^- + 2OH^-$

(d) $ClO^- + 2NH_3 \longrightarrow N_2H_4 + Cl^- + H_2O$

29.(a) Rb   (b) Ti   (c) Ca

30.(a) $Mg + 2HCl \longrightarrow MgCl_2 + H_2$

(b) $2Al + 6HCl \longrightarrow 2AlCl_3 + 3H_2$

(c) N.R.

(d) $Ni + 2HCl \longrightarrow NiCl_2 + H_2$

(e) $Sn + 2HCl \longrightarrow SnCl_2 + H_2$

31.(a) $2K + 2H_2O \longrightarrow 2KOH + H_2$

(b) $Sr + 2H_2O \longrightarrow Sr(OH)_2 + H_2$

32.(a) NO_2 (b) NO

33.(a) $Ag + NO_3^- + 2H^+ \longrightarrow Ag^+ + NO_2 + H_2O$

(b) $3Ag + NO_3^- + 4H^+ \longrightarrow 3Ag^+ + NO + 2H_2O$

34. 1 part conc. HNO_3, 3 parts conc. HCl (by volume)

35.(a) $Ni^{2+}(aq) + Mn(s) \longrightarrow Ni(s) + Mn^{2+}(aq)$

(b) N.R.

(c) $Sn(s) + Pt^{2+}(aq) \longrightarrow Sn^{2+}(aq) + Pt(s)$

(d) N.R.

36. chlorine

37.(a) no reaction

(b) no reaction

(c) $2NaI + Br_2 \longrightarrow 2NaBr + I_2$

38.(a) $2Ca + O_2 \longrightarrow 2CaO$

(b) $4Al + 3O_2 \longrightarrow 2Al_2O_3$

(c) $S + O_2 \longrightarrow SO_2$

(d) $2C_{12}H_{26} + 37O_2 \longrightarrow 24CO_2 + 26H_2O$

(e) $2C_9H_{20} + 19O_2 \longrightarrow 18CO + 20H_2O$

(f) $2C_2H_6 + 3O_2 \longrightarrow 4C + 6H_2O$

(g) $CH_3SH + 3O_2 \longrightarrow CO_2 + SO_2 + 2H_2O$

(h) $2C_2H_4(OH)_2 + 5O_2 \longrightarrow 4CO_2 + 6H_2O$

8 IONIC REACTIONS IN SOLUTION - A CLOSER LOOK

Ionic reactions are so common that you are sure to encounter them sooner or later in the laboratory. In this chapter we examine first why metathesis reactions occur. This will allow you to predict when these reactions occur and what the products will be. It also permits you to design experiments to make ionic compounds. In this chapter we also study the stoichiometry of ionic reactions in detail, both metathesis and redox, and illustrate how they are used in chemical analyses.

8.1   METATHESIS REACTIONS: WHY THEY OCCUR

Objectives

To examine the factors that determine whether or not a metathesis reaction will take place. You should learn how to predict the outcome of metathesis reactions.

Review

If all the ions in an ionic equation for a reaction do not cancel, then there is a net ionic equation and a reaction will occur. However, if all the ions do cancel, then there is no net ionic equation and no net reaction. Based on this, we can identify three factors that lead to a net reaction:

(a) one or more substances in the reaction is a solid

160

(b) one or more substances in the reaction is a weak electrolyte

(c) one of the products of the reaction is a gas

To predict precipitation reactions, you must know the solubility rules given on Pages 279 and 280. Study them carefully and study Examples 8.1 to 8.3 in the text.

When writing ionic equations, formulas for weak electrolytes are written in molecular form. These substances are the weak acids and bases that you learned about in Section 7.2 (Table 7.2, Page 236). Keep in mind that insoluble metal oxides react with acid in a neutralization reaction to form water as one of the products.

Study Table 8.1 so that you can recognize when a gas will be formed in a reaction.

Self-Test

1. Study the solubility rule before answering this question. Use this question to test your knowledge of the rules. If a substance is soluble, write S; if it is insoluble, write I.

    (a) KNO_3 _____   (e) ZnO   _____

    (b) $MgSO_4$ _____   (f) $PbSO_4$ _____

    (c) AgI   _____   (g) $Ni(OH)_2$ _____

    (d) $FeCO_3$ _____   (h) $(NH_4)_2CrO_4$ _____

2. Write ionic and net ionic equations for these reactions:

    (a) $CaCO_3 + 2HCl \longrightarrow H_2O + CO_2 + CaCl_2$

    (b) $(NH_4)_2SO_4 + 2NaOH \longrightarrow 2NH_3 + 2H_2O + Na_2SO_4$

    (c) $Na_2C_2O_4 + 2HCl \longrightarrow 2NaCl + H_2C_2O_4$

    (d) $BaCO_3 + H_2SO_4 \longrightarrow BaSO_4 + H_2O + CO_2$

    (e) $K_2SO_3 + H_2SO_4 \longrightarrow K_2SO_4 + H_2O + SO_2$

3. Write molecular, ionic and net ionic equations for the reaction, if any, that would occur between the following:

(a) $NiCl_2$ and Na_2CO_3

(b) $NaCl$ and $CaBr_2$

(c) $MgCl_2$ and $NaOH$

(d) Na_2SO_4 and $Mg(NO_3)_2$

(e) Na_2S and HCl

4. Write molecular, ionic, and net ionic equations for the reactions that occur, if any, between the following pairs of reactants in aqueous solution.

(a) $CuCl_2$ and $NaOH$

(b) NiO and H_2SO_4

(c) HNO_2 and KOH

(d) $HC_2H_3O_2$ and NH_3

(e) $AlCl_3$ and NH_3

New Terms

Solubility rules
See Page 279 in the text.

8.2   THE PREPARATION OF INORGANIC SALTS BY METATHESIS REACTIONS

Objectives

To learn methods that can be used to prepare salts by reactions in aqueous solution.

Review

The techniques discussed in this section call upon what you have learned in Section 8.1. Your ability to choose appropriate reactants to prepare a given salt obviously depends on how well you've learned this previous material. If you have difficulty with most of the questions in the Self-Test at the end of this section, go back and review the solubility rules and Table 8.1.

Precipitation Reactions. These make use of the formation of a precipitate to obtain the desired product. You need to remember the solubility rules to apply this method. Remember to use soluble reactants that give only one insoluble product.

Example 8.1

How can we prepare $CuCO_3$ by a precipitation reaction?

Solution

The product, $CuCO_3$, is insoluble; therefore we want the other product to be soluble. Also, we want to begin with a soluble carbonate and a soluble copper salt. Possible reactants are $CuCl_2$ and Na_2CO_3. Both are soluble and the choice of the sodium salt to provide the CO_3^{2-} ensures us that the other product in the metathesis reaction will be soluble.

$$CuCl_2 + Na_2CO_3 \longrightarrow 2NaCl + CuCO_3$$
$$(sol.) \qquad (sol.) \qquad\quad (sol.) \quad (insol.)$$

Neutralization Reactions. The desired salt is derived from the cation of a base and the anion of an acid. For instance, to prepare $CuBr_2$ you could use the reaction between $Cu(OH)_2$ and HBr,

$$Cu(OH)_2(s) + 2HBr(aq) \longrightarrow CuBr_2(aq) + 2H_2O$$

Since $Cu(OH)_2$ is insoluble, an excess of $Cu(OH)_2$ is used so that all of the HBr in solution is used up. Excess insoluble $Cu(OH)_2$ is removed by filtration and the solution that passes through the filter contains only $CuBr_2$ which can be recovered by evaporation.

This method is good because most metal hydroxides are insoluble and can be prepared from other readily available salts by reaction with a base. For instance,

$$Cu(NO_3)_2(aq) + 2NaOH(aq) \longrightarrow Cu(OH)_2(s) + 2NaNO_3(aq)$$

Reactions in Which a Product is a Gas. Reactions of metal carbonates were discussed in the text. Any metathesis reaction in which one product is a gas will leave the other product by itself in solution. Some sample reactions are:

$$K_2SO_3 + 2HClO_4 \longrightarrow 2KClO_4 + H_2O + SO_3(g)$$

$$FeS + 2HBr \longrightarrow FeBr_2 + H_2S(g)$$

Review also Examples 8.9 to 8.10 in the text before beginning the Self-Test.

Self-Test

5. How would you prepare the following by a precipitation reaction?

   (a) $Fe(NO_3)_3$ (b) $AgBr$ (c) $BaBr_2$ (d) $NaOH$

6. How would you prepare the following by a neutralization reaction?

   (a) $Cu(HSO_4)_2$ from $CuCl_2$ (c) $Mg(NO_3)_2$ from $MgCl_2$

   (b) $NiSO_4$ from $NiCl_2$ (d) $Ca(NO_3)_2$ from CaO

7. How would you prepare the following by a reaction that produces a gas?

   (a) $FeCl_2$ from $FeCO_3$ (d) $ZnCl_2$ from ZnS

   (b) $Co(NO_3)_2$ from $CoCO_3$ (e) $Ca(NO_3)_2$ from $CaCl_2$

   (c) $NaNO_2$ from NH_4NO_2

New Terms

8.3   STOICHIOMETRY OF IONIC REACTIONS

Objectives

> To learn how to solve problems that deal with the
> stoichiometry of ionic reactions in solution. You should
> learn in particular how to calculate the concentration of
> a particular ion in a solution of a salt and how to use
> this information along with either molecular or net ionic
> equations to solve stoichiometry problems.

Review

There are several ways of expressing concentration.
Parts per hundred (percent) and parts per million (ppm) were
discussed in the text. One of the most important concentration
units is molarity, the ratio of moles of solute to liters of solution.
If you know the number of moles of solute and the volume of the
solution (in liters), the ratio gives molarity.

Example 8.2

What is the molarity of a solution containing 0.843 mol of
NaCl in 750 mL of solution?

Solution

$$\text{molarity} = \frac{\text{moles}}{\text{liters}} = \frac{0.843 \text{ mol NaCl}}{0.750 \text{ L solution}}$$

$$\text{molarity} = 1.12 \text{ M}$$

Molarity is a convenient conversion factor relating moles
of solute to volume of solution. The molarity of the solution in
Example 8.2 can be used to construct two conversion factors,

$$\frac{1.12 \text{ mol NaCl}}{1.00 \text{ L}} \quad \text{and} \quad \frac{1.00 \text{ L}}{1.12 \text{ mol NaCl}}$$

which can be used in calculations.

Example 8.3

What volume of 1.12 M NaCl contains 0.420 mol of NaCl?

Solution

Moles must cancel. Therefore,

$$0.420 \text{ mol NaCl} \times \left(\frac{1.00 \text{ L}}{1.12 \text{ mol NaCl}} \right) = 0.375 \text{ L}$$

or

$$0.420 \text{ mol NaCl} \times \left(\frac{1000 \text{ mL}}{1.12 \text{ mol NaCl}} \right) = 375 \text{ mL}$$

The answer is 375 mL of solution.

Example 8.4

How many moles of NaCl are in 250 mL of 1.12 M NaCl solution?

Solution

$$250 \text{ mL} = 0.250 \text{ L}$$

$$0.250 \text{ L} \times \left(\frac{1.12 \text{ mol NaCl}}{1.00 \text{ L}} \right) = 0.280 \text{ mol NaCl}$$

We can also use milliliters directly,

$$250 \text{ mL} \times \left(\frac{1.12 \text{ mol NaCl}}{1000 \text{ mL}} \right) = 0.280 \text{ mol NaCl}$$

You should be able to calculate the concentration of a given ion in a solution of an electrolyte of known concentration. To do this, however, you _must_ be able to determine the number of ions of each kind that are liberated in the solution when the electrolyte dissolves. Stated another way, you must be able to identify the ions given by the compound when it dissolves. For example, consider the salt $(NH_4)_2C_2O_4$. What ions are found in an aqueous solution of it? To answer this question you must recognize the ions NH_4^+ and $C_2O_4^{2-}$. If you can't do this, review Section 5.5, especially Tables 5.2, 5.3 and 5.4.

The stoichiometry of reactions in solution was discussed in Chapter 2, and is extended just a bit more in this section. Examples 8.14 and 8.15 illustrate how net ionic equations are used. Notice that it is necessary to relate ion concentrations to overall solute concentrations to solve these kinds of problems. The following is another example that demonstrates this.

Example 8.5

How many milliliters of 0.200 M $Ba(NO_3)_2$ are needed to react completely with 75.0 mL of 0.150 M $Fe_2(SO_4)_3$ solution? The net ionic equation for the reaction is

$$Ba^{2+} + SO_4^{2-} \longrightarrow BaSO_4(s)$$

Solution

First we have to determine how many moles of sulfate ion are in the $Fe_2(SO_4)_3$ solution. Then we can calculate how many moles of barium ion are needed, and finally we can calculate the volume of the $Ba(NO_3)_2$ solution needed.

The molar concentration of SO_4^{2-} in the $Fe_2(SO_4)_3$ solution is

$$SO_4^{2-} \text{ concentration} = 3 \times (0.150 \text{ M}) = 0.450 \text{ M}$$

Therefore, in 75.0 mL of this solution there is

$$75.0 \text{ mL soln} \times \left(\frac{0.450 \text{ mol } SO_4^{2-}}{1000 \text{ mL soln}} \right) = 0.0338 \text{ mol } SO_4^{2-}$$

From the stoichiometry of the net ionic equation, it is obvious that the number of moles of Ba^{2+} needed for reaction is also 0.0338 mol.

$$0.0338 \text{ mol } SO_4^{2-} \sim 0.0338 \text{ mol } Ba^{2+}$$

The volume of $Ba(NO_3)_2$ solution required is obtained from the molarity of the solution. In this solution the Ba^{2+} concentration is 0.200 M because each formula unit of $Ba(NO_3)_2$ contains one Ba^{2+}. Therefore,

$$0.0338 \; \cancel{mol \; Ba}^{2+} \; x \left(\frac{1000 \; mL \; soln}{0.200 \; \cancel{mol \; Ba}^{2+}} \right) = 169 \; mL \; soln$$

The volume of the barium nitrate solution needed is 169 mL.

You should study Example 8.15 on Page 292 of the text to see how limiting reactant calculations are handled for solution stoichiometry.

Self-Test

8. Calculate the molarity of the following solutions:

    (a) 1.14 mol KI in 1.50 L of solution _____

    (b) 0.240 mol $CaCl_2$ in 500 mL of solution _____

    (c) 3.50 g of NaCl in 0.0500 L of solution _____

    (d) 4.25 g $MgSO_4$ in 75.0 mL of solution _____

9. How many moles of $KClO_3$ are in 500 mL of 0.150 M solution?

    _____

10. How many moles of urea are in 250 mL of urine if the urea concentration is 0.320 M?

    _____

11. A normal adult excretes about 1500 mL of urine per day. If the urea concentration is 0.320 M, how many grams of urea are excreted per day? Urea has the formula, $CO(NH_2)_2$.

    _____

12. What is the molar concentration of each ion in the following solutions?

    (a) 0.300 M $AlCl_3$ _____

    (b) 0.150 M $(NH_4)_2Cr_2O_7$ _____

    (c) 0.200 M Na_3PO_4 _____

    (d) 0.400 M $Cr_2(SO_4)_3$ _____

    (e) 0.0100 M $Ba(OH)_2$ _____

13. How many milliliters of 0.250 M $CaCl_2$ are required to react completely with 300 mL of 0.150 M $AgNO_3$ according to the equation,

$$Ag^+ + Cl^- \longrightarrow AgCl(s)$$

14. How many moles of solid AgCl will be formed if 300 mL of 0.240 M $AgNO_3$ are added to 200 mL of 0.480 M HCl? The reaction is: $Ag^+ + Cl^- \longrightarrow AgCl$

15. In Question 14, what will be the molar concentrations of any ions remaining in solution after the reaction is complete?

16. In an experiment, a student mixed 300 mL of 0.200 M $Ba(OH)_2$ with 500 mL of 0.100 M $CuSO_4$.

    (a) Write net ionic equations for any chemical reactions that occur in this mixture.

    (b) For any solids formed, calculate their amounts in moles.

    (c) Calculate the molar concentrations of any ions that remain in solution after reaction is complete.

New Terms

Parts per million
   Usually expressed on a weight basis. The number of grams of the component in question per million grams of solution. It is weight fraction multiplied by 10^6.

$$ppm\ X = \frac{grams\ X}{grams\ solution} \times 10^6$$

8.4   CHEMICAL ANALYSIS AND TITRATIONS

Objectives

To see how the principles of stoichiometry are used in practical applications.

Review

There are two important approaches to chemical analysis discussed in this section. The first involves the analysis of a substance by forming and weighing a compound of known composition that contains all of one component of the original sample being analyzed. This is illustrated in Example 8.16. Another example is presented below in which a sample is analyzed for the metal silver. The analysis makes use of the fact that Ag^+ forms an insoluble precipitate with Cl^-. If no other components of the sample do the same, then addition of Cl^- to a solution of the ore sample will separate the silver as insoluble AgCl which can be filtered and weighed. From the known composition of AgCl, the weight of Ag in the precipitate can be calculated. This must be the weight of silver in the sample because all the silver came from the ore sample.

Example 8.6

A 1.00-g sample of an ore known to contain silver was dissolved in HNO_3 and treated with Cl^-. 0.275 g of AgCl was obtained. What was the percent by weight Ag in the ore?

Solution

From the weight of AgCl we calculate the weight of Ag. In one mole of AgCl (143.4 g) there is one mole of silver (107.9 g). Therefore,

$$0.275 \text{ g AgCl} \times \left(\frac{107.9 \text{ g Ag}}{143.4 \text{ g AgCl}} \right) = 0.207 \text{ g Ag}$$

(If you don't understand this calculation, review Section 2.5.) All of this 0.207 g of Ag came from the ore. Therefore, the percent silver in the ore is

$$\%Ag = \frac{0.207 \text{ g}}{1.00 \text{ g}} \times 100 = 20.7\%$$

The second analytical approach discussed here is titration, which is a procedure that employs calibrated glassware to measure accurately volumes of solutions. By measuring the volume of a solution of known concentration needed to react completely with the contents of another solution, the amount of reactant in the other solution can be calculated. This section introduces you to a variety of new terms; be sure you learn them.

Self-Test

17. A 0.833-g sample of a mixture of NaCl and $CaCl_2$ was dissolved in water and treated with Na_2CO_3 to precipitate $CaCO_3$. The precipitate was filtered and dried and found to weigh 0.415 g. What percent of the original sample was $CaCl_2$?

_____

18. A 0.400-g sample of an alloy of iron and nickel was dissolved in HCl to give Fe^{2+} and Ni^{2+}. The resulting solution was titrated with 22.3 mL of 0.0400 M $KMnO_4$, causing Fe^{2+} to be oxidized to Fe^{3+}. What percent of the alloy is iron? The net ionic equation for the reaction is

$$5Fe^{2+} + MnO_4^- + 8H^+ \longrightarrow 5Fe^{3+} + Mn^{2+} + 4H_2O$$

_____

New Terms

Buret
   A graduated glass tube fitted with a valve (stopcock) at one end. It is used to dispense measured volumes of solutions.

Chemical analysis
   The experimental determination of the composition of a substance.

Endpoint
   That point in a titration when delivery of the titrant is halted because the indicator changes color or some other event signals the completion of the reaction.

Standardizing a solution
   Measuring accurately the concentration of solute in a solution.
   A standard solution is one whose solute concentration is ac-
   curately known.

Stopcock
   A valve (for example, at the end of a buret) that is used to
   control the flow of a liquid or sometimes a gas.

Titrant
   The solution dispensed from a buret.

Titration
   An analytical procedure in which a solution, generally of
   known concentration, is added gradually from a buret to
   another solution where the solutes react. When the completion of the reaction is signaled by an indicator, the volume
   of the solution added from the buret is read and recorded.

Volumetric analysis
   An analytical procedure that makes use of reactions in
   solution, where volumes and concentrations of solutions are
   carefully measured.

8.5   OXIDIZING AND REDUCING AGENTS
       IN THE LABORATORY

Objectives

   To learn about common laboratory oxidizing and reducing
   agents. You should learn the formulas of the compounds
   that serve as sources of these ions, the reactions they
   undergo, and any color changes that might be observed
   during these reactions.

Review

Oxidizing agents

   Potassium permanganate, $KMnO_4$. The permanganate ion
is purple in solution. In acidic solutions it is reduced to the
nearly colorless Mn^{2+} ion. In basic or neutral solutions, insoluble MnO_2 is formed.

Chromate ion, CrO_4^{2-}, and dichromate ion, $Cr_2O_7^{2-}$, usually as their sodium or potassium salts. The ions can be converted from one to the other by changing the acidity of the solution. In acidic solution, the oxidizing agent is $Cr_2O_7^{2-}$; in basic solution it is CrO_4^{2-}. Both contain Cr^{VI} (meaning chromium in the +6 oxidation state). The products of reduction depend on the acidity of the reaction mixture. In acidic solutions, the product is Cr^{3+}; in slightly basic solutions, the product is insoluble $Cr(OH)_3$; in strongly basic solution the product is CrO_2^-.

Reducing agents

Tin(II), usually as $SnCl_2$. This is a mild reducing agent and is oxidized to Sn^{4+}.

Sulfites and bisulfites, usually as their sodium or potassium salts. The actual reactant in solution depends on the acidity of the solution. If strongly acidic, the active reducing agent is H_2SO_3; if slightly acidic, HSO_3^- is the reducing agent; if basic, SO_3^{2-} is the reducing agent. The product of oxidation is sulfate ion.

Thiosulfate ion, usually as $Na_2S_2O_3$. Strong oxidizing agents give sulfate as the oxidation product. One of the principle uses of $S_2O_3^{2-}$ is in titrations of iodine, which are described on Pages 300 to 302. Study Example 8.20.

Self-Test

19. Write balanced net ionic equations for the reactions that would occur between

    (a) $SnCl_2$ and $Na_2Cr_2O_7$ in an acidic solution

    _____

    (b) K_2CrO_4 and $Na_2S_2O_3$ in a slightly basic solution

    _____

    (c) $NaHSO_3$ and $KMnO_4$ in an acidic solution

    _____

    (d) H_2SO_3 and Na_2CrO_4 in a very acidic solution

    _____

20. What is the formula of the triiodide ion? _____

21. When a solution containing copper(II) ion is added to a solution containing I^- ion, the following reaction occurs.

$$2Cu^{2+} + 5I^- \longrightarrow 2CuI + I_3^-$$

In a chemical analysis of a copper ore, a sample weighing 0.2314 g was dissolved in acid and excess NaI solution was added. The I_3^- that was formed was titrated with 0.02000 M $Na_2S_2O_3$ solution. The titration required 22.94 mL of the $Na_2S_2O_3$ solution. What was the percentage by weight of copper in the ore? _____

New Terms

8.6   EQUIVALENT WEIGHTS AND NORMALITY

Objectives

To learn how a quantity called an equivalent is defined for acid/base and redox reactions, and to learn how to use it in stoichiometric calculations. You should also learn how the concept is extended to solution stoichiometry through a concentration unit called normality.

Review

The equivalent is always defined so that in any reaction 1 equivalent of reactant A combines with exactly 1 equivalent of reactant B, regardless of the coefficients in the balanced chemical equation. This leads to different definitions for acid/base and redox reactions. The key to working with equivalents is to be able to relate them to the more familiar stoichiometric quantity, the mole. This requires that you determine the number of equivalents per mole, which is the integer n in Equations 8.1 and 8.2.

Acid-Base Reactions

One equivalent of acid supplies 1 mol H^+; one equivalent of base supplies 1 mol OH^-. For acids, this means that the number of equivalents per mole is equal to the number of H^+ supplied by each molecule of the acid. This can be obtained by examining the formulas of the reactants and products. For instance, consider the reaction of H_3PO_4 to give HPO_4^{2-}. The acid loses <u>two</u> H^+ to give the product, so there are <u>two</u> equivalents per mole in this case.

For bases, the number of equivalents per mole is equal to the number of hydroxides in the formula. Aluminum hydroxide, $Al(OH)_3$, provides three equivalents per mole.

Redox Reactions

One equivalent is the amount of reactant that gains or loses one mole of electrons. To determine the number of equivalents per mole, you must calculate the number of electrons transferred by each formula unit of the <u>reactant</u>. (Notice that it is the reactant that we focus our attention on. We need to know what the product is to calculate changes in oxidation number, but ultimately we determine the total change for the reactant.) For example, consider the reaction of $KMnO_4$ to give MnO_2 as the product. The manganese undergoes a change of 3 electrons. Since each $KMnO_4$ has only one manganese that changes, each formula unit of $KMnO_4$ undergoes a 3 electron change.

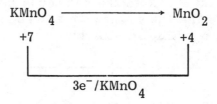

In this reaction, there are 3 equivalents per mole of $KMnO_4$.

Consider now a reaction in which $K_2Cr_2O_7$ is converted to $CrCl_3$. In this reaction each Cr changes by 3 electrons. The reactant, $K_2Cr_2O_7$, has two Cr atoms, so one formula unit of $K_2Cr_2O_7$ undergoes a 6-electron change.

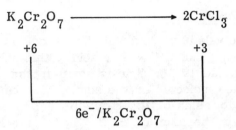

This means there are 6 equivalents per mole for $K_2Cr_2O_7$ in this reaction.

Equivalent weights

The equivalent weight is simply the weight of one equivalent. It can be calculated by Equation 8.2 on Page 303, and it is a useful quantity for working stoichiometry problems that involve weights of reactants.

Normality

This is a concentration unit that is similar to molarity. In fact, as pointed out on Page 306, these two units of concentration are related to each other by the number of equivalents per mole. Remember that for titrations involving solutions whose concentrations are expressed in normality,

$$N_A V_A = N_B V_B$$

where N_A and V_A are the normality and volume of the solution of reactant A, and N_B and V_B are the normality and volume of the solution of reactant B. Note the distinction between the endpoint in a titration and the equivalence point. The following example illustrates using normality in a problem.

Example 8.7

How many mL of 0.180 N $Ba(OH)_2$ are required to react completely with 22.0 mL of 0.0800 N HCl?

Solution

	acid	base
N	0.0800	0.180
V	22.0 mL	x

$$N_1V_1 = N_1V_2$$

$$(0.0800 \text{ N})(22.0 \text{ mL}) = (0.180 \text{ N})(x)$$

$$x = \frac{(0.0800 \text{ N})(22.0 \text{ mL})}{(0.180 \text{ N})} = 9.78 \text{ mL}$$

The volume of $Ba(OH)_2$ solution required is 9.78 mL.

In this section there are six equations set in blue type. They are all important and should be learned. Several of them relate mole quantities to the number of equivalents per mole, which is why this is such an important quantity to be able to calculate.

Self-Test

22. Calculate the equivalent weight for the following substances. The products produced when they react are given in parentheses.

    (a) $NaBiO_3$ (Bi^{3+}) _____

    (b) $NaIO_3$ (I^-) _____

    (c) H_2SO_4 (SO_4^{2-}) _____

    (d) H_2SO_4 (HSO_4^-) _____

    (e) $Na_2S_2O_3$ $(S_4O_6^{2-})$ _____

23. $Na_2S_2O_4$ reacts with $CuSO_4$ in solutions containing ammonia to produce SO_3^{2-} and metallic copper. How many grams of $Na_2S_2O_4$ are needed to completely reduce 15.0 g of $CuSO_4$?

    _____

24. How many grams of K_2CrO_4 are needed to prepare 300 mL of 0.100 N solution if the solution will be used in a reaction in which the Cr is reduced to the +3 oxidation state?

    _____

25. How many mL of 0.100 N HCl react with 19.5 mL of 0.220 N KOH?

    _____

26. What is the normality of an H_2SO_4 solution if 27.0 mL of the solution is required to neutralize 14.3 mL of 0.35 N NaOH?

_____

New Terms

Equivalence point
  That point in a titration when equal numbers of equivalents of reactants have been combined. Ideally, the equivalence point should occur at the endpoint during a titration.

Equivalent (eq)
  For acids and bases, the amount of substance that produces or reacts with one mole of H^+. For redox reactions, the amount of substance that gains or loses one mole of electrons.

Equivalent weight
  The weight of one equivalent.

Normality
  The number of equivalents of solute per liter of solution.

Answers to Self-Test Questions

1.(a) S, rules 1 and 3   (b) S, rule 5   (c) I, rule 4   (d) I, rule 8   (e) I, rule 6   (f) I, rule 5   (g) I, rule 7   (h) S, rule 2

2. (a) $CaCO_3 + 2H^+ + 2Cl^- \longrightarrow H_2O + CO_2 + Ca^{2+} + 2Cl^-$

$CaCO_3 + 2H^+ \longrightarrow H_2O + CO_2 + Ca^{2+}$

(b) $2NH_4^+ + SO_4^{2-} + 2Na^+ + 2OH^- \longrightarrow 2NH_3 + 2H_2O + 2Na^+ + SO_4^{2-}$

$2NH_4^+ + 2OH^- \longrightarrow 2NH_3 + 2H_2O$; dividing through by 2 gives $NH_4^+ + OH^- \longrightarrow NH_3 + H_2O$

(c) $2Na^+ + C_2O_4^{2-} + 2H^+ + 2Cl^- \longrightarrow 2Na^+ + 2Cl^- + H_2C_2O_4$

$C_2O_4^{2-} + 2H^+ \longrightarrow H_2C_2O_4$

(d) $BaCO_3 + 2H^+ + SO_4^{2-} \longrightarrow BaSO_4 + H_2O + CO_2$
(net is same as above)

(e) $2K^+ + SO_3^{2-} + 2H^+ + SO_4^{2-} \longrightarrow 2K^+ + SO_4^{2-} + H_2O + SO_2$
$SO_3^{2-} + 2H^+ \longrightarrow SO_2 + H_2O$

3. (a) $NiCl_2 + Na_2CO_3 \longrightarrow 2NaCl + NiCO_3$
$Ni^{2+} + 2Cl^- + 2Na^+ + CO_3^{2-} \longrightarrow 2Na^+ + 2Cl^- + NiCO_3(s)$
$Ni^{2+} + CO_3^{2-} \longrightarrow NiCO_3(s)$

(b) $2NaCl + CaBr_2 \longrightarrow 2NaBr + CaCl_2$
$2Na^+ + 2Cl^- + Ca^{2+} + 2Br^- \longrightarrow 2Na^+ + 2Br^- + Ca^{2+} + 2Cl^-$
(no net reaction)

(c) $MgCl_2 + 2NaOH \longrightarrow Mg(OH)_2 + 2NaCl$
$Mg^{2+} + 2Cl^- + 2Na^+ + 2OH^- \longrightarrow Mg(OH)_2(s) + 2Na^+ + 2Cl^-$
$Mg^{2+} + 2OH^- \longrightarrow Mg(OH)_2(s)$

(d) $Na_2SO_4 + Mg(NO_3)_2 \longrightarrow 2NaNO_3 + MgSO_4$
$2Na^+ + SO_4^{2-} + Mg^{2+} + 2NO_3^- \longrightarrow 2Na^+ + 2NO_3^- + Mg^{2+} + SO_4^{2-}$
(no net reaction)

(e) $Na_2S + 2HCl \longrightarrow 2NaCl + H_2S$
$2Na^+ + S^{2-} + 2H^+ + 2Cl^- \longrightarrow 2Na^+ + 2Cl^- + H_2S(g)$
$S^{2-} + 2H^+ \longrightarrow H_2S(g)$

4. (a) $CuCl_2 + 2NaOH \longrightarrow Cu(OH)_2 + 2NaCl$
$Cu^{2+} + 2Cl^- + 2Na^+ + 2OH^- \longrightarrow Cu(OH)_2(s) + 2Na^+ + 2Cl^-$
$Cu^{2+} + 2OH^- \longrightarrow Cu(OH)_2(s)$

(b) $NiO + H_2SO_4 \longrightarrow NiSO_4 + H_2O$
$NiO(s) + 2H^+ + SO_4^{2-} \longrightarrow Ni^{2+} + SO_4^{2-} + H_2O$
(net ionic equation same as above)

(c) $HNO_2 + KOH \longrightarrow KNO_2 + H_2O$
$HNO_2 + K^+ + OH^- \longrightarrow K^+ + NO_2^- + H_2O$
$HNO_2 + OH^- \longrightarrow NO_2^- + H_2O$

(d) $HC_2H_3O_2 + NH_3 \longrightarrow NH_4C_2H_3O_2$
$HC_2H_3O_2 + NH_3 \longrightarrow NH_4^+ + C_2H_3O_2^-$

(net ionic equation same as previous equation)

(e) $AlCl_3 + 3NH_3 + 3H_2O \longrightarrow Al(OH)_3 + 3NH_4Cl$

$Al^{3+} + 3Cl^- + 3NH_3 + 3H_2O \longrightarrow Al(OH)_3(s) + 3NH_4^+ + 3Cl^-$

$Al^{3+} + 3NH_3 + 3H_2O \longrightarrow Al(OH)_3(s) + 3NH_4^+$

5. One possible set of reactants for each is given here. However, there is more than one way to "skin a cat." If you have chosen different reactants, ask your teacher if they are satisfactory.

(a) $FeCl_3(aq) + 3AgNO_3(aq) \longrightarrow Fe(NO_3)_3(aq) + 3AgCl(s)$

(b) $AgNO_3(aq) + KBr(aq) \longrightarrow AgBr(s) + KNO_3(aq)$

in general: $Ag^+ + Br^- \longrightarrow AgBr(s)$

(c) $Ba(OH)_2(aq) + MgBr_2(aq) \longrightarrow BaBr_2(aq) + Mg(OH)_2(s)$

(d) $Ba(OH)_2(aq) + Na_2SO_4(aq) \longrightarrow BaSO_4(s) + 2NaOH(aq)$

6. (a) $CuCl_2(aq) + 2NaOH(aq) \longrightarrow Cu(OH)_2(s) + 2NaCl(aq)$

$Cu(OH)_2(s) + 2H_2SO_4 \longrightarrow Cu(HSO_4)_2(aq) + 2H_2O$

(b) $NiCl_2(aq) + 2NaOH(aq) \longrightarrow 2NaCl(aq) + Ni(OH)_2(s)$

$Ni(OH)_2(s) + H_2SO_4(aq) \longrightarrow NiSO_4(aq) + 2H_2O$

(c) $MgCl_2(aq) + 2NaOH(aq) \longrightarrow Mg(OH)_2(s) + 2NaCl$

$Mg(OH)_2(s) + 2HNO_3(aq) \longrightarrow Mg(NO_3)_2(aq) + 2H_2O$

(d) $CaO(s) + 2HNO_3(aq) \longrightarrow Ca(NO_3)_2(aq) + H_2O$

7. (a) $FeCO_3(aq) + 2HCl(aq) \longrightarrow FeCl_2(aq) + H_2O + CO_2(aq)$

(b) $CoCO_3(aq) + 2HNO_3(aq) \longrightarrow Co(NO_3)_2(aq) + H_2O + CO_2(g)$

(c) $NH_4NO_2(aq) + NaOH(aq) \longrightarrow NaNO_2(aq) + H_2O + NH_3(g)$

(d) $ZnS(s) + 2HCl(aq) \longrightarrow ZnCl_2(aq) + H_2S(g)$

(e) $CaCl_2(aq) + 2NaOH(aq) \longrightarrow CaCO_3(s) + 2NaCl(aq)$

$CaCO_3(s) + 2HNO_3(aq) \longrightarrow Ca(NO_3)_2(aq) + H_2O + CO_2(g)$

8. (a) 0.760 M (b) 0.480 M (c) 1.20 M (d) 0.471 M

9. 0.0750 mol $KClO_3$ 10. 0.0800 mol urea 11. 28.8 g of urea

12. (a) 0.300 M Al^{3+}, 0.900 M Cl^-

    (b) 0.300 M NH_4^+, 0.150 M $Cr_2O_7^{2-}$

    (c) 0.600 M Na^+, 0.200 M PO_4^{3-}

    (d) 0.800 M Cr^{3+}, 1.20 M SO_4^{2-}

    (e) 0.0100 M Ba^{2+}, 0.0200 M OH^-

13. 90.0 mL

14. 0.0720 mol AgCl (Cl^- in excess)

15. 0.192 M H^+, 0.144 M NO_3^-, 0.048 M Cl^-

16. (a) $Ba^{2+} + SO_4^{2-} \longrightarrow BaSO_4(s)$

       $Cu^{2+} + 2OH^- \longrightarrow Cu(OH)_2(s)$

    (b) 0.0500 mol $BaSO_4$, 0.0500 mol $Cu(OH)_2$

    (c) 0.0125 M Ba^{2+}, 0.0250 M OH^-

17. 55.2% $CaCl_2$

18. 62.3% Fe

19. (a) $3Sn^{2+} + Cr_2O_7^{2-} + 14H^+ \longrightarrow 3Sn^{4+} + 2Cr^{3+} + 7H_2O$

    (b) $8CrO_4^{2-} + 3S_2O_3^{2-} + 17H_2O \longrightarrow 8Cr(OH)_3 + 6SO_4^{2-} + 10OH^-$

    (c) $5HSO_3^- + 2MnO_4^- + H^+ \longrightarrow 5SO_4^{2-} + 2Mn^{2+} + 3H_2O$

    (d) $3H_2SO_3 + Cr_2O_7^{2-} + 2H^+ \longrightarrow 3SO_4^{2-} + 2Cr^{3+} + 4H_2O$

20. I_3^-

21. 12.59% Cu

22. (a) 140 g $NaBiO_3$ (b) 33.0 g $NaIO_3$ (c) 49.0 g H_2SO_4

    (d) 98.1 g H_2SO_4 (e) 158 g $Na_2S_2O_3$

23. 16.4 g $Na_2S_2O_4$ (eq. wt. $Na_2S_2O_4$ = 87.06 g; $CuSO_4$ = 79.8 g)

24. 1.94 g K_2CrO_4 25. 42.9 mL   26. 0.18 N

9 PROPERTIES OF GASES

In this chapter we examine the physical and chemical behavior of gases. This includes the way the properties of a gas depend on pressure, volume, and temperature. We will see that it is a relatively simple matter to measure the molecular weights of gaseous substances. The study of gases has also led to knowledge about the microscopic behavior of gases, including information about molecular size and the kinds of attractive forces that exist between gaseous atoms and molecules.

9.1 VOLUME AND PRESSURE

Objectives

To learn how pressure and volume are defined. You should learn how the pressure of a gas is measured and the units in which pressure is expressed.

Review

Gases expand to fill whatever container they are placed in. The volume of a gas is therefore the volume of its container.

Pressure is force per unit area. In the English system pressure can be expressed in pounds per square inch (psi). The pressure of a gas is usually given in terms of the height of a mercury column that exerts the same pressure as the gas. Remember that a mercury column 1 mm high exerts a pressure of 1

torr. At sea level, the pressure exerted by the atmosphere fluc-
tuates about 760 torr. One standard atmosphere (1 atm) is defined as precisely 760 torr. The SI unit of pressure is the
pascal (Pa). A standard atmosphere = 101,325 Pa (although we
won't be using pascals in our calculations). You should be able
to convert pressures from torr to atm, and vice versa using the
relationship, 1 atm = 760 torr.

   Gas pressures are normally measured using manometers.
In the text you see that for an open-end manometer the equation
used to calculate the gas pressure depends on whether the gas
pressure is greater than or less than the atmospheric pressure.
Don't try to memorize these equations - it's too easy to get them
confused. It is much better if you can learn how to analyze the
manometer. Remember that the lower of the two liquid levels is
always chosen as the reference level. At this level the pressures
on both the left and right sides are the same. Figure out what
they are, equate them, and then solve for the pressure of the
gas.

   Sometimes a liquid other than mercury is used in a manometer. To express the pressure in torr it is necessary to convert
the difference in heights of the liquid columns to the difference
in heights that would have been found had mercury been in the
manometer. This is obtained by multiplying the difference in
heights of the liquid by a ratio of the densities of the liquid and
mercury. Mercury is the most dense liquid ever used in a manometer. Therefore, the height of the mercury column will always be
less than the height of the liquid column. Always set up the
ratio of densities so that the calculated equivalent column of mercury is less than that of the liquid. Review Example 9.2 in the
text and Example 9.1 below. Equation 9.1 is useful to remember
for working problems of this kind.

Example 9.1

   A liquid having a density of 1.22 g/mL is used in a manometer. In measuring the pressure of a gas, a difference of 15.6
cm was observed between the liquid levels in the two arms. What
is the mercury equivalent, in torr, of this column of liquid. The
density of mercury is 13.6 g/mL.

Solution

   The mercury equivalent of the liquid column is obtained by

multiplying the height of the liquid column (15.6 cm) by a ratio of densities.

$$P_{Hg} = P_{liquid} \times \text{(ratio of densities)}$$

We can use Equation 9.1, or we can determine what the ratio must be by reasoning. Since P_{Hg} will be less than P_{liquid}, the ratio of densities must have some value smaller than 1, so that when P_{liquid} is multiplied by this ratio a smaller value is obtained. A value less than 1 is only obtained as 1.22/13.6. Therefore,

$$P_{Hg} = 15.6 \text{ cm} \times \left(\frac{1.22}{13.6}\right) = 1.40 \text{ cm Hg}$$

Since 1 cm = 10 mm and 1 torr = 1 mm Hg,

$$P_{Hg} = 14.0 \text{ mm Hg} = 14.0 \text{ torr}$$

Self-Test

1. If a gas exerts a pressure of 1.35 atm, what is its pressure in torr?

2. If a gas exerts a pressure of 630 torr, what is its pressure in atm?

3. A gas in a container is attached to an open-end manometer filled with mercury. The mercury level in the arm connected to the container is 18.5 mm below the level in the open arm. The atmospheric pressure is 755.3 torr. Calculate the pressure of the gas. (It will help if you sketch a picture of the apparatus.)

4. A gas contained in a vessel exerts a pressure of 1.14 atm. The vessel is connected to an open-end manometer filled with mercury. The atmospheric pressure is 766 torr. What will be the difference in heights (measured in cm) between the levels of mercury in the two arms?

5. Two gases in the cylinders shown in Figure 9.1 (next page) exert pressures of 785 torr and 790 torr. If the manometer

is filled with water (d = 1.00 g/mL), what will be the difference in heights between the liquid levels?

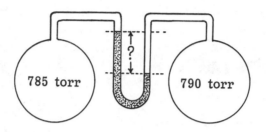

Figure 9.1

6. Calculate the pressure, in atm, exerted on a skin diver at a depth of 12 fathoms on a day when the atmospheric pressure is 752 torr (a barometric pressure of 29.6 inches of mercury). The density of sea water is 1.02 g/mL; 1 fathom equals 6 feet.

New Terms

Barometer
    A tube in which a column of mercury is supported by the atmospheric pressure and that is used to measure the pressure exerted by the atmosphere by measuring the height of the mercury column.

Manometer
    A U-shaped tube, filled partially with a liquid, that is used to measure pressures of trapped gases.

Pascal
    The SI unit for pressure. A pressure of 1 newton per square meter. $1 \text{ Pa} = 1 \text{ N/m}^2$

Pressure
    Force per unit area. In the SI, its units are pascals, $1 \text{ Pa} = 1 \text{ N/m}^2$.

Standard atmosphere (atm)

A unit of pressure sufficient to support a column of mercury 760 mm high. It corresponds to exactly 101,325 Pa.

Torr

A unit of pressure. 1 torr = 1 mm Hg.   760 torr = 1 atm.

9.2   BOYLE'S LAW

Objectives

To learn how the volume of a gas varies with the pressure exerted on it when the amount of gas and its temperature are held constant.

Review

Remember that as the pressure on a gas increases, the gas is squeezed into a smaller volume. Boyle's law says that at constant temperature the product, PV, for a fixed quantity of gas is constant. For real gases this is not quite true, although near atmospheric pressure and room temperature most gases follow Boyle's law quite well. An ideal gas is a hypothetical gas that would obey Boyle's law perfectly under all conditions.

You will be expected to be able to perform calculations dealing with Boyle's law. There are two ways to approach these problems:

(1)   You can memorize the equation, $P_1V_1 = P_2V_2$. This equation can be used, for example, to calculate the final pressure of a gas if you know its initial pressure and volume, and its final volume.

(2)   You can use the fact that the final volume of a gas is equal to its initial volume multiplied by a ratio of pressures, and then use the behavior of the gas to set up the ratio. For example, an increase in pressure causes the final volume to be smaller than the initial volume. The ratio of pressures must therefore be smaller than one so that when the initial volume is multiplied by the ratio the result is a smaller volume. Since this reasoning approach requires some practice, another example is presented on the following page.

Example 9.2

A gas, initially occupying 2.00 L at 780 torr, is placed in a container (at the same temperature) in which its pressure is 740 torr. What is the volume of the container?

Solution

Remember to set up a table of initial and final conditions to avoid confusion.

	initial	final
P	780 torr	740 torr
V	2.00 L	?

Next, reason through the problem. The pressure on the gas has decreased ($780 \longrightarrow 740$). Therefore, the gas must have expanded. This means that the final volume must be larger than 2.00 L. Which ratio of pressures do we choose to multiply the initial volume by?

$$\frac{780 \text{ torr}}{740 \text{ torr}} \quad \text{or} \quad \frac{740 \text{ torr}}{780 \text{ torr}}$$

Obviously (780/740) is the correct choice since it is the only one that will make the final volume larger. The answer is then obtained as

$$V_f = 2.00 \text{ L} \times \left(\frac{780 \text{ torr}}{740 \text{ torr}}\right) = 2.11 \text{ L}$$

As a final note, remember that it is absolutely necessary to have the units of the two quantities (P or V) in a ratio the same. The units in the ratio must cancel.

Self-Test

7. A gas at 745 torr occupies 250 mL. What volume will it occupy at 300 torr if the temperature remains the same?

8. A gas occupies a volume of 180 mL at a pressure of 450 torr. If the gas is transferred to a 2.00-L container at the same

temperature, what will be the new pressure?_____

9. Gasoline vapor mixed with air at atmospheric pressure (1 atm) is drawn into a 610-mL cylinder in an auto engine. Before the mixture is exploded the piston compresses the gas to a volume of 73.1 mL. What is the pressure of the gas when the mixture is ignited? (Assume no temperature change.)

_____

New Terms

Boyle's law
  At constant temperature, for a fixed quantity of gas, PV = constant.

Ideal gas
  A hypothetical gas that would obey the gas laws perfectly under all conditions.

9.3 CHARLES' LAW

Objectives

  To learn how the volume of a gas is related to its temperature.

Review

  Remember that absolute zero occurs at -273.15°C (usually rounded to -273°C). Temperatures used in gas law calculations are always expressed in kelvins. The kelvin temperature is obtained by adding 273 to the Celsius temperature.

$$K = °C + 273$$

  Calculations involving Charles' law, like those with Boyle's law, can also be approached in two ways:

(1) You can use the equation,

$$\frac{V_1}{T_1} = \frac{V_2}{T_2}$$

(2) You can use the fact that as the temperature of a gas increases, at constant pressure, its volume increases. Stated more simply, the gas expands as it gets hot.

     As before we have a situation where the final volume is equal to the initial volume multiplied by a ratio of absolute temperatures, or the final absolute temperature is equal to the initial absolute temperature multiplied by a volume ratio.

Example 9.3

     A gas occupies 250 mL at 25°C. If the pressure remains constant, at what temperature (in °C) will the gas occupy 300 mL?

Solution

     First we collect the data in a table and convert the temperature to kelvins.

	initial	final
V	250 mL	300 mL
T	25 + 273 = 298 K	?

We can compute the final temperature T_f as follows:

$$T_f = 298 \text{ K} \times (\text{ratio of volumes})$$

Since the volume is increasing, the temperature must be rising because gases expand as they are heated. This means that $T_f > T_i$, so the initial temperature must be multiplied by a volume ratio that is larger than one.

$$T_f = 298 \text{ K} \times \left(\frac{300 \text{ mL}}{250 \text{ mL}}\right)$$

$$= 358 \text{ K}$$

Converting to Celsius (by subtracting 273), the final temperature is 85°C.

Self-Test

10. A gas occupies a volume of 650 mL at 30°C. What volume will it occupy at 100°C, assuming that its pressure remains constant?

_____

11. A gas occupies a volume of 26.5 mL at 300°C. While being held at constant pressure, its volume decreases to 15.7 mL. What has the temperature of the gas become (in °C)?

_____

New Terms

Absolute temperature
   The temperature measured on the Kelvin scale.
   K = °C + 273.15 (usually rounded to the nearest whole degree: K = °C + 273).

Absolute zero
   0 K = -273.15 °C

Charles' law
   At constant pressure and for a fixed quantity of a gas, V/T = constant, where T is the temperature in kelvins.

9.4   GAY-LUSSAC'S LAW

Objectives

   To learn how the pressure of a gas is related to its temperature.

Review

   Warming a confined gas increases its pressure. Thus

$$P \propto T$$

or

$$\frac{P_1}{T_1} = \frac{P_2}{T_2}$$

As with the other gas laws, we can approach problems involving

Gay-Lussac's law by the reasoning method. This is shown in
Example 9.5 in the text.

Self-Test

12. A gas in a container of fixed volume exerts a pressure of
     855 torr at 350°C. When the temperature of the gas is
     changed the pressure rises to 980 torr. What is the new
     temperature of the gas (in °C)?

     _____

13. A sample of methane (natural gas) exerts a pressure of 350
     torr at a temperature of 18°C. What pressure will this sam-
     ple exert if its volume is held constant and its temperature
     is raised to 45°C?

     _____

New Terms

Gay-Lussac's law
     For a fixed quantity of gas at a constant volume, P/T =
     constant, where T is the temperature in kelvins.

9.5   THE COMBINED GAS LAW

Objectives

     To combine the preceding three gas laws into one expres-
     sion. You should learn the meaning of standard tempera-
     ture and pressure.

Review

     Reference conditions for gases have been chosen to be
0°C (standard temperature) and 760 torr (standard pressure).
STP is the abbreviation used to specify standard temperature and
pressure.

     As with the other gas laws, calculations with the combined
gas law can be solved using the reasoning approach; for example,

$$V_f = V_i \text{(ratio of pressures)(ratio of temperatures)}$$

You can also use the equation,

$$\frac{P_1 V_1}{T_1} = \frac{P_2 V_2}{T_2}$$

Review Examples 9.6 and 9.7 in the text.

Self-Test

14. A gas at 25°C and 740 torr occupies 840 mL. What volume will it occupy at 14°C and 650 torr?

_____

15. A sealab having an open hatch at the bottom is submerged to a depth at which the pressure is 8.5 atm and the temperature is 13°C. At the surface (P = 1 atm) its volume is 5000 ft^3 and the temperature is a balmy 30°C. If no air is pumped into the sealab, how much usable air space will remain when it is submerged?

_____

16. A sample of air at 35°C has a volume of 365 mL at a pressure of 850 torr. If it is transferred to a 280-mL container at a temperature of 50°C, what will be its pressure?

_____

17. If a sample of a gas occupies 265 mL at 920 torr and 37°C, what volume will it occupy at STP?

_____

New Terms

Combined gas law
   For a fixed quantity of gas, $P_1 V_1 / T_1 = P_2 V_2 / T_2$

Standard temperature and pressure (STP)
   The reference conditions for problems involving gases: 0°C and 760 torr.

9.6   DALTON'S LAW OF PARTIAL PRESSURES

Objectives

   To observe how gases behave in mixtures.

Review

Dalton's law is very simple. Each gas in a mixture behaves independently of any other gases present and exerts a pressure (called its partial pressure) that is the same as it would exert if it were alone in the container. The total pressure of the mixture is simply the sum of the pressures of each of the gases.

A practical application of Dalton's law is the calculation of the pressure of a gas collected over a liquid such as water. Review Examples 9.8 and 9.9 in the text before attempting the Self-Test below.

Self-Test

18. 300 mL of argon at a pressure of 420 torr and 300 mL of helium at 240 torr are placed into the same 300-mL container. The temperatures of the separate gases and the mixture are the same. What is the partial pressure of each gas in the mixture and the total pressure of the mixture?

19. 200 mL of N_2 at 30°C and 750 torr is mixed with some O_2 and transferred to a 500-mL container at 30°C. The total pressure of the mixture is found to be 680 torr. What is the partial pressure of each gas in the mixture?

20. 400 mL of oxygen was collected over water at 25°C at a total pressure of 765 torr. What is the partial pressure of the trapped oxygen?

New Terms

Dalton's law of partial pressures
For a mixture of gases, A, B, C, etc., the total pressure P_T is given by

$$P_T = p_A + p_B + p_C + \ldots$$

where p_A, p_B, etc. are the partial pressures of each of the gases.

Partial pressure
The pressure that is exerted by a particular gas in a mixture of gases.

Vapor pressure
> The equilibrium pressure exerted by the vapor of a liquid in an enclosed space above the liquid.

9.7 CHEMICAL REACTIONS BETWEEN GASES

Objectives

To learn the quantitative relationships between volumes of gases involved in chemical reactions. You should learn the volume occupied by one mole of gas at STP.

Review

Gay-Lussac's law of combining volumes states that at constant temperature and pressure the volumes of gases consumed and/or produced in a chemical reaction are related to one another as ratios of small whole numbers. In fact, under conditions of constant T and P, the volume ratios are the same as the ratios of the coefficients in the balanced chemical equation.

Also of historical importance is Avogadro's principle - equal volumes of gas at the same T and P contain equal numbers of molecules. This can also be expressed as the volume of a gas at constant temperature and pressure is proportional to the number of moles of gas present. For an ideal gas, the volume occupied by one mole at STP (the molar volume of the gas) is 22.4 liters.

Self-Test

21. What volume of O_2 is required to completely react with 150 mL of C_2H_6 (both volumes measured at the same T and P) according to the equation

$$2C_2H_6(g) + 7O_2(g) \longrightarrow 4CO_2(g) + 6H_2O(g) ?$$

_____

22. What volume of air (composed of 20% O_2 by volume) at 25°C and 1.00 atm is required to react with 500 mL of C_2H_6 (measured at 30°C and 850 torr)? (This problem requires several steps - think about how to solve the problem before working with the numbers.)

_____

23. What volume (in liters) would 24.6 g of C_2H_6 occupy at STP?

_____

24. How many liters of oxygen, measured at STP, are needed to oxidize 14.6 g of iron according to the equation
$$4Fe + 3O_2 \longrightarrow 2Fe_2O_3 \ ?$$

_____

New Terms

Avogadro's principle
   Equal volumes of gases at the same temperature and pressure contain equal numbers of molecules.

Gay-Lussac's law of combining volumes
   When measured at the same temperature and pressure, the volumes of gases consumed or produced in a chemical reaction are in ratios of small whole numbers..

9.8   THE IDEAL GAS LAW

Objectives

   To obtain an equation that encompasses all of the gas laws that we have examined in previous sections.

Review

   You should learn the ideal gas law,

$$PV = nRT$$

   The gas constant, R, can have different numerical values depending on the units used to express pressure and volume. The value used most frequently in the text is 0.0821 L atm mol^{-1} K^{-1}. If you learn this value, it's important that you also learn the units that go with it. If you use this value in the ideal gas law, remember that the pressure must be expressed in atm and the volume in liters; otherwise incorrect numerical answers will result regardless of how good you are at arithmetic.

   A very important application of the ideal gas law is in the determination of molecular weights of gaseous substances. Review Examples 9.14 and 9.15 in the text as well as the Example below.

Example 9.4

A sample of a gas was found to have a density of 1.64 g/L at 30°C and 0.930 atm. What is the molecular weight of the gas?

Solution

When you are asked to compute a molecular weight, you actually are being asked to calculate the number of grams per mole. The necessary data for this are P, V, T and a weight of gas (in grams). From the P, V, T data you can calculate the number of moles of gas from the ideal gas law. The molecular weight is then obtained simply by taking the ratio of grams of gas to moles of gas.

The density in this question gives the weight of one liter of gas. Therefore, we have: P = 0.930 atm, V = 1.00 L, T = 273 + 30 = 303 K, mass = 1.64 g. Solving the ideal gas law for n,

$$n = \frac{PV}{RT} = \frac{(0.930 \text{ atm})(1.00 \text{ L})}{(0.0821 \text{ L atm/mol K})(303 \text{ K})}$$

$$n = 0.0374 \text{ mol}$$

Then,

$$\text{M.W.} = \frac{1.64 \text{ g}}{0.0374 \text{ mol}} = 43.9 \text{ g/mol}$$

Self-Test

25. Calculate the numerical value of R in the units,

    (a) mL atm/mol K _____

    (b) L torr/mol K _____

26. How many moles of gas are present in 3.00 L at 800 torr and 40°C?

    _____

27. Calculate the pressure in atm exerted by 0.10 mol of argon at -20°C in a 10-L container.

    _____

28. 0.625 g of an unknown gas occupies 500 mL at STP.   What is its molecular weight?

29. What volume would 28 g of O_2 occupy at 800 torr and 27°C?

30. Calculate the density of N_2 at STP.

31. Butane, from a cigarette lighter, has a density of 2.30 g/L at 22°C and 730 torr.   What is the molecular weight of butane?

   If its empirical formula is C_2H_5, what is its molecular formula?

New Terms

Ideal gas law
   $PV = nRT$

Gas constant (universal gas constant)
   $R = 0.0821 \text{ L atm mol}^{-1} \text{ K}^{-1}$

9.9   GRAHAM'S LAW OF EFFUSION

Objectives

   To learn how the rates of effusion (and diffusion) of gases are related to their molecular weights.

Review

   Diffusion and effusion are similar, although not identical, processes. Both refer to the rates at which gas molecules move from one place to another. Graham's law is summarized in the equation,

$$\frac{\text{rate of effusion of gas (A)}}{\text{rate of effusion of gas (B)}} = \sqrt{\frac{M_B}{M_A}}$$

where M_A and M_B are the molecular weights of A and B, respectively.

32. Which of the following molecules diffuses faster?

 (a) H_2O or H_2S _____

 (b) NH_3 or H_2O _____

 (c) CO_2 or NO_2 _____

33. Calculate the ratio of the rates of effusion, R_{NO}/R_{NO_2}.

_____

34. How many times faster does $^{235}UF_6$ diffuse than $^{238}UF_6$?

_____

35. What would the molecular weight of a gas be if it diffuses only one sixth as fast as H_2?

_____

New Terms

Diffusion
    The mixing of two fluids, one into the other.

Effusion
    The escape of a gas under pressure through a very small opening into a region of low pressure.

Graham's law
    The rate of effusion of a gas is inversely proportional to the square root of the molecular weight of the gas. Comparing two gases,

$$\text{Rate (1)/Rate (2)} = \sqrt{M_2/M_1}$$

where M is the molecular weight.

9.10   KINETIC MOLECULAR THEORY AND THE GAS LAWS

Objectives

    To learn and understand the postulates of the theory that was developed to explain the gas laws that we discussed in earlier sections. You should learn how the distribution of molecular speeds and molecular kinetic energies are related to the absolute temperature.

Review

The kinetic molecular theory was developed to explain why gases behave the way they do. The theory is described by a set of postulates presented in detail in the text. In summary, the kinetic molecular theory (or simply the kinetic theory) views a gas as being composed of very tiny molecules, having negligible volume themselves, separated by very large distances from one another. The molecules are in rapid random motion, colliding with the walls of the container and with each other. The pressure exerted by a gas results from collisions of the molecules with the walls. It is further postulated that the molecules do not attract each other and that there is a distribution of molecular speeds, ranging from very slow molecules to extremely fast ones. Associated with the distribution of molecular speeds there is a corresponding distribution of kinetic energies. To account for Graham's law it is necessary to postulate that the average kinetic energy of a gas depends only on the absolute temperature. This is perhaps the most important aspect of the kinetic theory because it applies to any collection of molecules. At a given temperature the average kinetic energy is the same for any collection of molecules, regardless of their chemical makeup or whether they are in a gas, a liquid, or a solid. Study Figure 9.12. In particular, note the following:

(1)   At any temperature the fraction of molecules having zero kinetic energy is zero.

(2)   The fraction of molecules having very large kinetic energies gradually approaches zero at high kinetic energies.

(3)   The maximum on the curve at a given temperature represents the kinetic energy possessed by the largest fraction of molecules. This is termed the most probable kinetic energy since it is the one most likely to be found if the molecules were sampled at random.

(4)   At successively higher temperatures the height of the maximum decreases. The total area under the curve represents the sum of all of the fractions, and must equal 1.00. Since the curve gets higher at large kinetic energies, it must get lower elsewhere so that the area remains constant.

(5) At any given temperature the average kinetic energy occurs at a slightly higher kinetic energy than the most probable kinetic energy. This is a consequence of the unsymmetrical shape of the distribution curve.

(6) The average kinetic energy increases as the temperature increases.

Self-Test

36. (Multiple choice). How does kinetic theory account for Boyle's law?
     (a) The average kinetic energy depends only on temperature.
     (b) A gas is mostly empty space.
     (c) There are no attractive forces between molecules.
     (d) The molecules are in rapid random motion.
     _____

37. (Multiple choice). How does kinetic theory account for Charles' law?
     (a) There is a distribution of molecular speeds between gas molecules.
     (b) The molecules have negligibly small volumes.
     (c) Molecules collide with each other.
     (d) On the average, molecules move faster at higher temperature.
     _____

38. After studying this section, sketch the kinetic energy distribution for a gas at two different temperatures on the axes which follow. Indicate the average and most probable kinetic energies at both temperatures.

New Terms

Kinetic molecular theory
    The theoretical model that explains the properties of gases
    and accounts for the gas laws. It states that an ideal gas
    is composed of point-sized particles in rapid random motion
    and that the temperature of the gas is directly proportional
    to the average kinetic energy of its particles.

Mole fraction
    A concentration unit that is the ratio of the number of
    moles of a given component to the total number of moles in
    the solution.

9.11   REAL GASES

Objectives

    To see how the postulates of the kinetic theory must be
    modified to account for the properties of real gases,
    which do not obey the ideal gas law exactly.

Review

    There are two defects in the kinetic theory that was
presented in Section 9.10.

(1) Molecules do have attractive forces between them. An ex-
     ample is the dipole-dipole attractions between polar molecules.

(2) Molecules themselves do have a finite volume that is not neg-
     ligible compared to the total volume when the molecules are
     squeezed close together.

    The van der Waals equation,

$$\left(P + \frac{n^2 a}{V^2}\right)\left(V - nb\right) = nRT$$

attempts to apply corrections to the pressure and volume of a gas
in the ideal gas law. The actual pressure and volume are modi-
fied to give a pressure and volume that the gas would have if it
were an ideal gas (i.e., if there were no attractive forces and if

the gas molecules had zero volume). In the equation, the constant a is proportional to the strengths of the attractive forces
and b is proportional to the size of the molecules.

Self-Test

39. Use the data in Table 9.3 to answer the following:

  (a) Which gas has the larger molecules, CH_4 or H_2O?_____

  (b) Which gas has the greater attractive forces between
      molecules, NH_3 or H_2O?

                                                      _____

  (c) Which gas has the larger molecules, H_2O or C_2H_5OH?

                                                      _____

  (d) Which gas has the greater attractive forces, O_2 or
      CH_4?

                                                      _____

New Terms

Excluded volume
    The volume that one molecule in a gas prevents other
    molecules from occupying.

Van der Waals equation of state
    A modified form of PV = nRT in which corrections for the
    finite volume of the gas molecules and intermolecular attrac-
    tions are applied to the measured volume and measured
    pressure of a real gas.

Answers to Self-Test Questions

1. 1026 torr 2. 0.829 atm 3. 773.8 torr 4. 100 mm 5. 68 mm
6. 3.16 atm (2.17 atm from sea water, 0.99 atm from atmosphere)
7. 621 mL 8. 40.5 torr 9. 8.34 atm 10. 800 mL 11. 66°C
12. 441°C 13. 382 torr 14. 921 mL 15. 555 ft^3 (This question
illustrates why underwater laboratories open to the sea are pres-
surized - to keep the water out!) 16. 1.16 x 10^3 torr
17. 283 mL 18. P_{Ar} = 420 torr, P_{He} = 240 torr, P_T = 660 torr

19. p_{N_2} = 300 torr, p_{O_2} = (680 - 300) = 380 torr

20. 741 torr   21. 525 mL   22. 9.62 L   23. 18.4 L   24. 4.39 L
25.(a) 82.1 mL atm/mol K   (b) 62.4 L torr/mol K   26. 0.123 mol
27. 0.21 atm   28. 28.0 g/mol   29. 20 L   30. 1.25 g/L
31. 58.0 g/mol, C_4H_{10} 32.(a) H_2O (b) NH_3 (c) CO_2:   The

lighter (lower molecular weight) molecule diffuses faster.
33. 1.24   34. 1.004   35. 72 amu   36. b   37. d
38. See Figure 9.12.
39. (a) CH_4 (b) H_2O (c) C_2H_5OH (d) CH_4

10 STATES OF MATTER AND INTERMOLECULAR FORCES

This chapter focuses on the physical properties of liquids and solids, and how these properties are affected by the attractive forces between the particles (molecules or ions) of which they are composed. As you study this chapter you will learn the reasons for many of the properties of gases, liquids, and solids that we take for granted on a day-to-day basis. Perhaps you will see the world around you in a new light.

10.1 COMPARING THE PROPERTIES OF GASES, LIQUIDS, AND SOLIDS

Objectives

To learn why gases, liquids, and solids differ so greatly in their properties and to examine some specific properties of liquids and solids.

Review

The physical properties of all gases are nearly alike because the molecules are very far apart and the attractive forces between them are very weak. In a liquid or solid, the particles are very close together, with very little empty space. In addition, in a liquid or solid the attractive forces are relatively strong and depend on the kinds of particles. For this reason, different chemical substances behave differently in their liquid and solid states.

Compressibility and rates of diffusion are properties that are determined primarily by the tightness of packing in the various states.

Volume and shape depend on the strengths of the attractive forces. In a solid the attractions between molecules or ions prevent them from easily moving past each other.

Surface tension is the energy needed to increase the surface area of a liquid and depends strongly on the attractions between the molecules. Liquids of low surface tension are able to wet surfaces easily.

The rate of evaporation of a liquid or solid depends on the strengths of intermolecular attractions and increases with increasing temperature. It also depends on its surface area. Be sure to study Figures 10.6 and 10.7, with their accompanying explanations. Remember that evaporation is an endothermic process, and produces a cooling effect.

Self-Test

1. (Multiple choice). The fact that moist grains of sand stick together is attributed to liquid water's
    (a)   small molecular size
    (b)   surface tension
    (c)   inability to be compressed
    (d)   ability to change its shape
                                                    _____

2. (Multiple choice). Water evaporates faster at high temperatures than at low temperatures primarily because
    (a)   increasing the temperature of a liquid causes it to expand
    (b)   at high temperature the molecules are further apart
    (c)   water wets a surface faster at high temperature
    (d)   at the higher temperature more molecules have high kinetic energies
                                                    _____

3. Alcohol evaporates faster than water when they are at the same temperature.
    (a)   Which substance has the weaker attractive forces between its molecules?
                                                    _____

    (b)   Which would be expected to have the lower surface tension?
                                                    _____

4. (Multiple choice). The reason molecules diffuse more slowly
    in liquids than in gases is
    (a) the molecules move more slowly in a liquid than in a
         gas
    (b) the strong attractive forces in a liquid hold the mole-
         cules in place
    (c) the molecules move slowly because the liquid cannot
         expand easily
    (d) the molecules are constantly colliding with others,
         thereby interfering with their movement
                                                    _____

5. How does a surfactant increase the ability of water to wet
    a surface?
    _____

    _____

New Terms

Compressibility
    The ease with which a gas, a liquid, or a solid can be
    compressed to a smaller volume.

Diffusion
    The mixing of two fluids, one into the other.

Evaporation
    The conversion of a liquid to a gas.

Mean free path
    The average distance traveled by a molecule between
    collisions.

States of matter
    Solid, liquid, or gas.

Sublimation
    Conversion of a solid directly to a vapor without passing
    through the liquid state.

Surface tension
    A measure of the amount of energy needed to expand the
    surface area of a liquid.

Surfactant
    A substance that lowers the surface tension of a liquid and
    promotes wetting.

Wetting
    The spreading of a liquid across a solid surface.

10.2   INTERMOLECULAR ATTRACTIVE FORCES

Objectives

    To learn about the kinds of intermolecular attractive forces
    and their relative strengths.

Review

    Intermolecular attractions are the attractive forces between
neighboring molecules. There are three principal types: dipole-
dipole attractions, hydrogen bonds, and London forces.

    Dipole-dipole attractions occur between polar molecules and
are generally about 1% as strong as normal covalent bonds. Hydrogen bonding is an especially strong dipole-dipole attraction
that occurs when hydrogen is bonded to a small, very electronegative element - principally fluorine, oxygen, and nitrogen. Their
strengths are about 5% to 10% as strong as covalent bonds.
London forces (instantaneous dipole-induced dipole forces) occur
between all particles, but they are especially important in nonpolar substances where they are the only intermolecular forces
present.

Self-Test

6. What kinds of attractive forces occur in the liquid state be-
    tween molecules of

    (a) HBr   _____

    (b) CO_2 _____

    (c) H_2O _____

    (d) CH_3Cl _____

    (e) CH_3OH _____

7. Why are London forces normally weak compared to dipole-
    dipole forces? _____

_____

New Terms

Dipole-dipole attraction
    Attractions between molecules that are dipoles.

Hydrogen bond
    An extra strong dipole-dipole attraction that occurs between
    molecules in which hydrogen is covalently bonded to nitrogen,
    oxygen, or fluorine.

Induced dipole
    A dipole created when the electron cloud of an atom, mole-
    cule, or ion is distorted by a neighboring dipole or by an
    ion.

Instantaneous dipole
    A momentary dipole caused by the erratic movement of elec-
    trons in an atom, molecule, or ion.

Intermolecular forces of attraction
    The attractive forces that occur between neighboring
    molecules.

London forces
    Weak attractive forces caused by instantaneous dipole-induced
    dipole attractions.

10.3   HEAT OF VAPORIZATION

Objectives

    To examine the energy changes that accompany the evapo-
    ration of a liquid and to learn what they tell us about the
    strengths of intermolecular attractions.

Review

    The molar heat of vaporization is the energy required to
convert one mole of liquid to one mole of vapor. Quantitatively,

it is the difference between the heat content of the vapor and the heat content of the liquid.

$$\Delta H_{vap} = H_{vapor} - H_{liquid}$$

Remember that neither H_{vapor} nor H_{liquid} can actually be measured; it is only their difference that is observed.

The heat of vaporization is useful because it provides a direct measure of the strengths of the attractive forces that exist between the molecules in the liquid.

Variations in ΔH_{vap} show that among hydrocarbons the attractive forces (London forces) increase with chain length. London forces also increase with molecular size because large molecules are more polarizable than small ones. In this section we see that hydrogen bonding is important for HF, H_2O and NH_3. In general, hydrogen bonding is most significant in molecules having O—H or N—H bonds.

Self-Test

8. Using the data in Table 10.1, arrange the following compounds in order of increasing strengths of intermolecular attractive forces: C_2H_6, HCl, H_2S, HF, SiH_4, NH_3.

   _____

9. Without referring to Table 10.1, choose the compound in each of the following pairs with the stronger intermolecular attractive forces.
   (a) PH_3 or AsH_3 _____
   (b) SiH_4 or CH_4 _____
   (c) H_2O or H_2S _____

New Terms

Molar heat of vaporization, (Heat of vaporization), ΔH_{vap}
    The amount of heat absorbed when one mole of liquid is converted to a vapor at constant temperature and pressure. Usually, it is measured at the boiling point of the substance.

Polarizability
    The ease with which the electron cloud of an atom, molecule, or ion is distorted, thereby causing the particle to become

a dipole.

10.4   VAPOR PRESSURES OF LIQUIDS

Objectives

To understand why the vapor pressure of a liquid depends
only on the temperature. You should understand the concept of dynamic equilibrium and you should learn how the
effects of outside influences on an equilibrium can be predicted by application of Le Châtelier's principle. In particular, you should learn how temperature affects the vapor pressure of a liquid.

Review

A dynamic equilibrium exists when two opposing processes
occur at the same speed.

The equilibrium vapor pressure of a liquid (usually just
called its vapor pressure) is the pressure exerted by its vapor
when the vapor is in dynamic equilibrium with the liquid. In
this case molecules are evaporating from the liquid into a closed
container at the same rate that molecules are returning to the
liquid.

Le Châtelier's principle states that when a system at equilibrium is disturbed (so as to upset the equilibrium) the system
readjusts in a way that minimizes, or counteracts, the stress
placed upon it. If the pressure on the system is increased by a
decrease in volume, the system will respond (if it can) in a way
that tends to reduce the pressure. If heat is added to a system,
the system responds by undergoing a change that absorbs heat.
In each case the system changes in a way that tends to absorb
the stress placed on it. You will encounter Le Châtelier's principle again in Chapters 14, 15 and 16. Learning to apply it now
will make things easier for you later on.

The vapor pressure of a liquid increases with temperature.
A graph of vapor pressure versus temperature gives a vapor
pressure curve, illustrated in Figure 10.15 in the text. The vapor pressure curve ends at the critical temperature - the temper-

ature above which a gas can no longer be condensed to liquid by the application of pressure. At the critical temperature a gas can be liquefied by application of the critical pressure.

Self-Test

10. Consider the process, vapor $\rightleftharpoons$ liquid + heat

    (a) A decrease in pressure will increase the amount of

    _____

    (b) An increase in temperature will decrease the amount of

    _____

11. (Multiple choice). The vapor pressure of a liquid increases with increasing temperature primarily because as the temperature rises,
    (a) the molecules of the vapor move more rapidly
    (b) a greater fraction of molecules can escape the liquid
    (c) the attractive forces between the molecules in the vapor decrease
    (d) the rate of return to the liquid increases   _____

12. Refer to Table 8.1 to answer this question. Should HBr or HCl be expected to have the larger vapor pressure at -75°C?

    _____

13. Ethylene glycol has a very low vapor pressure at room temperature.
    (a) Does ethylene glycol evaporate rapidly at room temperature?

    _____

    (b) What does the information in this question tell you about the strengths of the attractive forces in ethylene glycol?

    _____

    _____

New Terms

Critical pressure, P_c
    The vapor pressure of a substance at its critical temperature.

Critical temperature, T_c
   The temperature above which a substance cannot exist as a
   separate liquid phase, regardless of the pressure.

Equilibrium vapor pressure of a liquid
   The pressure exerted by a vapor that is in dynamic equilibrium with its liquid.

Vapor pressure
   The pressure exerted by the vapor above a liquid. Usually,
   this term means the equilibrium vapor pressure, which is
   the vapor pressure when the liquid is in equilibrium with its
   vapor.

Vapor pressure curve
   A graph of equilibrium vapor pressure versus temperature.

Le Châtelier's principle
   When a system that is in dynamic equilibrium is subjected to
   a disturbance that upsets the equilibrium, the system undergoes a change in a direction that counteracts the disturbance
   and restores equilibrium.

Supercritical fluid
   A substance as it exists at a temperature above its critical
   temperature.

10.5   BOILING POINT

Objectives

   To define more precisely the term, boiling point, and to
   understand why boiling point changes with pressure. You
   should also learn how boiling point provides a measure of
   the strengths of the intermolecular attractive forces in a
   liquid.

Review

   The boiling point is the temperature at which the vapor
pressure of the liquid equals the prevailing atmospheric pressure.
The normal boiling point (standard boiling point) is the temperature at which the vapor pressure equals 760 torr.

The boiling point provides an indication of the strengths of the attractive forces between liquid molecules. If the attractive forces are high, the vapor pressure at a given temperature is low because only a small fraction of molecules can escape the liquid. These liquids must be heated to high temperatures to bring their vapor pressures up to atmospheric pressure. On the other hand, when weak attractive forces are present, a large fraction can escape and the vapor pressure is high. Liquids that have low vapor pressures at a given temperature have high boiling points, while those with high vapor pressures have low boiling points.

The abnormally high boiling points of NH_3, H_2O and HF provide evidence for hydrogen bonding in these substances.

Self-Test

14. Why does HF have a lower boiling point than H_2O even though it forms stronger hydrogen bonds?

_____

_____

15. What effect does an increase in pressure have on the boiling point of a liquid?

_____

16. What is inside the bubbles in boiling water? _____

New Terms

Boiling point
    The temperature at which the vapor pressure of a liquid equals the prevailing external pressure.

Normal boiling point
    The temperature at which the vapor pressure of a liquid equals 1 atm.

10.6   FREEZING POINT

Objectives

    To define freezing point in terms of dynamic equilibrium and to consider the energy changes that take place upon freezing and melting.

Review

At the freezing point of a liquid there is a dynamic equilibrium between molecules in the solid and liquid. Molecules leave
the solid and enter the liquid at the same rate that molecules
leave the liquid and attach themselves to the solid. The energy
that must be removed from one mole of liquid to convert it to solid is called the molar heat of crystallization. This is equal in
magnitude, but opposite in sign, to the molar heat of fusion -
the energy needed to melt one mole of solid. Fusion means the
same as melting (That is how an electrical fuse works.). Remember that ΔH_{fus} is always much less than ΔH_{vap}.

Self-Test

17. Why doesn't the value of ΔH_{fus} give a direct measure of the
    strengths of the attractive forces in the solid? _____

    _____

    _____

18. What difference is there between the freezing point of a
    liquid and the melting point of a solid? _____

New Terms

Freezing point
    At a particular pressure, the temperature at which an equi-
    librium can exist between the liquid and solid forms of a
    substance.

Melting point
    The temperature at which a substance melts. It is the same
    temperature as the freezing point of the substance.

Molar heat of crystallization (heat of crystallization), ΔH_{cryst}
    The heat evolved when one mole of a liquid freezes. It is
    equal in magnitude, but opposite in sign to the molar heat
    of fusion.

Molar heat of fusion (heat of fusion), ΔH_{fus}
　　The amount of heat absorbed when one mole of solid melts to give a mole of liquid at constant temperature and pressure.

10.7　CRYSTALLINE SOLIDS

Objectives

To learn what features identify crystalline solids and to learn how their structures are investigated using X-ray diffraction.

Review

A crystal normally has a very regular, symmetrical form that is the result of the very orderly pattern of particles within it.

The structures of crystals are studied by X-ray diffraction. When an X-ray beam is directed on a crystal the atoms composing the crystal scatter the beam in all directions. The X rays emerging from the crystal are only in phase in certain directions, however, and an intense X-ray beam is observed to come out of the crystal only at certain angles with respect to the incoming beam. The key point in this section is that the distance of separation between planes of atoms in a crystal is related to the angle at which an X-ray beam is observed to be reflected.

The Bragg equation relates the angle of reflection (θ), the distance between planes of atoms (d) and the wavelength of the X rays (λ). Using X rays of known wavelength, the distances between atoms in the crystal can be calculated. Bragg's equation is

$$n\lambda = 2d \sin \theta$$

where n is an integer (n = 1 or 2 or 3, etc.)

Self-Test

19. X rays of wavelength 154 pm are reflected from layers of atoms in a crystal of potassium chloride at an angle of 14.1°. What is the distance between the layers? (Assume n = 1)

New Terms

Bragg equation

$n\lambda = 2d \sin \theta$. The equation is used to analyze X-ray diffraction data obtained from crystals.

Crystalline solid

A solid in which the particles are arranged in an orderly, repeating pattern.

X-ray diffraction

The diffraction of X rays by the atoms in a crystalline solid. It is a technique for studying the structures of crystalline solids.

10.8   LATTICES

Objectives

To find a way of describing a repeating pattern, such as the structure of a crystal, in terms of a lattice.

Review

One of the main themes throughout this section is that it is possible to describe the structures of millions of different crystals in terms of a very small set of only 14 three-dimensional lattices.

A lattice may be a one-, two- or three-dimensional geometric array of points. To describe a crystal, of course, a three-dimensional lattice is required. The properties of the entire lattice are embodied in the unit cell. The entire lattice can be constructed by moving the unit cell along its edges by distances equal to the lengths of the edges. The unit cell is characterized by the lengths of its edges, $\underline{a}$, $\underline{b}$ and $\underline{c}$, and the angles opposite them, α, β and γ, respectively (see Figure 10.26 in the text).

Three common types of lattices are described by the cubic unit cells.

(1)   simple cubic (primitive cubic): lattice points only at the corners.

(2) body-centered cubic: lattice points at the corners plus one in the center of the cell.

(3) face-centered cubic: lattice points at the corners plus one in the center of each face.

Remember that only 1/8 of a corner point lies within a given unit cell, 1/4 of a point along an edge lies in a given cell, 1/2 of a face-centered point lies within a given cell, and any point within the cell contributes one entire point to the cell.

Measurement of unit cell dimensions allows the calculation of the sizes of atoms and ions. The procedure is essentially a problem in applied geometry, as shown on Page 379.

Self-Test

20. Consider the unit cell drawn below. How many lattice points are within it?

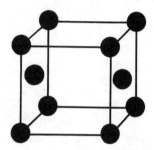

21. Cesium chloride, CsCl, forms crystals having a simple cubic lattice. If cesium ions are located at the corners of the unit cells, where must the choride ions be located?

22. Iron crystallizes in a body-centered cubic lattice, with atoms touching along the body diagonal of the cube - the line running from one corner through the center of the cube to the opposite corner. The atomic radius of iron is 126 pm. What is the length of the edge of the unit cell expressed in picometers?

23. Potassium chloride crystallizes with a face-centered cubic structure. One face of a unit cell is shown on p 218. The unit cell edge is 628 pm long and the radius of the Cl^- ion is 181 pm.

(a) What is the ionic radius of K^+ in picometers? _____

(b) What is the radius in angstroms?   _____

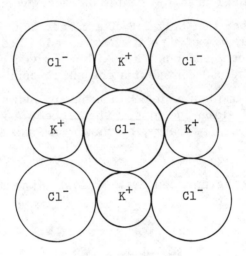

New Terms

Body-centered cubic unit cell
> A cubic unit cell that has identical atoms, molecules, or ions at the corners, plus one in the center of the cell.

Crystal lattice
> The repeating symmetrical pattern of atoms, molecules, or ions that occurs in a crystal.

Face-centered cubic (fcc) unit cell
> A cubic unit cell that has atoms, molecules, or ions at the corners and in the center of each face.

Lattice
> A repeating pattern of points. In a crystal, it corresponds to the repeating pattern formed by the particles of the substance.

Primitive lattice
> A lattice in which the unit cell has lattice points only at the corners.

Simple cubic unit cell

A cubic unit cell with identical atoms, molecules, or ions located only at the corners.

Unit cell

The smallest portion of a lattice that can be used to generate the entire lattice by repeatedly moving the unit cell in directions parallel to its edges by distances equal to the lengths of those edges. In a less formal sense, it is the smallest portion of a crystal that can be repeated over and over in all directions to give the entire crystal lattice.

10.9   TYPES OF CRYSTALS

Objectives

To understand how the properties of a crystalline substance depend on the kinds of species that occupy sites in the lattice and on the nature of the attractive forces between them.

Review

The key points of this section are summarized in Table 10.5 in the text. Study this table well before answering the following Self-Test.

Self-Test

24.   What crystal type is observed for

   (a)   NaCl   _____

   (b) SO_2 _____

   (c)   Ni   _____

   (d) $MgCl_2$ _____

   (e)   SiC   _____

25. CO_2 forms soft crystals (dry ice) that sublime (evaporate) at $-78°C$. SiO_2, on the other hand, forms hard high melting crystals (sand). What crystal type does each of these form?

_____

26. UF_6 forms soft crystals that melt at 64.5°C. What is the probable type of crystal formed by UF_6? _____

27. An element, formerly called columbium, melts at 2468°C, is soft and shiny, and conducts electricity. What is this type of crystal? _____

New Terms

Covalent crystal
    A crystal in which lattice positions are occupied by atoms that are covalently bonded to other atoms at neighborning lattice sites.

Ionic crystal
    A crystal in which the particles are positive and negative ions.

Metallic crystal
    A solid having only positive ions at the lattice points, which are attracted to a "sea of electrons" that extends throughout the entire crystal.

Molecular crystal
    A crystal composed of molecules (such as water) or individual atoms (such as the noble gases).

10.10 LIQUID CRYSTALS

Objectives

    To learn the properties of these substances that have some properties of both liquids and crystals.

Review

    Substances that form liquid crystals have rodlike molecules. The three classes of liquid crystals are nematic, smectic, and cholesteric. Their differences are shown in Figure 10.34.

Self-Test

28. What type of liquid crystal is used in liquid crystal display in wristwatches and calculators?

_____

29. What type of liquid crystal changes color dramatically when its temperature is changed?

_____

New Terms

Liquid crystal
    A substance that is able to flow like a liquid but which has some physical properties normally associated with crystals.

Cholesteric liquid crystal
    Rodlike molecules, similar in structure to cholesterol, that are arranged in layers in which the parallel rods in one layer are oriented in a different direction than the parallel rods in an adjoining layer.

Nematic liquid crystal
    A liquid crystal composed of long rodlike molecules packed like short pieces of uncooked spaghetti.

Smectic liquid crystal
    A liquid crystal that consists of rodlike molecules arranged in layers of parallel rods.

10.11   HEATING AND COOLING CURVES; CHANGES OF STATE

Objectives

    To observe what changes take place when heat is gradually added to a solid, or gradually removed from a gas. You should learn the kinds of energy changes that take place along the various segments of a heating or cooling curve. Learn the definition of supercooling and amorphous solid.

Review

    On those portions of a heating or cooling curve where the temperature is changing (the slanted line segments in Figures

10.37 and 10.38) the kinetic energy of the molecules is changing. The horizontal segments, where the temperature remains constant, correspond to changes in potential energy during a phase change (gas ←→ liquid, liquid ←→ vapor).

Supercooling is a phenomenon that occurs when a liquid is cooled so rapidly that its temperature drops below the ordinary freezing point before the molecules have an opportunity to assemble themselves into the proper arrangement to form a crystal. Amorphous solids such as glass are actually supercooled liquids.

Self-Test

30. Refer to the cooling curve which follows to answer the following:
     (a) Which line segment corresponds to the conversion of vapor to liquid?

     _____

     (b) Which line segments correspond to changes in kinetic energy?

     _____

     (c) Which line segments correspond to changes in potential energy?

     _____

     (d) Use a dotted line to indicate the effect of supercooling.

     (e) What is the boiling point of the substance? _____

     (f) What is the melting point of the substance? _____

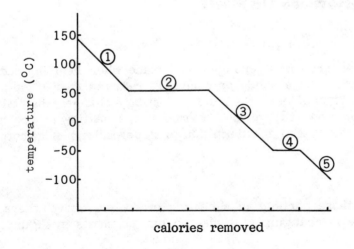

calories removed

New Terms

Change of state
   Transformation of matter from one state to another, for example, from liquid to solid.

Cooling curve
   For a particular substance, a graph of temperature versus
   amount of heat removed. Temperatures corresponding to
   condensation of the vapor and freezing of the liquid can be
   read from the graph.

Heating curve
   For a particular substance, a graph of temperature versus
   amount of heat added. Temperatures corresponding to the
   melting and boiling points of the substance can be read from
   the graph.

Supercooled liquid
   A liquid at a temperature below its freezing point. An
   amorphous solid. A glass.

Supercooling
   Cooling a liquid to a temperature below its freezing point.

Amorphous solid
   A noncrystalline solid. It lacks the long-range order found
   in crystals. It is also called a supercooled liquid. Glass is
   an example.

10.12 VAPOR PRESSURES OF SOLIDS

Objectives
   To learn how solids, like liquids, are able to evaporate by
   sublimation.

Review
   Sublimation is the direct conversion of solid to vapor without passing through the liquid state. If the solid is placed in a
closed container, the vapor can come to equilibrium with the solid.
The pressure exerted by the vapor is called the vapor pressure
of the solid. It too rises with increasing temperature.

Self-Test

31. The heat of sublimation, ΔH_{subl}, is the energy required to convert one mole of solid directly to one mole of vapor. The value of ΔH_{subl} is always greater than ΔH_{vap}. Why is this so?

_____

_____

32. Which substance would have a higher vapor pressure at -90°C, solid H_2O or solid CO_2? Why? _____

_____

New Terms

Equilibrium vapor pressure of a solid
    The pressure exerted by a vapor that is in dynamic equilibrium with its solid.

10.13   PHASE DIAGRAMS

Objectives

    To learn how a phase diagram can be used to define the limits of temperature and pressure over which the different states of a substance can exist.

Review

    The type of phase diagram discussed in this section contains three lines that define pressures and temperatures at which equilibria can exist between two phases. The solid-vapor equilibrium line is the vapor pressure curve for a solid. The liquid-vapor line, which terminates at the critical temperature and pressure, is the vapor pressure curve for the liquid. The solid-liquid line gives the melting point at different pressures. These lines serve as boundaries to temperature/pressure regions where only one phase can exist. Review Figure 10.41 and learn which regions of the diagram correspond to solid, liquid, and vapor. Remember that the three equilibrium lines intersect at the triple point - the temperature and pressure at which all three states can coexist in dynamic equilibrium.

The relationships between temperature, pressure and phase changes are covered in detail in Figures 10.42 to 10.44. Review this material, too, so you can follow the changes that take place moving either horizontally or vertically on a phase diagram.

For most substances the solid-liquid line slants to the right. This is because in most cases the solid is more dense than the liquid. Application of pressure to a liquid (moving up vertically at constant temperature) converts the liquid to the more dense (more compact) solid phase. You should be able to make this prediction on the basis of Le Châtelier's principle.

Self-Test

33. Sketch a phase diagram for a substance whose triple point occurs at -10°C, 25 torr and whose normal melting and boiling points are -5°C and 120°C, respectively. Identify the solid-liquid (S-L), liquid-vapor (L-V) and solid-vapor (S-V) lines. Indicate the solid, liquid, and vapor regions.

New Terms

Phase diagram
>   A pressure-temperature graph on which are plotted temperatures and pressures at which equilibrium exists between the states of a substance. It defines temperature-pressure regions in which the solid, liquid, and gaseous states of the substance can exist.

Triple point
>   The temperature and pressure at which the liquid, solid, and vapor states of a substance can coexist in equilibrium.

Answers to Self-Test Questions

1. b   2. d   3.(a) alcohol   (b) alcohol   4. d   5. It lowers the surface tension of the liquid.   6.(a) dipole-dipole and London (b) London   (c) hydrogen bonding and London   (d) dipole-dipole and London   (e) hydrogen bonding and London
7. London forces are intermittent because the dipoles come and go, existing only briefly.   8. $SiH_4 < C_2H_6 < HCl < H_2S < NH_3 <$

HF (arranged in order of increasing ΔH_{vap})
9.(a) AsH$_3$ (b) SiH$_4$ (c) H$_2$O   10.(a) vapor (b) liquid   11. b
12. HCl   13.(a) no (b) they are large   14. Because HF can
form only two hydrogen bonds while H$_2$O can form four.   Four
weaker bonds turn out to be stronger than two strong bonds.
15. Increasing pressure raises the boiling point.   16. steam
17. It gives a measure of the difference between the strengths of
attractive forces in two phases that each contain relatively strong
attractive forces.   18. None. They are identical.   19. 316 pm
20. Two   21. Entirely within the unit cells so that the Cs$^+$ to Cl$^-$
ratio can be 1:1   22. 291 pm   23.(a) 133 pm (b) 1.33 Å
24.(a) ionic (b) molecular (c) metallic (d) ionic (e) covalent
25. CO$_2$ – molecular; SiO$_2$ – covalent   26. molecular   27. metallic
(the element is now called niobium)   28. nematic   29. cholesteric
30.(a) 2 (b) 1, 3, 5 (c) 2, 4 (d) See Figure 10.39 in the text.
(e) 50°C (f) –50°C   31. The strengths of the attractive forces
are greater in the solid than in the liquid.   Therefore, more energy must be added to convert the solid to a gas than to change
the liquid to a gas.   32. CO$_2$, because it has weaker attractive
forces (CO$_2$ is nonpolar, H$_2$O is polar and exhibits hydrogen
bonding).
33.

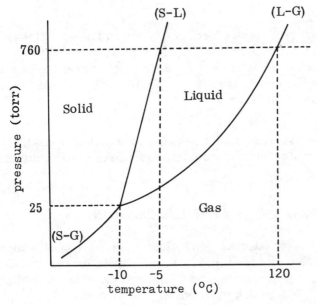

11 PHYSICAL PROPERTIES OF SOLUTIONS AND COLLOIDS

Now that you have learned some of the properties of pure substances - liquids, solids, and gases - we turn our attention to the properties of mixtures. Our emphasis in this chapter will be on solutions, although we begin by examining other kinds of mixtures as well. Our goal will be to learn how the composition of a solution affects such physical properties as boiling point, melting point, and vapor pressure. As you will see, the ways that these properties are affected by the presence of a solute in a solvent have some very practical applications.

11.1   KINDS OF MIXTURES:
SUSPENSIONS, COLLOIDS, AND SOLUTIONS

Objectives

To learn how mixtures are categorized according to the sizes of their particles. In this section you should pay particular attention to the properties of colloidal dispersions.

Review

Mixtures are divided into three categories: suspensions, colloids, and solutions. In suspensions, the particle size is large enough that the mixture separates into its components under the influence of gravity. A mixture of sand and water is an example. In a solution, the particles are of the size of individual atoms,

227

molecules, or ions. Because of their small size they mingle with the particles of the solute and never separate, no matter how long the solution is allowed to stand. Between these two extremes are mixtures called colloids, or colloidal dispersions. In a colloid, the particle size is much larger than in a solution, but not so large that they separate on standing.

Study Table 11.1 which describes the various kinds of colloids. Notice that colloids are formed in all three states - gases, liquids, and solids. One of the special properties of colloids is that they demonstrate the Tyndall effect - the scattering of light by the colloidal particles so that the light beam can be seen when viewed at right angles to its direction of travel through the mixture. Solutions do not exhibit the Tyndall effect.

Colloids are stabilized by preventing their particles from sticking together. For liquids dispersed in liquids, this is accomplished by emulsifying agents. Sols are often stabilized by the adsorption of ions on their surfaces. These like-charges repel, which keeps the particles apart.

Often it is necessary or desirable to destabilize a colloid and cause it to coalesce or coagulate. For colloids stabilized by adsorption of ions, addition of an ion of opposite charge neutralizes the charge on the colloidal particle and permits coagulation. Aerosols are destabilized by neutralizing the charges picked up by their colloidal particles.

Self-Test

1. What is the approximate size range for colloidal particles?

    _____

2. Foam rubber is a colloid.

    (a) What is the dispersed phase?   _____

    (b) What is the dispersing medium?   _____

    (c) What kind of colloid is this?   _____

3. What kind of colloid is fog?   _____

    What is the dispersing medium?   _____

4. Why can't a colloid be separated by filtering it through filter paper?

    _____

New Terms

Colloidal dispersion

A mixture in which particles of one of the components are of a size intermediate between those in a true solution and those in a suspension.

Dispersed phase

In a colloidal dispersion, the substance analogous to the solute in a solution. It is the substance dispersed in the dispersing medium.

Dispersing medium

In a colloidal dispersion, the substance analogous to the solvent in a solution. It is the substance into which the colloidal substance is dispersed.

Suspension

Relatively large particles of one substance are suspended in another. For example, fine sand suspended in the wind, or mud suspended in water. Suspensions settle and separate upon standing.

Tyndall effect

The scattering of light at large angles by colloidal particles. This makes a light beam passing through a colloid visible when viewed from the side.

11.2   TYPES OF SOLUTIONS

Objectives

To review the different kinds of solutions that can be formed.

Review

Solutions can be formed between: gas-gas (gaseous solutions); liquid-gas, liquid-liquid, liquid-solid (liquid solutions); solid-gas, solid-liquid, solid-solid (solid solutions).

Solid solutions can be of two types, substitutional and interstitial. Review the meanings of these.

Self-Test

5. What kind of solutions do the following represent?

    (a) black coffee (without sugar) _____

    (b) brass _____

    (c) a carbonated beverage _____

    (d) auto exhaust _____

    (e) a martini (without the olive) _____

New Terms

Alloy
    A solid solution of two or more metals.

Interstitial solid solution
    A solid solution in which the solute particles fit into empty
    spaces between particles of the solvent.

Substitutional solid solution
    A solid solution in which a particle of the solute (e.g., an
    atom or a molecule) replaces a particle of the solvent in the
    lattice of the solvent.

11.3   CONCENTRATION UNITS

Objectives

    To define additional concentration units that are useful in
    treating the physical properties of solutions. You should
    learn to convert among the different units.

Review

    Be sure you know the definitions of the following units.
The most common reason that students have difficulty handling
concentration units is because they fail to learn the definitions.

$$\text{mole fraction} \qquad X_A = \frac{n_A}{n_A + n_B + n_C + \ldots}$$

n_A, n_B, n_C, etc. are the number of moles of each component of the solution. Mole percent (mol percent) equals 100 x mole fraction.

weight fraction $$w_A = \frac{\text{weight of A}}{\text{total weight of solution}}$$

Weight percent, of course, equals 100 x weight fraction,
$$\% \text{ A (w/w)} = 100 \times w_A$$

molarity $$M = \frac{\text{moles of solute}}{\text{liters of solution}}$$

normality $$N = \frac{\text{equivalents of solute}}{\text{liters of solution}}$$

molality $$m = \frac{\text{moles of solute}}{\text{kilograms of solvent}}$$

(Be careful to clearly distinguish between molarity and molality; they sound and look alike but are defined quite differently.)

Conversions among molality, mole fraction, and weight fraction are straightforward and require only the molecular weights of solute and solvent (see Examples 11.1 - 11.3 in the text). To convert any of these to molarity (or vice versa) requires the density of the solution, as shown in Example 11.4 and the additional example below.

Example 11.1

An aqueous solution of $CuSO_4$, having a mole fraction of $CuSO_4$ equal to 0.0127, has a density of 1.106 g/mL. What is the molarity of the $CuSO_4$?

Solution

We begin by assuming that we have a total of 1 mol of solute and solvent. Then there are

$$0.0127 \text{ mol } CuSO_4$$
$$0.9873 \text{ mol } H_2O$$

To obtain the volume of the solution, which we need to compute the molarity, we first must calculate the total mass of the solution and then apply the density.

$$0.0127 \text{ mol } CuSO_4 \times \left(\frac{159.5 \text{ g } CuSO_4}{1 \text{ mol } CuSO_4}\right) = 2.03 \text{ g } CuSO_4$$

$$0.9873 \text{ mol } H_2O \times \left(\frac{18.02 \text{ g } H_2O}{1 \text{ mol } H_2O}\right) = 17.79 \text{ g } H_2O$$

Total weight of solution = 19.82 g

$$\text{volume of solution} = 19.82 \text{ g} \times \frac{1 \text{ mL}}{1.106 \text{ g}} = 17.92 \text{ mL}$$

We now have both the number of moles of $CuSO_4$ and the volume of the solution. The molarity is:

$$\text{molarity} = \frac{0.0127 \text{ mol } CuSO_4}{0.01792 \text{ liter soln.}}$$

$$= 0.709 \text{ M}$$

Self-Test

6. Calculate (a) the molality, (b) mole fraction of solute, and (c) weight fraction of solute in a solution prepared by dissolving 100 g of paraffin (molecular weight 370) in 500 g of benzene, C_6H_6. This solution could be used as a paint remover.

7. A solution of NaBr in water has a weight fraction of NaBr equal to 0.40. What is the (a) mole fraction, (b) mole percent, and (c) molality?

8. The density of the solution in Question 7 is 1.414 g/mL. What is the molarity of the NaBr?

9. A solution of propylene glycol, $C_3H_8O_2$, in water has a molality of 2.65 m. What is the weight percent $C_3H_8O_2$ in the solution?

New Terms

Molality
> A concentration unit that is the ratio of the number of moles of solute to the number of kilograms of solvent.

Molar concentration
> A ratio of moles of solute to liters of solution. It is the number of moles of solute per liter of solution.

Mole fraction
> A concentration unit that is the ratio of the number of moles of a given component to the total number of moles in the solution.

Mole percent (mol %)
> Mole percent = 100 x mole fraction

Percentage by weight
> The number of grams of the component in question per 100 grams of solution.

Volumetric flask
> A special flask having a long thin neck that has a mark etched around it. When filled to this mark with water, it contains precisely the volume specified. It is used to prepare solutions of accurately known concentration.

Weight fraction
> The number of grams of solute divided by the total number of grams of solution.

Weight percent
> Weight percent = weight fraction x 100

11.4   THE SOLUTION PROCESS IN LIQUID SOLUTIONS

Objectives

> To learn what factors control the solubility of substances in liquid solvents.

Review

The key point in this section is that in order for substances to be appreciably soluble in each other, they must possess similar intermolecular attractive forces. Particles that attract each other very strongly tend to congregate and separate from those to which they are weakly attracted.

Remember that when a solute particle is placed in solution it becomes solvated, that is, surrounded by solvent molecules to which it is attracted. When the solvent is water, the term hydration is used.

Soaps and detergents also work on the principle of "like dissolves like." Nonpolar tails of soap anions dissolve in oil and grease globules. The polar heads keep the particles suspended in water so they can be washed away.

Self-Test

10. How does hydration of ions help keep them in solution?

    _____

    _____

11. What does the term "like dissolve like" mean on a molecular level?

    _____

    _____

12. Why do soap anions form micelles in aqueous solutions?

    _____

    _____

New Terms

Miscible
     Two liquids are miscible if they are soluble in each other in all proportions.

Hydration
     The act of a molecule or ion becoming surrounded by water molecules.

Solvation
   The surrounding of a solute particle by molecules of the
   solvent.

Hydrophilic
   A hydrophilic substance is attracted strongly to water
   molecules and tends to be soluble in water.

Hydrophobic
   A hydrophobic substance is attracted very weakly to water
   molecules and tends to be insoluble in water.

Micelle
   A particle formed by the grouping together of fatty acid
   anions (soap anions) with their nonpolar tails intermingling
   and their anionic heads facing outward toward the aqueous
   environment.

Soap
   A solution of fatty acid anions.

11.5   HEATS OF SOLUTION

Objectives

   To study the energy changes that occur when a solution
   is formed. You should learn the definition of ideal solution
   and why some solution processes are exothermic and some
   are endothermic.

Review

   The heat of solution is the energy absorbed or liberated
when a solution is formed. In this section you saw that it is
possible to divide the total energy change into various contribu-
tions, some of which are endothermic and some of which are exothermic.

   For liquid solutions formed from a solvent (A) and solute
(B), an ideal solution results when the A-B attractions are the
same as the A-A and B-B attractions. For an ideal solution,
$\Delta H_{soln} = 0$. When the A-B attractions are greater than the A-A
and B-B attractions, $\Delta H_{soln} < 0$ and the solution process is

exothermic. When the A-B attractions are weaker, $\Delta H_{soln} > 0$ and the solution process is endothermic. These are summarized in Figures 11.10 - 11.12.

For solutions of solids in liquids the lattice energy (the energy required to separate the solute particles from a crystal) and hydration energy (or solvation energy - the energy released when the solute particle is placed into the solvent cage) must be considered. This is summarized in Figure 11.13 in the text.

Self-Test

13. When acetone (a component of nail polish remover) is dissolved in water, the resulting solution becomes warm. What conclusions can you draw about the relative strengths of the attractive forces between acetone and water molecules?

14. Acetone and water (Question 13 above) are completely soluble in each other in all proportions. Does this mean they form ideal solutions?

_____

15. For LiCl, $\Delta H_{soln} < 0$. What does this imply about the relative values of the hydration energy of the ions and the lattice energy of LiCl?

_____

_____

New Terms

Heat of solution, ΔH_{soln}
    The amount of heat absorbed or evolved when a given amount of solute dissolves in a solvent to form a solution.

Hydration energy
    The amount of energy liberated when an ion or other solute particle becomes surrounded by water molecules. It is usually expressed in kJ per mol of solute hydrated.

Ideal solution
    A solution for which $\Delta H_{soln} = 0$, and in which solute-solute, solvent-solvent, and solute-solvent attractions are all equal.

Solvation energy
    The energy liberated when a solute particle becomes surrounded by solvent molecules. Hydration energy is a special case in which the solvent is water.

11.6   SOLUBILITY AND TEMPERATURE

Objectives

> To examine the factors that determine the effect of temperature on solubility, and to learn how substances are purified by fractional crystallization.

Review

A rise in temperature increases solubility if the dissolving of additional solute is endothermic. A fairly good rule of thumb is that the solubility of most solids and liquids in a liquid solvent increases with increasing temperature. The solubilities of gases, however, almost always decrease with increasing temperature.

In the procedure called fractional crystallization, a solid substance containing a soluble impurity is dissolved in a minimum of hot solvent. The solution is cooled and some of the pure desired solid crystallizes, leaving the impurity behind in the solution along with some of the desired material. Even though some of the desired substance is lost, that which is recovered is usually of much higher purity.

Self-Test

16. Why do gases usually become less soluble in liquids as the temperature of the solution is raised?

_____

_____

_____

17. A solid is known to contain 80 g of $NaNO_3$ and 5 g of NaCl. The solubility of NaCl is 36 g/100 g H_2O at 0°C and 40 g/100 g H_2O at 100°C. The solubility of $NaNO_3$ is 73 g/100 g H_2O at 0°C and 180 g/100 g H_2O at 100°C.

(a) What is the minimum amount of boiling water (100°C) necessary to dissolve all of the solid?

_____

(b) If the solution is cooled to 0°C, how much $NaNO_3$ will separate as pure solid?

_____

New Terms

Fractional crystallization
    A procedure for purifying substances in which the impure
    solid is dissolved in a minimum amount of hot solvent. The
    solution is then gradually cooled, which causes crystals of
    the pure substance to precipitate. These are collected by
    filtration, while the impurities remain in the solution.

11.7   THE EFFECT OF PRESSURE ON SOLUBILITY

Objectives

    To learn how, and under what circumstances, pressure
    influences solubility.

Review

        Pressure has virtually no effect on the solubility of solids
or liquids in liquid solvents. The solubilities of gases, however,
are very markedly affected by pressure changes. This can be
predicted by Le Châtelier's principle, since an increase in pressure favors a decrease in the number of moles of gas (this would
tend to bring the pressure back down). Check with your instructor whether he expects you to treat the effect of pressure
on the solubility of a gas quantitatively. If so, review the material below on Henry's law.

        Henry's law relates the concentration of a dissolved gas,
C_g, to its partial pressure, p_g, over the solution.

$$C_g = k_g p_g$$

k_g is the Henry's law constant.

Self-Test

18. Why are the solubilities of solids in liquids virtually unaf-
     fected by pressure?

19. Calculate the solubility of a gas, X, in water at 20°C if its
     partial pressure is 720 torr ($k = 3.5 \times 10^{-3}$ g/L torr at
     20°C).

New Terms

Henry's law

$C_g = k_g p_g$, where C_g is the concentration of a gas dissolved in a solvent at a particular temperature, p_g is the partial pressure of the gas over the solution, and k_g is a proportionality constant called the Henry's law constant.

11.8   VAPOR PRESSURES OF SOLUTIONS

Objectives

To learn how the vapor pressure of a solution depends on the relative amounts of solute and solvent.

Review

When a nonvolatile, nondissociating solute is dissolved in a solvent, the vapor pressure of the solvent is diminished because a portion of the surface becomes occupied by molecules unable to enter the vapor phase. Raoult's law relates the vapor pressure to the mole fraction of the solvent in the solution,

$$P_{solution} = X_{solvent} P^{\circ}_{solvent}$$

where $P^{\circ}_{solvent}$ is the vapor pressure of the pure solvent.

When two volatile liquids are mixed, the vapor above the solution contains molecules of both. The vapor pressure of the solution is the sum of the partial pressures of each substance. The partial pressures are also determined by Raoult's law. For some substance, A, its partial pressure is

$$P_A = X_A P^{\circ}_A$$

where P_A is the partial pressure of A above the solution and X_A is the mole fraction of A in the solution. As before, P°_A is the vapor pressure of pure A.

Deviations from Raoult's law occur when the solution is nonideal (recall the definition of an ideal solution in Section 11.5). When ΔH_{soln} is negative, meaning heat is evolved as the solution is formed, the actual partial pressure of each component is less than that calculated from Raoult's law. The reason for this is that the solute and solvent are held more tightly in the solution than in either pure substance. These extra strong solute-solvent attractive forces are responsible for both a negative ΔH_{soln} and negative deviations from Raoult's law. Positive deviations occur when ΔH_{soln} is positive. In this case the A-B attractive forces are less than either A-A or B-B attractions. Molecules are held less tightly than predicted for an ideal solution and the vapor pressure is greater than that calculated from Raoult's law.

Self-Test

20. The vapor pressure of water at 100°C is 760 torr. What is the vapor pressure of a solution of 200 g of sugar, $C_{12}H_{22}O_{11}$, in 1000 g of H_2O at this same temperature? Will the solution boil at 100°C under an atmospheric pressure of 760 torr?

21. At 85°C, ethylene bromide ($C_2H_4Br_2$) has a vapor pressure of 170 torr and propylene bromide ($C_3H_6Br_2$) has a vapor pressure of 127 torr. These substances form very nearly an ideal solution. What is the vapor pressure of a solution containing 100 g of each?

New Terms

Negative deviations (from Raoult's law)
Solutions that exhibit negative deviations from Raoult's law have vapor pressures that are lower than predicted by Raoult's law.

Positive deviations (from Raoult's law)
Solutions that exhibit positive deviations have vapor pressures that are higher than predicted by Raoult's law.

Raoult's law
$P_A = X_A P_A^o$, where P_A^o is the vapor pressure of pure substance A, X_A is the mole fraction of A in the solution, and P_A is the vapor pressure of A over the solution.

11.9   FRACTIONAL DISTILLATION

Objectives

To see how a distillation process can often be used to separate mixtures of volatile liquids.

Review

Remember that at the boiling point the sum of the partial pressures of the components above a mixture equals the atmospheric pressure.

$$P_{atm} = p_A + p_B = P_{Total}$$

The partial pressures, p_A and p_B, in turn, are found by Raoult's law.

$$p_A = X_A P_A^o$$

Remember that with Raoult's law X_A and X_B are the mole fractions of A and B in the liquid.

In the vapor the mole fraction is found from Dalton's law. For example,

$$p_A = X_A P_{Total}$$

which gives

$$X_A = \frac{p_A}{P_{Total}} = \frac{p_A}{p_A + p_B}$$

Be careful not to confuse the mole fraction in the liquid with the mole fraction in the vapor.

When a liquid mixture boils, the vapor always contains a larger proportion of the more volatile component than does the liquid. Remember this, because it can help you see when you've made a mistake in a calculation.

A boiling point diagram is shown in Figure 11.20 in the text. Remember that the upper curve gives the composition of the vapor; the lower curve gives the composition of the liquid.

The compositions of vapor and liquid in equilibrium are connected by a tie line. Review how repeated boiling and condensation of the vapor gradually gives a liquid richer in the more volatile component.

Mixtures having large deviations from Raoult's law form azeotropes. These mixtures have either maxima or minima in their boiling point curves. They can only be separated into one pure component plus the liquid mixture having the composition at the maximum or minimum of the curve.

Self-Test

22. Two substances, A and B, have vapor pressures at 85°C of 800 torr and 300 torr, respectively. What will be the composition of a mixture of these substances that boils at 85°C under 1 atm pressure? (Hint – use Raoult's law and remember that $X_B = 1 - X_A$) _____

23. If mixtures of two liquids show large positive deviations from Raoult's law, do they form a maximum boiling azeotrope or a minimum boiling azeotrope? _____

New Terms

Fractional distillation
    A method used to separate mixtures of volatile liquids into their components. It involves boiling the mixture, condensing the vapor, then boiling this vapor, then condensing the new vapor, and so on. In each step, the vapor becomes richer in the more volatile component.

Tie line
    A horizontal line on a boiling point diagram that connects the boiling point curve to the vapor composition curve. It allows one to read the boiling point of a solution having a particular composition and to determine the composition of the vapor that is in equilibrium with the boiling solution.

Azeotrope
    A mixture that has either a higher boiling point or a lower boiling point than either of the two pure components in a liquid mixture.

Boiling point diagram
A graph on which is plotted the boiling points of mixtures of varying composition. Also plotted is a curve showing the compositions of the vapor given off when solutions of different compositions boil. A vapor composition can be obtained from a liquid composition by a tie line running horizontally between the two curves.

11.10 COLLIGATIVE PROPERTIES OF SOLUTIONS

Objectives

To see how the vapor pressure lowering of a solution by a nonvolatile solute causes a boiling point elevation and freezing point depression. You should learn how this phenomenon permits the determination of molecular weights. In addition, you should learn how the dissociation of an electrolyte produces abnormally large changes in boiling and freezing points.

Review

You should examine Figure 11.22 in the text to be sure you understand why a nonvolatile solute raises the boiling point and lowers the freezing point.

Remember that

$$\Delta T_b = K_b m$$

and $$\Delta T_f = K_f m$$

where m is the molality – the number of moles of solute particles per 1000 g (1 kilogram) of solvent. The specific values of K_b and K_f depend on the solvent (Table 11.6).

These relationships are useful in two ways. Knowing m and K_b or K_f, you can calculate the changes in boiling and freezing points. This might be important, for example, if you wanted to know the properties of an antifreeze solution. The important application to chemistry is in the determination of molecular weights. Here we measure ΔT, and knowing K we can calculate the molality. From a knowledge of the weights of solute and solvent we can obtain a relationship between weight and number of moles, from which the molecular weight can easily be computed.

Example 11.2

5.48 g of a solid are dissolved in 200 g of water to give a solution having a freezing point of -0.850°C. What is the molecular weight of the substance?

Solution

From the freezing point depression, 0.850°C, we can calculate the molality.

$$m = \frac{\Delta T}{K} = \frac{0.850°C}{1.86°C/molal} = 0.457 \text{ molal}$$

This translates to the ratio,

$$\frac{0.457 \text{ mol solid}}{1.00 \text{ kg } H_2O} \tag{1}$$

Next we calculate the ratio of mass of solid to kilograms of water.

$$\text{ratio} = \frac{5.48 \text{ g solid}}{0.200 \text{ kg } H_2O}$$

Dividing numerator and denominator by 0.200 we get,

$$\text{ratio} = \frac{27.4 \text{ g solid}}{1.00 \text{ kg } H_2O} \tag{2}$$

Ratio (1) must equal ratio (2) because we are dealing with the same solution. Since their denominators are the same, their numerators must be equal. The next step then is to equate numerators.

$$0.457 \text{ mol solid} = 27.4 \text{ g solid}$$

Finally, divide through by 0.457 to get the weight of one mole.

$$1 \text{ mol solid} = 60.0 \text{ g}$$

The molecular weight, therefore, is 60.0 g/mol.

Self-Test

24. Calculate the boiling point elevation and the actual boiling point of a solution of 35.0 g of a solute having a molecular weight of 210 in 450 g of benzene. Use the data in Table 11.6.

_____

25. What is the molecular weight of an unknown substance if a solution of 0.00213 g X in 0.100 g of camphor has a freezing point of 174.5°C? Use the data in Table 11.6.

_____

26. Calculate the freezing point depression produced by a solution of 0.100 g of a compound having a molecular weight of 10,000 dissolved in 100 g of water.

_____

New Terms

Colligative property

A property that depends only on the number of particles in a solution, and not on their chemical identity. Examples are freezing point depression, boiling point elevation, vapor pressure lowering, and osmotic pressure.

Molal boiling point elevation constant

A constant, which is characteristic of each particular solvent, that relates the boiling point elevation for a solution to the molal concentration of the solute.

Molal freezing point depression constant

A constant, which is characteristic of each particular solvent, that relates the freezing point depression for a solution to the molal concentration of the solute.

11.11   OSMOTIC PRESSURE

Objectives

To see how osmosis provides a means of determining very large molecular weights.

Review

If you worked through the solution to Question 26 on the preceding page, you saw that when the molecular weight is large, ΔT_f is very small. This makes it nearly impossible to measure. Measurements of osmotic pressure provide means of calculating very high molecular weights because the osmotic pressure produced by even very dilute solutions is measurable.

The van't Hoff equation is easy to remember - it looks like the ideal gas law.

$$\pi V = nRT$$

If you know π, V, R, and T, you can calculate the number of moles of solute in the solution. A form of this equation that is often more convenient in solving problems is

$$\pi = MRT$$

where M is the molar concentration of the solute.

Example 11.3

A 0.010-g sample of starch in 5.0 mL of water at 25°C produces a solution having an osmotic pressure of 2.3 torr. What is the average molecular weight of the starch molecules?

Solution

First, let's express π in atm.

$$\pi = 2.3 \text{ torr} \times \left(\frac{1 \text{ atm}}{760 \text{ torr}}\right) = 3.0 \times 10^{-3} \text{ atm}$$

We also have

$$V = 0.005 \text{ L}$$
$$R = 0.0821 \text{ L atm/mol K}$$
$$T = 298 \text{ K}$$

Solving the van't Hoff equation for n gives

$$n = \frac{\pi V}{RT}$$

and substituting,

$$n = \frac{(3.0 \times 10^{-3} \text{ atm})(0.005 \text{ L})}{(0.0821 \text{ L atm/mol K})(298 \text{ K})}$$

$$n = 6.1 \times 10^{-7} \text{ mol}$$

From the quantity of starch placed in the solution we have

$$6.1 \times 10^{-7} \text{ mol} = 0.010 \text{ g}$$

$$1 \text{ mol} = 1.6 \times 10^4 \text{ g} = 16,000 \text{ g}$$

The molecular weight is 16,000.

Self-Test

27. A solution of 0.20 g of a water-soluble polymer in 10 mL of
     water at 20°C has an osmotic pressure of 0.10 torr. What
     is the molecular weight of the polymer?

New Terms

Dialysis
> The passage of water and small molecules and ions, but not
> large molecules, through a membrane.

Isotonic solutions
> Solutions having the same osmotic pressure.

Osmosis
> The selective passage of solvent through a semipermeable
> membrane from a solution of low solute concentration to a
> solution of high solute concentration.

Osmotic pressure
> The pressure that must be exerted on the more concentrated
> solution to prevent osmosis from occurring.

Semipermeable membrane
> A membrane that permits the passage of solvent molecules
> but not solute molecules.

11.12   SOLUTIONS OF ELECTROLYTES

Objectives

To learn how the dissociation of an electrolyte in an aqueous solution affects the colligative properties. You should also learn that in solutions of electrolytes the ions are not totally independent of each other.

Review

Electrolytes dissociate to produce more moles of particles than moles of solute. One mole of NaCl produces 2 mol of particles. The freezing point and boiling point changes are therefore larger than they would be if no dissociation occurred. To obtain the actual ΔT, multiply the ΔT calculated using the molal concentration of salt by the number of ions produced when one formula unit dissociates. For example, for a 1.00 m solution of $CaCl_2$ we would calculate $\Delta T = 1.86°C$. Since $CaCl_2$ produces three ions per $CaCl_2$ formula unit, the actual ΔT is three times as large as we originally calculated.

$$\Delta T_{actual} = 3(\Delta T_{calculated})$$

$$\Delta T_{actual} = 3(1.86°C) = 5.58°C$$

Weak electrolytes produce freezing point depressions and boiling point elevations that are intermediate between those calculated for a nonelectrolyte and those calculated for strong electrolytes. Association of solute particles – the coming together of two or more solute particles in the solution – produces fewer particles and therefore smaller ΔT_f and ΔT_b than expected.

As the concentration of an electrolyte increases, its ions influence each other to a greater extent and are less independent. One way that this can happen is by the formation of ion pairs – groups of oppositely charged ions. As the concentration of ions increases, there is a greater chance for ions of opposite charge to encounter one another and an equilibrium concentration of ion pairs can be created. This, in effect, reduces the number of independent particles that are available to alter the properties of the solution.

The van't Hoff factor, i, is the ratio of the observed freezing point depression (or boiling point elevation) to the freezing point depression (or boiling point elevation) that the substance would exhibit if it were a nonelectrolyte.

Self-Test

28. What value of ΔT_f do you expect for 0.100 m solutions of:

    (a) NaCl _____ (b) $Al_2(SO_4)_3$ _____

29. What is the limiting i factor (at infinite dilution) for the following:

    (a) $MgSO_4$ _____ (c) $Al_2(SO_4)_3$ _____

    (b) K_2SO_4 _____

New Terms

Association

The joining together of two or more molecules in a solution to produce a particle of higher apparent molecular weight. The forces of attraction between the particles are usually of dipole-dipole type, including hydrogen bonding.

Dimer

A particle formed by the joining together of two smaller particles.

van't Hoff factor

The ratio of the measures ΔT_f to the ΔT_f calculated assuming the solute in a solution to be a nonelectrolyte.

Answers to Self-Test Questions

1. 1 nm to 1000 nm   2.(a) air (b) rubber   (c) solid foam
3. liquid aerosol, air   4. The particles are too small to be caught by the filter paper. 5.(a) solid in a liquid (b) solid-solid (c) gas in a liquid (d) gas-gas (e) liquid-liquid
6.(a) 0.541 m (b) 0.0404 (c) 0.167 7.(a) 0.104
(b) 10.4 mol % (c) 6.48 m 8. 5.50 M 9. 16.8% (w/w) $C_3H_8O_2$

10. The polar water molecules help shield ions of opposite charge from each other. 11. Substances tend to be soluble in each other only if they have about equal intermolecular attractive forces. 12. Their nonpolar tails "dissolve" in one another, which leaves their anionic heads facing the aqueous environment. 13. Acetone attracts water more than acetone attracts acetone or water attracts water. 14. No. In Question 13 you saw that $\Delta H_{soln} < 0$. For an ideal solution $\Delta H_{soln} = 0$. 15. The hydration energies of the ions must be greater than the lattice energy. 16. Because ΔH_{soln} for a gas is usually negative (exothermic). Increasing the temperature requires adding heat. Le Châtelier's principle predicts that an endothermic change should occur which requires that gas leave the liquid. 17.(a) 44.4 g H_2O (b) 48 g. Note that all of the NaCl is soluble in 44.4 g H_2O. 18. Because they are incompressible. 19. 2.52 g/L 20. P_{H_2O} = 752 torr. No, the vapor pressure is less than atmospheric pressure. 21. 149.3 torr
22. <u>Solution</u>

$$P_A + P_B = 760$$

$$X_A P_A^o + X_B P_B^o = 760$$

$$X_A P_A^o + (1 - X_A)P_B^o = 760$$

$$X_A(800) + (1 - X_A)(300) = 760$$

$$800X_A + 300 - 300X_A = 760$$

$$500X_A = 760 - 300 = 460$$

$$X_A = 460/500$$

$$X_A = 0.92$$

$$X_B = 1 - X_A = 0.08$$

23. Minimum boiling azeotrope
24. ΔT_b = 0.94°C, T_b = 80.1 + 0.94 = 81.0°C
25. 188 g/mol
26. ΔT_f = 0.000186°C
27. 3.7 x 10^6 g/mol
28. (a) 0.372°C (b) 0.930°C
29. (a) 2 (b) 3 (c) 5

12 CHEMICAL THERMODYNAMICS

As pointed out in the text, Chapters 12 and 13 deal with the two factors that control whether or not the products of a chemical reaction will form. Thermodynamics controls the feasibility of a reaction in the sense that it determines whether a reaction is possible and how much products can be formed; kinetics (Chapter 13) controls how fast the products are formed.

Thermodynamics deals with energy changes and is applied to physical as well as chemical changes. You will see that a number of thermodynamic principles are developed here using physical systems as examples, followed by the extension of the principles to chemical systems. The applications of thermodynamics range from simple chemical reactions to complex reactions in living organisms.

12.1   SOME COMMONLY USED TERMS

Objectives

To become familiar with some of the terminology to be used in later discussions.

Review

This section defines in a precise way some terms that have been used rather loosely before. It also introduces some new terms. Be sure of their meaning before moving on.

Self-Test

1. Fill in the blanks.

    (a) A process that occurs without a change in temperature is said to be

    _____

    (b) A quantity whose value is independent of the prior history of a sample is called

    _____

    (c) A change that occurs without heat being transferred between the system and its surroundings is said to be

    _____

    (d) The energy required to raise the temperature of 1 g of a substance by 1°C is called

    _____

    (e) The energy required to raise the temperature of the entire system by 1°C is called the _____ of the system.

    (f) The energy required to raise the temperature of one mole of a substance by 1°C is called

    _____

New Terms

Thermodynamics
   The study of energy changes and the flow of energy from one substance to another.

System
   That particular portion of the universe upon which we wish to focus our attention.

Surroundings
   That which exists outside a system.

Isothermal
   A change that occurs at constant temperature.

Adiabatic
   A change that occurs without heat transfer between the system and its surroundings.

State
>   A particular set of conditions of pressure, temperature,
>   volume, and number of moles of each component of a system.

Equation of state
>   An equation relating state variables.

Equation of state for an ideal gas
>   The ideal gas law, $PV = nRT$.

Heat capacity
>   The amount of heat needed to raise the temperature of a
>   system by 1 °C.

Molar heat capacity
>   The amount of heat required to raise the temperature of one
>   mole of a substance by 1 °C.

Specific heat
>   The amount of heat needed to raise the temperature of 1 g
>   of a substance by 1 °C.

State function
>   A quantity whose value depends only on the current state
>   of the system and not on the system's prior history. The
>   magnitude of the change in a state function depends only
>   on the initial and final states of the system and is independ-
>   ent of the path followed between these states.

State variable
>   A state function.

12.2   THE FIRST LAW OF THERMODYNAMICS

Objectives

>   To see how the law of conservation of energy applies to
>   heat transfer and the performing of work. You should
>   also learn what is meant by a reversible process and that
>   the maximum work can only be obtained if a change occurs
>   by a "reversible process."

Review

For any process that ultimately returns a system to its original state, the net energy change is zero. This is the first law of thermodynamics. For changes between different states we are concerned with the internal energy E.

$$E = (total\ K.E.) + (total\ P.E.)$$

For a change, we have

$$\Delta E = q - w$$

Remember the following:

$$\Delta E = E_{final} - E_{initial}$$

Also, q is heat added to the system.

> w is energy removed from the system when the system performs work.

> ΔE depends only on the initial and final states; E is a state function.

The entire discussion on the isothermal (constant temperature) expansion of an ideal gas was designed to show you that the magnitudes of q and w depend on the way the expansion is carried out; q and w are not state functions. Since ΔE is the same regardless of the path between initial and final states, E is a state function.

Remember that one way a system can perform work is to expand against an externally applied pressure. Under a constant opposing pressure,

$$w = P\Delta V$$

If the opposing pressure is zero, no work will be accomplished. This applies not only to gases, but also to chemical systems such as the discharge of a battery described on p 453.

A reversible change is one that takes place in an infinite number of steps, each of which occurs with the opposing force just barely less than the driving force for the process. In the reversible expansion of a gas, for instance, the external pressure is initially high and equal to the internal pressure exerted by the gas. As the gas expands the external pressure is dropped at the same rate as the internal pressure drops, so the

driving and restraining forces are essentially balanced throughout the entire expansion.

Self-Test

2. A compressed gas (assumed to be ideal) in a cylinder pushes
   back a piston against a constant opposing force of 8.00 atm.
   The initial and final volumes of the gas are 25 mL and
   600 mL. How much work, expressed in joules, is done by
   the gas during the expansion?

   _____

   Express this answer in calories.

   _____

3. Calculate the work done by a gas (in liter atm) as it expands from an initial 4 L at 20 atm to 20 L at 4 atm

   (a) by a one-step process against an opposing pressure of
       4 atm.

       _____

   (b) by a two-step process in which the opposing pressure
       in the first step is 10 atm and in the second step is
       4 atm.

       _____

New Terms

First law of thermodynamics
   When a system undergoes a series of changes that ultimately
   brings it back to its original state, the net energy change
   for the system is zero. This is a formal statement of the
   law of conservation of energy, and is the basis of Hess's
   law. Often stated mathematically as $\Delta E = q - w$, where
   ΔE is the change in the internal energy, q is the heat
   added to the system, and w is the work done by the
   system.

Internal energy, E
   The total kinetic and potential energy of a system.

Reversible process
   A process that occurs by an infinite number of steps during
   which the driving force for the change is just barely greater than the force that resists the change. Any slight increase in the resisting force causes the change to reverse
   direction.

Work

The energy involved in moving an opposing force a given distance.

12.3   HEATS OF REACTION: THERMOCHEMISTRY

Objectives

To express energy changes in chemical reactions in terms of thermodynamic quantities.

Review

For changes at constant volume (and temperature), the heat of reaction is equal to ΔE.

$$\Delta E = q_V$$

Heats of reaction measured with a bomb calorimeter are equal to ΔE because $\Delta V = 0$ (therefore, $P\Delta V = 0$) for reactions in this apparatus.

For changes at constant pressure (and temperature), the heat of reaction is ΔH.

$$\Delta H = q_p$$

H is the enthalpy (also called heat content) and, like E, is a state function. The enthalpy is defined as

$$H = E + PV$$

and at constant pressure

$$\Delta H = \Delta E + P\Delta V$$

A calorimeter is a device used to measure heats of reaction. As noted earlier, a bomb calorimeter has a constant volume. When reactions take place in it, the heat liberated is absorbed by the calorimeter and its temperature increases. From the temperature change and a knowledge of the heat capacity of the calorimeter, the amount of heat evolved in the reaction can be calculated (Example 12.2 in the text). The heat of reaction at constant pressure (ΔH) is measured in a similar way, but the contents of the calorimeter are kept at constant pressure.

Usually ΔH and ΔE are computed on a "per mole" basis to make them intensive properties, rather than extensive ones. For a reaction at constant pressure, the difference between ΔH and ΔE depends on the size of the volume change that accompanies the reaction. For reactions involving only liquids and solids, $\Delta H \approx \Delta E$. When gases are consumed or produced, the PV work is given by

$$P\Delta V = \Delta nRT$$

where Δn is the change in the <u>number of moles of gas</u>. Review Example 12.3 in the text.

Self-Test

4. One slice of bread plus sufficient oxygen for complete combustion are placed in a bomb calorimeter having a heat capacity of 36,500 cal/°C. The initial temperature of the calorimeter was 25.00°C. After the combustion was completed, the temperature rose to 26.64°C. How many nutritional Calories (1 Calorie, written with a capital C, equals 1000 calories, or 1 kcal) are contained in one slice of bread, assuming the products of metabolism are the same as the products of combustion?

    _____

5. When 0.500 mol of methane, CH_4 (natural gas), is oxidized by oxygen to produce 0.500 mol of CO_2 and 1.00 mol of water vapor, 401 kJ of heat energy are evolved. The balanced equation for the reaction is:
    $$CH_4(g) + 2 O_2(g) \longrightarrow CO_2(g) + 2H_2O(g)$$
    (a) What is ΔH in the units kJ/mol CH_4? _____

    (b) What is ΔE at 25°C (expressed in the same units)?

    _____

6. Methanol may someday replace gasoline as a fuel in automobiles. It burns according to the equation,
    $$2CH_3OH(\ell) + 3 O_2(g) \longrightarrow 2CO_2(g) + 4H_2O(g)$$
    Oxidation of 1.000 mol of CH_3OH at 25°C and constant pressure liberates 1280 kJ. What is ΔE for this reaction expressed in kJ/mol?

    _____

New Terms

Bomb calorimeter
> A constant-volume calorimeter. Heats of reaction measured with this apparatus correspond to ΔE for the reaction.

Calorimeter
> A device used for the measurement of heats of reaction.

Enthalpy, H
> Also called *heat content*. Defined by the equation, $H = E + PV$. At constant T and P, $\Delta H = \Delta E + P\Delta V$. ΔH is also the heat of reaction at constant pressure.

12.4   HESS'S LAW OF HEAT SUMMATION

Objectives

> To use the fact that H is a state function in calculating values of ΔH. You should learn how to combine ΔH values when chemical equations are added or subtracted to produce new equations, as well as the definition of heat of formation.

Review

A chemical equation written to show the energy change that takes place is called a thermochemical equation. Thermochemical equations are always interpreted on a mole basis; they therefore may be written with fractional coefficients. Remember to always indicate the physical state (solid, liquid or gas) of the substances written in a thermochemical equation.

Hess's law says, in effect, that the ΔH for some net reaction is the sum of all of the ΔH's for steps along the way. When thermochemical equations are added together to obtain some final equation, the ΔH for the final equation is the sum of the ΔH's of the thermochemical equations that were combined. Study Example 12.4 in the text as well as the following example before working the Self-Test.

Example 12.1

Add the thermochemical equations below to obtain the value of ΔH for the reaction,

$$2Na_2O_2(s) + 4HCl(g) \longrightarrow 4NaCl(s) + 2H_2O(\ell) + O_2(g)$$

Equations:

$$2Na_2O_2(s) + 2H_2O(\ell) \longrightarrow 4NaOH(s) + O_2(g) \qquad \Delta H = -30.2 \text{ kcal}$$

$$NaOH(s) + HCl(g) \longrightarrow NaCl(s) + H_2O(\ell) \qquad \Delta H = -42.8 \text{ kcal}$$

Solution

When combining thermochemical equations, pay attention to what must appear in the final equation <u>and</u> what must cancel, so that it doesn't appear. The first given equation has $2Na_2O_2$ on the left, which is just what we need. It also has $4NaOH$ on the right, and we see that this must be eliminated because it doesn't appear in the final equation. Now look at the second given equation. It has $NaOH$ on the left. If we give it a coefficient of 4, then $4NaOH$ on the left of the second equation can cancel the $4NaOH$ on the right of the first. Therefore, the second equation, and its ΔH, must be multiplied by 4 before adding it to the first.

$$2Na_2O_2(s) + 2H_2O(\ell) \longrightarrow 4NaOH(s) + O_2(g) \qquad \Delta H \doteq -30.2 \text{ kcal}$$

$$4NaOH(s) + 4HCl(g) \longrightarrow 4NaCl(s) + 4H_2O(\ell) \qquad \begin{aligned} \Delta H &= 4(-42.8 \text{ kcal}) \\ &= -171.2 \text{ kcal} \end{aligned}$$

Adding the equations gives

$$2Na_2O_2(s) + 2H_2O(\ell) + 4NaOH(s) + 4HCl(g) \longrightarrow$$
$$4NaOH(s) + O_2(g) + 4NaCl(s) + 4H_2O(\ell)$$

Adding their ΔH values,

$$\Delta H = (-30.2 \text{ kcal}) + (-171.2 \text{ kcal}) = -201.4 \text{ kcal}$$

Remember that in problems of this type, if you have to reverse an equation in order to get cancellation of unwanted formulas, you <u>must</u> also reverse the sign of ΔH.

The heat of formation, ΔH_f, is the enthalpy change that occurs when <u>one mole</u> of a substance is formed <u>from its elements</u>. Note the two underlined portions of this definition, because students often have difficulty knowing which ΔH values to label with the subscript "f." For example, consider these reactions:

(1) $S(s) + 3/2 O_2(g) \longrightarrow SO_3(g)$ $\Delta H = -396$ kJ

(2) $SO_2(g) + 1/2 O_2(g) \longrightarrow SO_3(g)$ $\Delta H = -99$ kJ

(3) $H_2SO_4(\ell) \longrightarrow SO_3(g) + H_2O(\ell)$ $\Delta H = +132$ kJ

In each case SO_3 is "formed," but only ΔH for the first reaction is properly labeled ΔH_f. Only in reaction 1 is <u>one mole</u> of SO_3 formed <u>from the elements</u>.

A useful form of Hess's law can be stated in terms of heats of formation:

$$\Delta H_{reaction} = \left(\begin{array}{c} \text{sum of } \Delta H_f \\ \text{of the products} \end{array} \right) - \left(\begin{array}{c} \text{sum of } \Delta H_f \\ \text{of the reactants} \end{array} \right)$$

Self-Test

7. Use the equations
    $CaO(s) + SO_3(g) \longrightarrow CaSO_4(s)$ $\Delta H = -95.9$ kcal

    $Ca(OH)_2(s) \longrightarrow CaO(s) + H_2O(g)$ $\Delta H = +26.1$ kcal

    to obtain the value of ΔH for the reaction,
    $Ca(OH)_2(s) + SO_3(g) \longrightarrow CaSO_4(s) + H_2O(g)$

    _____

8. Use the equations
    $2C_2H_2(g) + 5 O_2(g) \longrightarrow 4CO_2(g) + 2H_2O(g)$ $\Delta H = -2512$ kJ

    $N_2(g) + \frac{1}{2}O_2(g) \longrightarrow N_2O(g)$ $\Delta H = +104$ kJ

    to obtain ΔH for the reaction,
    $C_2H_2(g) + 5N_2O(g) \longrightarrow 2CO_2(g) + H_2O(g) + 5N_2(g)$

    _____

9. Use the equations
    $2NO(g) + O_2(g) \longrightarrow 2NO_2(g)$ $\Delta H = -105$ kJ

    $2N_2O(g) + 3 O_2(g) \longrightarrow 4NO_2(g)$ $\Delta H = -55$ kJ

    $NO_2(g) + SO_2(g) \longrightarrow NO(g) + SO_3(g)$ $\Delta H = -47$ kJ to calculate ΔH for the reaction,

$$2NO(g) + SO_2(g) \longrightarrow N_2O(g) + SO_3(g) \quad \underline{\hspace{3cm}}$$

New Terms

Enthalpy diagram
> A diagram that displays in graphical form the enthalpy changes that accompany the various thermochemical equations that combine to give some net change.

Heat of formation (Enthalpy of formation)
> The amount of heat liberated or absorbed when one mole of a compound is formed from its elements.

Hess's law of heat summation
> Also known simply as Hess's law. When thermochemical equations are added to give the net equation for a reaction, the corresponding heats of reaction are added to give the net heat of reaction. Also,
> $$\Delta H_{reaction} = (\text{sum } \Delta H_f \text{ products}) - (\text{sum } \Delta H_f \text{ reactants})$$

Thermochemical equation
> An equation whose coefficients are interpreted as representing numbers of moles of reactants and products, and which is accompanied by the energy change for the reaction.

12.5   STANDARD STATES

Objectives

To establish standard conditions for the comparison of heats of reaction. You should learn to apply Hess's law using standard heats of formation.

Review

Standard conditions are chosen to be 25°C (298 K) and 1 atm pressure. A substance in its natural state under these conditions is said to be in its standard state. Standard states are indicated by a superscript zero.

Standard heats of formation, such as those in Table 12.1 in the text, can be used to calculate standard heats of reaction following Hess's law.

$$\Delta H° = (\text{sum of } \Delta H_f° \text{ products}) - (\text{sum of } \Delta H_f° \text{ reactants})$$

This is illustrated in Examples 12.5 and 12.6 in the text. Remember that we always take $\Delta H_f°$ for any pure element in its standard state to be equal to zero.

Sometimes standard heats of formation cannot be measured directly. In these cases a reaction is carried out in which the heat of reaction is measured and the heats of formation of all reactants and products, except the one compound in question, are known. The unknown $\Delta H_f°$ can then be computed. Example 12.7 in the text illustrates this method using a measured heat of combustion.

Self-Test

10. Use the data in Table 12.1 to calculate $\Delta H°$ for the following reactions in kilojoules:

   (a) $CH_4(g) + 4Cl_2(g) \longrightarrow CCl_4(\ell) + 4HCl(g)$ _____

   (b) $Fe_2O_3(s) + 3CO(g) \longrightarrow 3CO_2(g) + 2Fe(s)$ _____

   (c) $C_2H_5OH(\ell) + O_2(g) \longrightarrow HC_2H_3O_2(\ell) + H_2O(g)$

   _____

11. The heat of combustion of octane, $C_8H_{18}(\ell)$, a component of gasoline, to produce $CO_2(g)$ and $H_2O(g)$ is -1213.6 kcal/mol of C_8H_{18}. What is the value of ΔH_f of $C_8H_{18}(\ell)$?

   _____

12. From the data in Table 12.1 can you suggest why using N_2O instead of O_2 in a combustion reaction produces a higher flame temperature?

   _____

   _____

New Terms

Standard state
   The natural state of a substance at 25°C and 1 atm.

Bar
   A unit of pressure. 1 bar = 10^5 Pa. It differs from 1 atm by about 1.3 percent.

Standard heat of formation, ΔH°_f

   The enthalpy change associated with the formation of one mole of a substance in its standard state from its elements in their standard states.

Standard heat of reaction, ΔH°

   ΔH° = (sum of ΔH°_f of products) - (sum of ΔH°_f of reactants)

12.6   BOND ENERGIES

Objectives

   To see how thermodynamic data can be used to obtain information about the strengths of chemical bonds. You should learn how to use bond energies to obtain an estimate of the heat of formation of a compound.

Review

   The bond energy is the energy required to break a bond to produce neutral fragments. The atomization energy, ΔH_{atm}, is the energy needed to break all of the bonds in a molecule to give neutral atoms.

   In many cases the tabulated average bond energies are additive in the sense that they may be used to calculate an atomization energy of a molecule. This can be used as one part of an alternative path from the free elements in their standard states to the compound in question in its standard state.

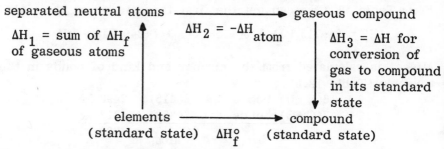

If the standard state of the compound is the gas, ΔH_3 can be ignored.

***

Example 12.2

Calculate the value of ΔH_f^o for dimethyl ether vapor,

$$
\begin{array}{ccc}
H & & H \\
| & & | \\
H-C-O-C-H \\
| & & | \\
H & & H
\end{array}
$$

Solution

The reaction whose ΔH we wish to calculate is as follows, with the alternative path indicated below it.

$$2C(s,\ graphite) + 3H_2(g) + \tfrac{1}{2}O_2(g) \xrightarrow{\Delta H_f^o} C_2H_6O(g)$$

$$2\Delta H_f[C(g)] \qquad 6\Delta H_f[H(g)] \qquad \Delta H_f[O(g)] \qquad -\Delta H_{atom}$$

$$2C(g) + 6H(g) + O(g)$$

The minus sign appears before the ΔH_{atom} because in the direction of the arrow the process is the reverse of atomization. When a reaction is reversed, remember that the sign of ΔH is reversed, too.

The sum of all ΔH's along the lower path must equal the ΔH along the upper path (that is, ΔH_f^o).

$$\Delta H_f^o = 2\Delta H_f[C(g)] + 6\Delta H_f[H(g)] + \Delta H_f[O(g)] - \Delta H_{atom}$$

From Table 12.2 we can get the first three terms on the right.

$$\Delta H_f^o = 2(+715\ kJ) + 6(+218\ kJ) + (+249\ kJ) - \Delta H_{atom}$$

ΔH_{atom} is calculated from the number and kind of bonds in the molecule (Table 12.3).

$$
\begin{array}{lr}
6(C-H)\ bonds & 6(415) = 2490\ kJ \\
2(C-O)\ bonds & 2(356) = 712\ kJ \\
\hline
& \Delta H_{atom} = 3202\ kJ
\end{array}
$$

Substituting,

$$\Delta H_f^o = 1430\ kJ + 1308\ kJ + 249\ kJ - 3202\ kJ$$

$$\Delta H^{\circ}_{f} = -215 \text{ kJ}$$

Since we are dealing with the formation of one mole of product,

$$\Delta H^{\circ}_{f} = -215 \text{ kJ/mol}$$

(The experimentally measured value is -185 kJ/mol.)

Self-Test

13. Calculate the atomization energy in kJ/mol for acetic acid.

14. Use the data in Tables 12.2 and 12.3 to calculate ΔH°_{f} for $C_2H_6(g)$ in kJ/mol. Compare your value with that found in Table 12.1. The structure of C_2H_6 is

15. Use the data in Tables 12.2 and 12.3 to calculate ΔH°_{f} for $C_6H_6(\ell)$ in kJ/mol. The heat of vaporization of C_6H_6 is 8.19 kcal/mol. The molecule is represented as a resonance hybrid.

How does your calculated value compare with that found in Table 12.1

New Terms

Atomization energy
>   The amount of energy needed to convert one mole of a compound into neutral gaseous atoms. It is the total energy needed to break all the bonds in a molecule to give gaseous atoms.

12.7   ENERGY, ENTROPY, AND THE SPONTANEITY OF CHEMICAL AND PHYSICAL CHANGES

Objectives
>   To learn about the factors that control the spontaneity of both chemical and physical events.

Review

A spontaneous change is one that occurs without continued outside help. It may need a push to get it started (the combustion of a mixture of H_2 and O_2, for instance) but once started, it continues on its own.

In this section you learn that there are two thermodynamic quantities that determine whether events are spontaneous. Spontaneity is favored if there is an energy decrease (if ΔH is negative, corresponding to an exothermic change.) Spontaneity is also favored if there is an increase in the degree of randomness (statistical probability) of a system. The thermodynamic quantity related to randomness is entropy, S. Spontaneity is favored by an entropy increase (if ΔS is positive).

For any given substance at a given temperature, its entropy depends on its physical state. Remember that

$$S_{solid} < S_{liquid} < S_{gas}$$

In general, gases have large entropies and solids have quite low entropies.

It is sometimes possible to anticipate the way the entropy changes in chemical reactions. Review the discussion on the top of Page 472 and Example 12.10 before working the Self-Test below.

Self-Test

16. You know that in tossing a coin there is an equal probability
     of it coming up either heads or tails. Suppose you had two
     coins, labeled A and B, and were to toss them. Make a
     table showing all of the possible combinations of heads and
     tails for the two coins. What is the probability that both
     coins would come up heads?

     _____

     Which state has the higher entropy, heads-heads or
     heads-tails?

     _____

17. Do the same thing as you did in Question 16, but for 4
     coins, labeled A, B, C, D. What is the probability of all
     four coins coming up heads when tossed? What is the prob-
     ability of there being two heads and two tails?

     _____

     Which combination of heads and tails has the largest entropy?

     _____

18. Predict the sign of the entropy change for the following
     reactions.

     (a) $NH_4Cl(s) + NaOH(s) \longrightarrow NaCl(s) + H_2O(\ell) + NH_3(g)$

     _____

     (b) $SO_2(g) + 1/2\ O_2(g) \longrightarrow SO_3(g)$

     _____

     (c) $SO_2(g) + CaO(s) \longrightarrow CaSO_4(s)$

     _____

New Terms

Entropy, S
     The thermodynamic quantity that describes the degree of
     randomness of a system. The greater the disorder, the
     higher the statistical probability of the state, and the higher
     the entropy.

Spontaneous change
     A change that occurs by itself without outside assistance.

12.8   THE SECOND LAW OF THERMODYNAMICS

Objectives

To obtain an equation that incorporates the two factors
that favor spontaneous changes (i.e., decrease in energy,
increase in entropy).

Review

Chemical and physical changes are favored when accompanied by a decrease in energy. A change also tends to be spontaneous if it occurs with an increase in entropy.

The second law of thermodynamics states, in essence, that
whenever a spontaneous change occurs, the entropy of the universe increases.

The Gibbs free energy is defined as

$$G = H - TS$$

At constant temperature and pressure,

$$\Delta G = \Delta H - T\Delta S$$

Remember that for a process to be spontaneous ΔG must be negative. In terms of the right side of the above equation, the difference, $\Delta H - T\Delta S$, must be negative. This section considers
three possibilities:

(1) ΔH negative, ΔS positive: ΔG will be negative at all temperatures. The process will be spontaneous regardless of the
temperature.

(2) ΔH positive, ΔS negative: ΔG will be positive at all temperatures. The process cannot be spontaneous at any tempera-
ture.

(3) ΔH and ΔS both positive or both negative: the sign of ΔG
depends on the value of T. If ΔH and ΔS are both positive,
for example, ΔG becomes the difference between two positive
quantities (ΔH and $T\Delta S$). At high temperature $T\Delta S$ can be
larger than ΔH; ΔG will be negative and the change will be
spontaneous. At low temperature ΔH will be larger than
$T\Delta S$; ΔG will be positive and the change won't be spontaneous.

Self-Test

19.   What will be the sign of ΔG at high temperature if both ΔH and ΔS are negative?

_____

20.   The conversion of liquid CCl_4 to gaseous CCl_4 at 1 atm occurs with ΔH = +32.8 kJ/mol and ΔS = +95.0 J/mol K.   Above
what temperature should bubbles be able to form within the
liquid spontaneously?

_____

New Terms

Gibbs free energy, G
      A thermodynamic quantity that relates energy (enthalpy, H),
      and entropy, S.   It is defined as G = H − TS.

Second law of thermodynamics
      Whenever a spontaneous event takes place, it is accompanied
      by an increase in the total entropy of the universe.

12.9   FREE ENERGY AND USEFUL WORK

Objectives

      To see how ΔG is related to the useful work that can be
      extracted from a system during a spontaneous change.

Review

      The free energy change, ΔG, is equal to the <u>maximum</u>
work that can be obtained from a spontaneous change.   Remember
that this maximum work can only be obtained if the change is reversible.   All real systems undergo changes in an irreversible
manner; therefore, the amount of work that can be extracted
from a real system is somewhat less than the maximum predicted
by ΔG.

New Terms

12.10 STANDARD ENTROPIES AND FREE ENERGIES

Objectives

To establish standard entropies and free energies of substances. You should learn the third law of thermodynamics. You should also learn to calculate $\Delta G°$ for reactions from $\Delta G_f°$.

Review

The third law of thermodynamics states that for any pure substance, $S = 0$ at 0 K. Absolute values of entropy can be obtained and some are given in Table 12.4. Values of $\Delta G°$ can be gotten from calculated $\Delta H°$ and $\Delta S°$, the latter obtained by suitably combining the $S°$ of products and reactants.

$$\Delta S° = (\text{Sum } S° \text{ products}) - (\text{Sum } S° \text{ reactants})$$

Table 12.5 tabulates values of $\Delta G_f°$. These can be used in Hess's law type calculations to compute values of $\Delta G°$ for reactions.

$$\Delta G° = (\text{Sum of } \Delta G_f° \text{ products}) - (\text{Sum of } \Delta G_f° \text{ reactants})$$

Self-Test

21. Calculate values of $\Delta S_f°$ for the following in units of J/mol K.

    (a) $Al_2O_3(s)$ _____

    (b) $C_3H_8(g)$ _____

    (c) $PbSO_4(s)$ _____

22. The standard entropy of $CS_2(g)$ is 237.7 J/mol K. Use the data in Tables 12.1 and 12.4 to calculate $\Delta G_f°$ of $CS_2(g)$.

    _____

23. Calculate $\Delta G°$ in kilojoules for the following reactions:

    (a) $H_2SO_4(\ell) + CaO(s) \longrightarrow CaSO_4(s) + H_2O(\ell)$ _____

    (b) $Ag(s) + 2HNO_3(\ell) \longrightarrow AgNO_3(s) + NO_2(g) + H_2O(\ell)$

    _____

New Terms

Third law of thermodynamics
  For a pure crystalline substance, $S = 0$ at 0 K.

Standard entropy, S°
  The entropy that one mole of a substance has at 25°C and
  1 atm.

Standard entropy change, ΔS°
  Formally, $\Delta S^\circ = S^\circ_{final} - S^\circ_{initial}$
  ΔS° = (Sum of S° of products) - (Sum of S° of reactants)

Standard free energy change, ΔG°
  $\Delta G^\circ = \Delta H^\circ - T\Delta S^\circ$.

  ΔG° = (Sum of ΔG°_f of the products) - (Sum of ΔG°_f of the
  reactants)

Standard free energy of formation, ΔG°_f
  The change in free energy when one mole of a compound in
  its standard state is formed from its elements in their standard states.

12.11 FREE ENERGY AND EQUILIBRIUM

Objectives

> To discover the relationship between free energy and
> equilibrium. You should learn the qualitative relationship
> between ΔG° and the position of equilibrium.

Review

  The main points in this section are that $\Delta G = 0$ when a
system is at equilibrium, and that ΔG° is related to the position
of equilibrium. Review the discussion centering on Figures 12.12
and 12.13. Notice that even with a ΔG° that is positive, some
reaction occurs. This is because ΔG starts out negative heading
in the direction of the products. Also note that the distinction
is made here between ΔG° and ΔG. ΔG° is the difference between
the free energy of the products in their standard states and the
free energy of the reactants in their standard states. We are

using ΔG, on the other hand, to stand for the way that the free energy is changing as we move along the free energy curve. Our earlier discussion about spontaneity applies in the sense that the free energy must be decreasing (ΔG negative) when the process is occurring spontaneously. Once the minimum is reached, equilibrium is established because the system cannot climb out of the free energy well.

In Figure 12.13, notice that the position of equilibrium is determined by the sign (and magnitude) of $\Delta G°$. Only when $\Delta G°$ is negative do we observe the formation of significant amounts of products. In this way we can use $\Delta G°$ as a predictor of reaction "spontaneity."

Self-Test

24. Sketch free energy curves for the reactions:

(a) $N_2(g) + \frac{1}{2} O_2(g) \longrightarrow N_2O(g)$ $\Delta G° = +104$ kJ

(b) $H_2(g) + Cl_2(g) \longrightarrow 2HCl(g)$ $\Delta G° = -191$ kJ

25. Is the reaction, $N_2(g) + O_2(g) \longrightarrow 2NO(g)$, "spontaneous" at room temperature? Is it more or less "spontaneous" at 1000°C? (Assume $\Delta H°$ and $\Delta S°$ are essentially independent of temperature.)

New Terms

Answers to Self-Test Questions

1.(a) isothermal (b) state function (c) adiabatic (d) specific heat (e) heat capacity (f) molar heat capacity 2. 466 J
3.(a) 64 L-atm (b) 88 L-atm 4. 59.9 Calories 5.(a) 802 kJ/mol
(b) 802 kJ/mol ($P\Delta V = 0$) 6. -1284 kJ/mol 7. -69.8 kcal
8. -1776 kJ 9. -177 kJ 10.(a) -429.1 kJ (b) -30 kJ
(c) -451 kJ 11. -59.4 kcal/mol 12. N_2O has a positive $\Delta H_f°$, so when it serves as a reactant it tends to make ΔH more negative (since ΔH of reactants are subtracted from those of the products).
13. 3136 kJ/mol 14. Calc. $\Delta H_f° = -100$ kJ/mol

15. Calc. ΔH_f° = +209 kJ/mol; actual ΔH_f° = +49.0 kJ/mol.
(Resonance stabilizes molecules and ions.)

16.

A	B
H	H
H	T
T	H
T	T

Probability of both heads = 1/4 = 0.25
Probability of one head and one tail is 2/4 =
0.50. The head-tail state has the greater
entropy.

17.

A	B	C	D	
H	H	H	H	*
H	T	H	H	
H	H	T	H	
H	H	H	T	
H	T	T	H	**
H	T	H	T	**
H	H	T	T	**
H	T	T	T	
T	H	H	H	
T	T	H	H	**
T	H	T	H	**
T	H	H	T	**
T	T	T	H	
T	T	H	T	
T	H	T	T	
T	T	T	T	

16 possible combinations

* = all heads
** = 2 heads, 2 tails

probability all heads = 1/16 = 0.0625

probability 2 heads, 2 tails = 6/16 =
0.375

Two heads and two tails has the
highest probability and therefore the
largest entropy.

18.(a) ΔS = (+)   (b) ΔS = (−)   (c) ΔS = (−)   19. ΔG will be
positive. 20. 345 K (72°C). When ΔG = 0, ΔH = $T\Delta S$,
$T = \Delta H/\Delta S$. Above this T, ΔG will be negative.
21.(a) −313.1 J/mol K   (b) −269.6 J/mol K   (c) −358 J/mol K
22. $\Delta G_f^\circ = \Delta H_f^\circ - (298\ K)\Delta S_f^\circ$; ΔG_f° = +66.8 kJ/mol   23.(a) −263 kJ
(b) −57.3 kJ

24.(a)   (b)

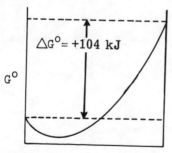

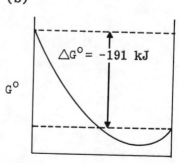

25. Since $\Delta G° = +174$ kJ, the reaction is not "spontaneous" because very little NO will be produced. At 1000°C (1273 K),

$$\Delta G = \Delta H° - (1273 \text{ K})\Delta S°$$
$$= +181 \text{ kJ} - (1273 \text{ K})(+24.7 \text{ J/mol K})$$
$$= +181 \text{ kJ} - 31.4 \text{ kJ} = +150 \text{ kJ}$$

Since ΔG is smaller, the reaction will be a little more "spontaneous" at the higher temperature.

13 CHEMICAL KINETICS: THE STUDY OF THE RATES OF REACTIONS

This chapter concerns itself with the rates at which chemical reactions take place. This subject is important for several reasons. First, unless a reaction proceeds at a measurable rate, no products will be observed regardless of how thermodynamically favorable the reaction might be. Second, a study of reaction rates and the factors that influence them provides insight into the sequence of chemical steps that occurs to produce the overall net reaction. Third, a study of the effect of temperature on reaction rate gives information about energy changes that occur along the path from reactants to products.

Remember the four factors that influence the rate of a reaction.
1. The chemical nature of the reactants and products.
2. The concentration of the reactants.
3. The effect of temperature.
4. The influence of catalysts.

13.1   REACTION RATES AND THEIR MEASUREMENT

Objectives

To see what is meant by reaction rate and to see how it is measured. You should also learn the units used to express reaction rates.

Review

The term "reaction rate" describes how fast the concentrations of reactants or products change with time and is usually expressed in the units mol/liter second (mol liter^{-1} s^{-1}). For most reactions the rate changes (decreases) as the reactants are consumed.

The rate of reaction can be obtained from a graph of the concentration of a reactant (or product) versus time (see Figure 12.2). The rate at some time, t, is obtained from the slope of the tangent to the concentration-time curve at time t. The procedure is described in Figure 12.2.

Remember that square brackets, [ ], denote molar concentration.

Self-Test

1. The rate of a reaction was found to be 3.0 x 10^{-4} mol/L^{-1}s^{-1}. What would be the rate if it were expressed in the units, mol L^{-1}min^{-1}?

   _____

2. From the concentration $\underline{vs}$ time curve below, estimate the rate of reaction at t = $\overline{10}$ s.

   _____

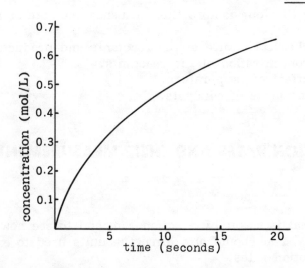

3. The sequence of chemical reactions that provides the net overall change in a chemical reaction is called

   _____

4. Consider the following reaction

$$4NH_3(g) + 3 O_2(g) \longrightarrow 2N_2(g) + 6H_2O(g)$$

If the rate of formation of N_2 at a particular instant is 0.800 mol $L^{-1}s^{-1}$, what is the rate of

(a) formation of H_2O? _____

(b) disappearance of NH_3? _____

(c) disappearance of O_2 _____

5. List the four factors that affect the rate of a chemical reaction.

_____

_____

New Terms

Rate

A ratio in which units of time appear in the denominator, for example, 40 mi/hr or 3.0 (mol L^{-1})/s.

Rate of reaction (Reaction rate)

How quickly the reactants disappear and the products form, expressed in units of mol $L^{-1} s^{-1}$.

13.2   RATE LAWS

Objectives

To learn what is meant by the term, rate law, and to see how it can be obtained from experimental data.

Review

The rate law for a reaction such as

$$A + B \longrightarrow products$$

is

$$Rate = k[A]^x[B]^y$$

where k is the rate constant. The exponents, x and y, are called the order of the reaction with respect to A and B, respectively. The overall order is (x + y).

It is very important to remember that the actual values of x and y can only be obtained by experiment. These experiments involve observing what effect altering the concentrations of the reactants has on the rate of reaction.

For a reaction, A $\longrightarrow$ B,

(1) if doubling the concentration of A doubles the rate, the exponent is 1.

$$Rate = k[A]^1$$

(2) if doubling the concentration of A quadruples the rate, the exponent is 2.

$$Rate = k[A]^2$$

Review Examples 13.2 and 13.3 in the text to see how these rules are applied. Notice that once the exponents in the rate law have been established, the rate constant can be evaluated from any of the sets of data.

Self-Test

6. Below are some typical rate laws. What are the orders of the reactions and the orders with respect to each reactant?

(a) Rate = $k[NO]^2[Br_2]$

$2NO + Br_2 \longrightarrow 2NOBr$ _____

(b) Rate = $k[NO]^2[H_2]$

$2NO + 2H_2 \longrightarrow N_2 + 2H_2O$ _____

7. The following data were collected for the reaction,
$$A + 2B \longrightarrow C + D$$

| concentrations | | rate of formation of C |
A	B	(mol L^{-1} s^{-1})
0.10	0.10	2.0×10^{-4}
0.10	0.20	4.0×10^{-4}
0.20	0.20	1.6×10^{-3}
0.30	0.20	3.6×10^{-3}

(a) The rate law for the reaction is   _____

(b) The value of the rate constant is   _____

(c)   The units of the rate constant are _____

New Terms

Order (of reaction)
> The sum of the exponents in the rate law is the overall order of the reaction. Each exponent gives the order with respect to a certain reactant.

Rate constant
> The proportionality constant in the rate law for a reaction. Its value is the rate of the reaction when all the reactant concentrations are 1 M.

Rate law
> An equation that relates the rate of a reaction to the molar concentrations of the reactants, each raised to some appropriate power.

13.3   CONCENTRATION AND TIME: HALF-LIVES

Objectives

> To learn how the concentrations of the reactants are related to time for first-order and second-order reactions. You should learn the concept of half-life and know how it is computed for first- and second-order reactions.

Review

For a first-order reaction with the rate law, rate = k[A], the concentration at any time, t, after the start of the reaction (t = 0) is

$$\ln \frac{[A]_o}{[A]_t} = kt$$

or, in terms of common logs,

$$2.303 \log \frac{[A]_o}{[A]_t} = kt$$

280   Chapter 13

For a second-order reaction with a rate law, rate = $k[B]^2$,. the relationship between concentration and time is

$$\frac{1}{[B]_t} - \frac{1}{[B]_o} = kt$$

The half-life, $t_{\frac{1}{2}}$, of a given reactant is the time it takes for the reactant's concentration to be reduced to half of its initial value. For a first-order reaction, remember that $t_{\frac{1}{2}}$ is independent of the reactant's initial concentration, and the first and successive half-lives are all equal. They can be computed from the rate constant

$$t_{\frac{1}{2}} = \frac{\ln 2}{k} = \frac{0.693}{k}$$

The half-life in a second-order reaction does depend on the reactant's initial concentration. Doubling the initial concentration halves the $t_{\frac{1}{2}}$; halving the initial concentration doubles the $t_{\frac{1}{2}}$. This means that successive half-lives in a second-order reaction increase by a factor of 2. In other words the second half-life is double the first because its initial concentration is only half the first. Similarly, the third half-life is double the second, and so on. The half-life can be calculated by the expression

$$t_{\frac{1}{2}} = \frac{1}{k[B]_o}$$

Self-Test

8. In a certain first-order reaction having the rate law, rate = $k[C]$, the rate constant has a value of 3.00×10^{-4} s^{-1}. If the initial concentration of the reactant C is 0.50 mol/L,

    (a) what will be its concentration after 30 minutes?

    _____

    (b) what is $t_{\frac{1}{2}}$ for the reaction?   _____

    (c) what will be the concentration of C after 4 half-lives?

    _____

9. In a certain second-order reaction having the rate law, rate = $k[D]^2$, the reaction was begun with a concentration of D equal to 1.00 M. The rate constant for the reaction is

$k = 5.0 \times 10^{-2}$ L mol^{-1} s^{-1}.

(a)   What is the initial half-life of D? _____

(b)   How long will it take for the concentration of D to be reduced to 0.125 M?

_____

New Terms

Half-life, $t_{\frac{1}{2}}$

The time required in a chemical reaction for the concentration of a given reactant to be reduced to half its initial value.

13.4   COLLISION THEORY

Objectives

To obtain a theory that accounts quantitatively for the dependence of reaction rate on concentration.

Review

The basis for the collision theory is the notion that molecules must collide in order to react with one another. We can predict the rate law if we know what collisions take place during a reaction. Usually reactions occur in a series of steps before the ultimate products have been formed and we don't actually know what these steps are. In fact, one of the goals of kinetics is to give us a way of guessing intelligently at what these steps might be.

Remember, if we have the following collision processes, their rate laws are:

A + B ⟶ products   Rate = k[A][B]

A + A ⟶ products

or   2A ⟶ products   Rate = k[A]^2

New Terms

Bimolecular collision
    A collision between two molecules.

Collision theory
    A theory of reaction rates that postulates that the rate of
    a reaction is proportional to the number of collisions that
    occur each second between the reactant molecules.

13.5 REACTION MECHANISMS

Objectives

    To see how collision theory helps us choose between alter-
    native possible mechanisms for a reaction. You should
    learn the meaning of "rate-determining step."

Review

    The individual reactions that make up a mechanism are
called elementary processes. The slowest step in the mechanism
is called the rate-determining step because the final products
can't be formed any faster than the products of the slowest step.

    Obtaining a satisfactory mechanism for a reaction is a very
difficult task. A chemist must draw on all his experience and
knowledge to arrive at a set of elementary processes that both
make sense chemically and fit the experimentally determined rate
law. With your limited chemical background you can't be expected
to derive chemically reasonable mechanisms. However, within
reason, you should be able to decide from a comparison of predicted and experimentally found rate laws whether a given mechanism is possible. You should also be able to decide which step
in a mechanism must be the slow step in order to yield the correct rate law.

    Remember that the predicted rate law should only include
the reactants in the overall equation. Any intermediate products
should not appear. In the very simple mechanisms that we are
dealing with you can get the exponents in the predicted rate law
by adding together all of the steps up to and including the rate-
determining step. The coefficients of the reactants at this point

are the exponents in the predicted rate law. Try this with the mechanism proposed for the reaction between NO and H_2 at the beginning of the section in the text. The second reaction is the rate-determining step.

Self-Test

10. Consider the following mechanisms:

$$(1) \quad 2A \longrightarrow Q$$
$$(2) \quad Q + B \longrightarrow C + C$$
$$(3) \quad B + D \longrightarrow 2M$$

(a) What is the equation for the overall reaction?

_____

(b) What is the rate law if step 1 is rate-determining?

_____

(c) What is the rate law if step 2 is rate-determining?

_____

11. The following mechanism was proposed to account for a chemical reaction. The rate law was found experimentally to be: Rate = $k[R]^2$

$$2R \longrightarrow X + Y$$
$$X + Z \longrightarrow T + U$$
$$U + Z \longrightarrow P$$

Which is the rate-determining step? _____

New Terms

Elementary process
    One of the individual steps in a reaction mechanism.

Mechanism of a reaction (Reaction mechanism)
    The series of individual steps in a chemical reaction that gives the net overall change.

Rate-determining step
    The slow step in a reaction mechanism, which determines how fast the products appear.

13.6   EFFECTIVE COLLISIONS

Objectives

To understand why reaction rates are nearly always much less than the rate of collision between molecules.

Review

The first thing to keep in mind here is that except for a very few cases, reactions proceed at a much slower rate than we would at first expect on the basis of the frequency of molecular collisions. Two factors tend to limit the number of collisions that are effective. One is the energy of the colliding molecules; the other is related to the orientation of the molecules when they collide.

New Terms

Effective collisions
Collisions between reactant molecules that lead to a net chemical change.

13.7   TRANSITION STATE THEORY

Objectives

To follow the energy changes that take place during an effective collision. Also, to see how the rate of reaction is affected by the energy required to produce an effective collision. You should become familiar with the potential energy diagram for a reaction.

Review

The minimum kinetic energy required between two colliding molecules in order to produce an effective collision is called the activation energy, E_a. Review the energy diagrams in Figures 13.6 to 13.8. You should be able to identify:

(1) the potential energy of the reactants

(2)   the potential energy of the products
(3)   the activation energy for the forward reaction
(4)   the activation energy for the reverse reaction
(5)   the heat of reaction
(6)   whether the forward reaction is endo- or exothermic

The species that exists at the top of the potential energy diagram (i.e., the high-energy species that is formed during an effective collision) is called the activated complex. The peak on the potential energy diagram is called the transition state. Transition state theory is concerned with the characteristics (geometry, energy) of the activated complex.

As a general rule, reactions having high activation energies tend to occur slowly, whereas fast reactions usually have low activation energies.

Self-Test

12. Identify the following by the numbers on the potential energy diagram which follows.

(a)   _____   the potential energy of the products

(b)   _____   the activation energy for the forward reaction

(c)   _____   the heat of reaction

(d)   _____   the potential energy of the reactants

(e)   _____   the activation energy of the reverse reaction

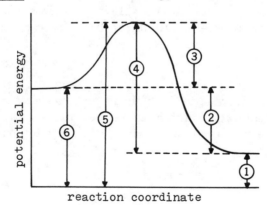

New Terms

Activated complex
    The chemical species that exists with partly broken and
    partly formed bonds in the transition state.

Activation energy, E_a
    The minimum kinetic energy that must be possessed by
    reactant molecules in order to give an effective collision
    (one that forms the products).

Reaction coordinate
    In an analysis of the energy changes that take place during
    a collision, it is the path followed as reactant molecules ap-
    proach each other in a collision, followed by bonds being
    broken as new ones are formed.

Transition state
    The brief moment during a reaction when the reactants have
    collided and are at the high point on the potential energy
    diagram for the reaction.

13.8   EFFECT OF TEMPERATURE ON REACTION RATES

Objectives

    To learn how and why temperature affects the rate of
    reaction. You should be able to calculate the activation
    energy from rate constants at two different temperatures.

Review

    In very nearly every case, increasing the temperature in-
creases the rate of reaction. This is because molecules move
faster, on the average, at higher temperatures and more molecular collisions have the minimum kinetic energy to produce a net
chemical change.

    The Arrhenius equation is

$$k = Ae^{-E_a/RT}$$

From this can be derived the expression,

$$\ln \frac{k_1}{k_2} = \frac{E_a}{R} \left(\frac{1}{T_2} - \frac{1}{T_1} \right)$$

or, in terms of common logarithms,

$$\log \frac{k_1}{k_2} = \frac{E_a}{2.303 \ R} \left(\frac{1}{T_2} - \frac{1}{T_1} \right)$$

If rate constants k_1 and k_2 are known at temperatures T_1 and T_2, the activation energy can be calculated.

Self-Test

13. As a rough rule of thumb, the rates of many reactions approximately double for every _____ °C rise in temperature.

14. The rate constant of a reaction at 15°C is 1.3×10^{-5} L/mol s, while at 50°C its rate constant is 8.0×10^{-3} L/mol s. What is the E_a for the reaction in kJ/mol?

_____

15. The activation energy for a certain reaction was found to be 25.0 kcal/mol. At 25°C the rate constant is 2×10^{-3} s^{-1}. What is the rate constant at 50°C?

_____

New Terms

Arrhenius equation
   The equation that relates the rate constant for a reaction, k, to the activation energy, E_a. $k = Ae^{-E_a/RT}$

13.9   CATALYSTS

Objectives

   To define what a catalyst is and to understand how it functions in affecting the rate of reaction.

Review

A catalyst is a substance that alters the rate of a reaction by providing an alternative path (mechanism) from reactants to products that has a lower activation energy than the uncatalyzed path. It is important to remember that a catalyst functions by changing the mechanism.

A homogeneous catalyst exists in the same phase as the reactants. Biological enzymes are examples of homogeneous catalysts that promote specific biochemical reactions.

A heterogeneous catalyst exists as a separate phase from the reactants and products and appears to function by adsorbing reactant molecules on its surface where the reaction can somehow proceed more readily. Heterogeneous catalysts are widely used in industrial applications because they don't have to be separated later from the products of reaction as would homogeneous catalysts.

An inhibitor is a substance that becomes adsorbed on the surface of the catalyst and thereby decreases, or inhibits, its activity. The catalyst is then said to be poisoned.

Self-Test

16. How does a catalyst alter the activation energy of a reaction?

_____

17. What type of catalyst is present in a catalytic muffler?

_____

18. What type of catalyst is a biological enzyme?

_____

New Terms

Catalyst

A substance that alters the rate of a chemical reaction by providing a lower energy path (mechanism) that leads from reactants to products. The catalyst is not used up as the reaction progresses.

Heterogeneous catalyst
> A catalyst that is in a different phase than the reactants. The reactants are adsorbed on the surface of the catalyst, which is where the reaction occurs.

Homogeneous catalyst
> A catalyst that is in the same phase as the reactants.

Inhibitor
> A substance that blocks the action of a catalyst.

13.10   CHAIN REACTIONS

Objectives

> To examine a type of mechanism that often occurs in systems with very complicated rate laws. You should learn that these reactions tend to propagate themselves once they have been started. You should learn the kinds of steps responsible for initiation, continuation, and termination of the chain.

Review

Chain reactions often involve free radicals - molecules or ions that contain unpaired electrons. These unpaired electrons tend to pair up with electrons in other molecules or ions, and free radicals are very reactive. The kinds of reactions that may be found in a chain mechanism are:

(1)   initiation - this is the step that generates the first free radical.

(2)   propagation - a product is formed plus another free radical. This continues the chain.

(3)   inhibition - this is a step that slows down the rate of formation of products. In the mechanism in the text it removes some product but still generates a free radical so the chain can continue.

(4)   termination - this is a step that removes free radicals and therefore interrupts the chain.

Self-Test

18. The reaction of methane with chlorine ($CH_4 + Cl_2 \longrightarrow$ $CH_3Cl + HCl$) is believed to occur by the following mechanisms. Identify the nature of each of these reactions.

(a) $Cl_2 \xrightarrow{\text{light}} 2Cl\cdot$ _____

(b) $Cl\cdot + CH_4 \longrightarrow HCl + CH_3\cdot$ _____

(c) $CH_3\cdot + Cl_2 \longrightarrow CH_3Cl + Cl\cdot$ _____

(d) $Cl\cdot + Cl\cdot \longrightarrow Cl_2$ _____

(e) $CH_3\cdot + CH_3\cdot \longrightarrow C_2H_6$ _____

(f) $CH_3\cdot + Cl\cdot \longrightarrow CH_3Cl$ _____

New Terms

Chain reaction
> A reaction in which a product of one step is the reactant in another. Usually, they involve free radicals and are very rapid once initiated.

Free radical
> An extremely reactive chemical species that contains one or more unpaired electrons.

Inhibition step
> In a chain reaction, a step in the mechanism that removes product molecules and thereby inhibits or slows the overall rate of production of the products.

Initiation step
> The first step in a chain reaction in which a reactant molecule is converted into one or more free radicals.

Propagation step
> A step in a chain reaction in which a free radical reacts with a reactant molecule to give a product molecule plus another free radical.

Termination step
> In a chain reaction, a step in the mechanism that removes free radicals and thereby terminates the chain.

Answers to Self-Test Questions

1. 1.8×10^{-2} mol L^{-1} min^{-1} 2. 0.026 mol L^{-1} s^{-1} 3. the
mechanism   4.(a) 2.4 mol L^{-1} s^{-1} (b) -1.6 mol L^{-1} s^{-1}
(c) -1.2 mol L^{-1} s^{-1} 5. nature of the reactants, concentration
of reactants, temperature, catalysts   6.(a) second order in NO,
first order in Br_2, third order overall   (b) second order in NO,
first order in H_2, third order overall   7.(a) Rate = $k[A]^2[B]$
(b) $k = 0.2$ (c) L^2 mol^{-2} s^{-1} 8.(a) 0.29 mol/L
(b) 2310 s = 38.5 min   (c) 0.031 mol/L   9.(a) 20 s   (b) 140 s
10.(a) $2A + 2B \longrightarrow C + 2M$ (b) Rate = $k[A]^2$ (c) Rate =
$k[A]^2[B]$ 11. The first step   12.(a) 1   (b) 3   (c) 2   (d) 6
(e) 4   13. $10°C$ 14. 142 kJ/mol   15. 5.2×10^{-2} s^{-1}
16. a catalyst provides a different, low energy mechanism
17. heterogeneous catalyst   18. homogeneous catalyst
19.(a) initiation   (b) propagation   (c) propagation
(d) termination   (e) termination   (f) termination

14 CHEMICAL EQUILIBRIUM

As a chemical reaction proceeds, the concentrations of the reactants decrease and the rate of the forward reaction decreases. At the same time, the concentrations of the products increase and the rate of the reverse reaction increases. Eventually both reactions occur at the same rate and dynamic equilibrium is achieved.

There is a simple relationship between the concentrations of reactants and products in an equilibrium system. This chapter deals with that relationship, how it can be understood from the standpoint of thermodynamics, and how it can be used in calculations relating equilibrium concentrations.

14.1 THE EQUILIBRIUM LAW FOR A CHEMICAL REACTION

Objectives

To establish the relationships between reactant and product concentrations in a chemical equilibrium. You should note that this section views the equilibrium law as a purely experimentally measurable phenomenon without attempting to present an explanation for it.

Review

Remember that the mass action expression (or reaction quotient) for <u>any</u> chemical reaction can be written from the balanced equation. The concentrations of the products always appear in the numerator, raised to powers that are equal to their coefficients in the balanced equation. The concentrations of reactants are multiplied together in the denominator where they are each raised to powers equal to their coefficients in the balanced equation.

At equilibrium, at a given temperature, the mass action expression for a given reaction is always equal to the same number, the equilibrium constant. Remember, there are no restrictions on the individual equilibrium concentrations. The only requirement is that when they are substituted into the mass action expression, the resulting fraction must equal the equilibrium constant. This defines the equilibrium law for the reaction.

For gaseous reactions the equilibrium constant expression can be written in terms of concentrations, thereby giving K_c, or in terms of partial pressures, giving K_p.

Self-Test

1. Write the mass action law (equilibrium law) giving both K_c and K_p for each of the following gaseous reactions:

   (a) $PCl_5 \rightleftharpoons PCl_3 + Cl_2$

   (b) $Br_2 + SO_2 + 2H_2O \rightleftharpoons H_2SO_4 + 2HBr$

   (c) $6XeF_4 + 12H_2O \rightleftharpoons 2XeO_3 + 4Xe + O_2 + 24HF$

   (d) $2NO_2 + F_2 \rightleftharpoons 2NO_2F$

2. Below are equilibrium concentrations of NO_2 and N_2O_4. The equilibrium equation is: $N_2O_4(g) \rightleftharpoons 2NO_2(g)$

Experiment	$[N_2O_4]$	$[NO_2]$
1	4.46×10^{-2} M	3.11 M
2	1.50×10^{-3} M	0.571 M
3	2.30×10^{-7} M	7.06×10^{-3} M
4	1 M	14.7 M

Show that they obey the equilibrium law. What is the value of the equilibrium constant?

New Terms

Equilibrium constant
    The value that the mass action expression has when a chemical system is at equilibrium. It is K_p when partial pressures are used in the mass action expression, and it is K_c when molar concentrations are used.

Mass action expression
    A fraction that can be constructed from the overall balanced equation for a reaction. For the general reaction
        $aA + bB \rightleftharpoons mM + nM$
    the mass action expression is

$$\frac{[M]^m [N]^n}{[A]^a [B]^b}$$

For reactions involving gases, partial pressures can be used in place of molar concentrations.

Reaction quotient
    The numerical value of the mass action expression.

Equilibrium law
    An equation that sets the mass action expression equal to the equilibrium constant. A condition that must be fulfilled for a reaction to be at equilibrium.

14.2   THE EQUILIBRIUM CONSTANT

Objectives

To see how the magnitude of K provides an immediate qualitative estimate of the extent to which a reaction proceeds toward completion.

Review

When K is large the reaction proceeds far toward completion; when K is small hardly any products are present at equilibrium.

Self-Test

3. Arrange the following reactions in order of increasing tendency to proceed toward completion:

(a) $CO(g) + Cl_2(g) \rightleftharpoons COCl_2(g)$ $K = 5 \times 10^9$

(b) $N_2O_4(g) \rightleftharpoons 2NO_2(g)$ $K = 217$

(c) $2SO_2(g) + O_2(g) \rightleftharpoons 2SO_3(g)$ $K = 8 \times 10^{25}$

(d) $2HCl(g) \rightleftharpoons H_2(g) + Cl_2(g)$ $K = 3.1 \times 10^{-17}$

New Terms

14.3   THERMODYNAMICS AND CHEMICAL EQUILIBRIUM

Objectives

To relate, quantitatively, the standard free energy change for a reaction to the equilibrium constant. After completing this section you should be able to compute K from $\Delta G°$, and vice versa.

Review

The free energy change for a reaction is related to the mass action expression (Q) by the equation,

$$\Delta G = \Delta G^\circ + RT \ln Q \qquad \text{(14.3 in text)}$$

or, in terms of common logarithms,

$$\Delta G = \Delta G^\circ + 2.303 \, RT \log Q$$

Important equations to remember are the following:

For gaseous reactions,

$$\Delta G^\circ = -RT \ln K_p \qquad \text{(14.5 in text)}$$

or $\qquad \Delta G^\circ = -2.303 \, RT \log K_p$

For reactions in solution,

$$\Delta G^\circ = -RT \ln K_c \qquad \text{(14.6 in text)}$$

or $\qquad \Delta G^\circ = -2.303 \, RT \log K_c$

The K's that you compute using these equations are called thermodynamic equilibrium constants. In using the equations, you must be sure to use the correct value of R, according to the energy units of ΔG°.

$$R = 1.987 \text{ cal mol}^{-1} \text{ K}^{-1}$$
$$R = 8.314 \text{ J mol}^{-1} \text{ K}^{-1}$$

Also, for ΔG° be sure to convert kJ to J or kcal to cal, and be sure to express the temperature in kelvins. This is emphasized again in the following example.

Example 14.1

What is the thermodynamic equilibrium constant, K_p, for the reaction, $2HBr(g) + Cl_2(g) \rightleftharpoons 2HCl(g) + Br_2(g)$, at 25°C? Work the problem using ΔG° in kilocalories.

Solution

First we calculate ΔG° from the appropriate ΔG°_f in Table 12.5 (Page 478). Let's use values in kcal/mol.

$$\Delta G^\circ = 2\Delta G_f^\circ(HCl) - 2\Delta G_f^\circ(HBr)$$

$$\Delta G^\circ = 2 \text{ mol}(-22.8 \text{ kcal/mol}) - 2 \text{ mol}(-12.7 \text{ kcal/mol})$$

$$\Delta G^\circ = -20.2 \text{ kcal}$$

Using a scientific calculator, it is simplest to work with natural logarithms. We therefore solve Equation 14.5 for $\ln K_p$.

$$\ln K_p = \frac{-\Delta G^\circ}{2.303 \, RT}$$

In these calculations, remember:

(1) use $R = 1.987$ cal mol^{-1} K^{-1} if ΔG° is in kcal; use $R = 8.314$ J/mol K if ΔG° is in kJ.

(2) make sure you express ΔG° in calories (or J), not kcal (or kJ).

(3) use the absolute temperature (298 K in this question).

Substituting,

$$\ln K_p = \frac{-(-20200)}{(1.987)(298)} = 34.1$$

To take the antilog, we use the e^x function on the calculator.

$$K_p = e^{34.1}$$
$$= 6 \times 10^{14}$$

If you don't have a scientific calculator with logarithm functions, you must use common logarithms. In that case,

$$\log K_p = \frac{-(-20200)}{2.303(1.987)(298)} = 14.8$$

Taking the antilogarithm gives

$$K_p = 6 \times 10^{14}$$

(Logarithms and antilogarithms are discussed in Appendix A of the textbook.)

Self-Test

4. Calculate the value of the thermodynamic equilibrium constant at 25°C for the reaction, $H_2(g) + I_2(g) \rightleftharpoons 2HI(g)$

    _____

5. What is the value of $\Delta G°$ if at 25°C a reaction has an equilibrium constant equal to 1.0?

    _____

6. What is the value of $\Delta G°$ in both kJ and kcal if at 25°C a reaction has an equilibrium constant of 1.5×10^{-12}?

    _____

New Terms

Thermodynamic equilibrium constant
     An equilibrium constant computed from the equation
     $\Delta G° = -RT \ln K$. For reactions involving gases, $K = K_p$.

Activity
     The effective concentration of a solute or the effective pressure of a gas in an equilibrium system. At low concentrations or low pressures, activities approach molar concentrations or pressures.

14.4   THE RELATIONSHIP BETWEEN K_p AND K_c

Objectives
     To see how we can convert from K_p to K_c, and vice versa.

Review
     Remember the relationship,

$$K_p = K_c(RT)^{\Delta n_g}$$

where Δn_g is the change in the number of moles of <u>gas</u> on going from reactants to products in the balanced equation. Review the sample calculation in Example 14.4 in the text. Notice that in this calculation $R = 0.0821$ L atm mol^{-1} K^{-1}. This is to make units cancel properly.

Self-Test

7. The reaction, $N_2(g) + 3H_2(g) \rightleftharpoons 2NH_3(g)$, has $K_p = 7.2 \times 10^5$ at 25°C. What is the value of K_c?

8. The reaction, $H_2(g) + I_2(g) \rightleftharpoons 2HI(g)$, has $K_p = 0.35$ at 25°C. What is the value of K_c?

New Terms

14.5   HETEROGENEOUS EQUILIBRIA

Objectives

To see how the mass action expression can be simplified in cases of equilibrium between two or more pure phases.

Review

Remember that the concentrations of pure liquid or solid phases are not included in the mass action expression. This is because they are constant and are included in the equilibrium constant.

Self-Test

9. Write the equilibrium constant expression for K_c for the following:

(a) $2H_2(g) + O_2(g) \rightleftharpoons 2H_2O(\ell)$

(b) $CO_2(g) + Li_2CO_3(s) + H_2O(g) \rightleftharpoons 2LiHCO_3(s)$

(c) $Cl_2(g) + 2KBr(s) \rightleftharpoons 2KCl(s) + Br_2(g)$

New Terms

Heterogeneous reaction
     A chemical reaction in which the reactants and products are
     not all in the same phase.

Homogeneous reaction
     A reaction in which the reactants and products are in the
     same phase.

14.6 LE CHÂTELIER'S PRINCIPLE AND CHEMICAL EQUILIBRIA

Objectives

     To learn how to apply Le Châtelier's principle to changes
     in concentration, pressure, and temperature in chemical
     systems.

Review

(1) When a reactant or product is added to a system at equilib-
     rium, the position of equilibrium shifts toward the opposite
     side of the equation.

(2) Decreasing the concentration of a reactant or product causes
     the position of equilibrium to shift in the direction of the
     substance removed.

(3) Increasing the pressure by decreasing the volume shifts the
     position of equilibrium in the direction of the fewest number
     of moles of gas.

(4) An increase in temperature causes the position of equilibrium
     to shift in the direction of the endothermic reaction.

     A very important point to remember is that the only thing
that changes K for a reaction is a change in temperature!

     Two final observations are made in this section. One is
that adding an inert (unreactive) gas to a system, without changing the volume, has no effect on the position of equilibrium. The
second is that a catalyst has no effect on the position of equilibrium. It only increases the speed with which the system reaches

equilibrium.

Self-Test

10. Use the letters, I = increase, D = decrease, N = no change,
     to indicate what effect each of the following changes will
     have upon the amount of $SO_2(g)$ in the system,

     $$2SO_2(g) + O_2(g) \rightleftharpoons 2SO_3(g) \qquad \Delta H = -193 \text{ kJ}$$

     (a) adding $O_2(g)$ _____

     (b) adding $SO_3(g)$ _____

     (c) removing $SO_3(g)$ _____

     (d) increasing the temperature   _____

     (e) increasing the volume of the container   _____

     (f) adding helium   _____

     (g) adding a catalyst   _____

11. Which, if any, of the changes described in Question 10 will
     alter the equilibrium constant?   _____

New Terms

Le Châtelier's principle
     When a system that is in dynamic equilibrium is subjected to
     a disturbance that upsets the equilibrium, the system under-
     goes a change in a direction that counteracts the disturbance
     and restores equilibrium.

14.7   EQUILIBRIUM CALCULATIONS

Objectives

     To learn how to use the equilibrium constant expression in
     numerical calculations.

Review

     There are basically two kinds of calculations that you have
to learn to do. One is to calculate K from either equilibrium con-

centrations or information from which you can deduce equilibrium concentrations. The other is to calculate information about equilibrium concentrations, having at your disposal the value of K. There are six sample calculations in the text illustrating these types of problems (Examples 13.6 to 13.11). These are worked out in great detail. Two additional sample calculations follow. A very important thing to notice in all of these is that the concentrations (or algebraic quantities representing concentrations) that are substituted into the mass action expression in the equilibrium law are always <u>equilibrium concentrations</u>.

The first example deals with the calculation of K from a set of equilibrium concentrations.

Example 14.2

At a certain temperature, 0.15 mol CO(g) and 0.15 mol $H_2O(g)$ are introduced into a 2.0-L container. At equilibrium the CO(g) concentration was measured to be 0.042 mol/L. What is the value of K_c for the reaction,

$$CO(g) + H_2O(g) \rightleftharpoons H_2(g) + CO_2(g)$$

Solution

First let's write the equilibrium constant expression.

$$K_c = \frac{[H_2][CO_2]}{[CO][H_2O]}$$

We need equilibrium concentrations of each gas. First let's calculate the initial concentrations. <u>Remember, always work with concentrations!</u>

$$[CO] = 0.15 \text{ mol}/2.0 \text{ L} = 0.075 \text{ M}$$
$$[H_2O] = 0.15 \text{ mol}/2.0 \text{ L} = 0.075 \text{ M}$$

How about the products? Their initial concentrations were zero. At equilibrium they are present because some CO and H_2O reacted to produce them. How much reacted?

We are given the equilibrium concentration of CO, 0.042 M. This is less than we started with. The difference between what is present at equilibrium and what we started with is the amount that reacted.

Amount of CO reacted = 0.075 mol/L - 0.042 mol/L
= 0.033 mol/L

How much H_2O reacted with the CO? From the equation we can see that the answer must also be 0.033 mol/L, and the concentration of H_2O remaining at equilibrium must be

$$[H_2O]_{equilibrium} = 0.075\ M - 0.033\ M = 0.042\ M$$

For the reactants at equilibrium,

$$[H_2O] = 0.042\ M$$
$$[CO] = 0.042\ M$$

How about the products? When 0.033 mol/L of CO reacts, it must produce 0.033 mol/L of both H_2 and CO_2. This we can see from the coefficients in the balanced equation. At equilibrium, then,

$$[H_2] = 0.033\ M$$
$$[CO_2] = 0.033\ M$$

The reasoning that we've just gone through is simplifed somewhat by setting up a concentration table similar to that in Example 14.6 in the text. Using the values in this problem,

	Initial Concentration	Change	Equilibrium Concentrations
CO	0.075 M	-0.033 M	0.042 M
H_2O	0.075 M	-0.033 M	0.042 M
H_2	0	+0.033 M	0.033 M
CO_2	0	+0.033 M	0.033 M

Substituting these equilibrium concentrations into the mass action expression, we can calculate K.

$$K_c = \frac{(0.033)(0.033)}{(0.042)(0.042)}$$

$$K_c = 0.62$$

The second example asks you to calculate equilibrium concentrations using the known value of K. This kind of question involves some very simple algebra. Don't panic over it. If you take your time and think it through slowly, you should be able to learn how to approach this kind of problem. Don't try to memorize how to solve specific problems. If you do, it only takes a small change in the problem to trip you up.

Example 14.3

In the last example we found that at a particular temperature $K_c = 0.62$ for the reaction,

$$CO(g) + H_2O(g) \rightleftharpoons H_2(g) + CO_2(g)$$

The equilibrium concentrations were: $[CO] = [H_2O] = 0.042$ M and $[H_2] = [CO_2] = 0.033$ M. Suppose an additional 0.010 mol/L of CO(g) and 0.010 mol/L of H_2O(g) are introduced into the container. What will the new equilibrium concentrations become?

Solution

As soon as the additional CO and H_2O are added, the equilibrium is upset, and we can treat the new concentrations as initial concentrations.

<u>initial concentrations</u>

$$[CO] = 0.042 + 0.010 = 0.052 \text{ M}$$
$$[H_2O] = 0.042 + 0.010 = 0.052 \text{ M}$$
$$[H_2] = 0.033 \text{ M}$$
$$[CO_2] = 0.033 \text{ M}$$

We now take into account that a reaction will take place that brings the system back to equilibrium. Let's let x equal the number of moles/L of CO that will react. The CO concentrations at equilibrium will therefore have been diminished by x. The H_2O concentration will also have been decreased by x mol/L (from the stoichiometry of the balanced equation). Similarly, the H_2 and CO_2 concentrations will each increase by x.

<u>equilibrium concentrations</u>

$$[CO] = 0.052 - x$$
$$[H_2O] = 0.052 - x$$
$$[H_2] = 0.033 + x$$
$$[CO_2] = 0.033 + x$$

The reasoning that we have just gone through is the key to solving the problem. It is made easier with the concentration table.

	Initial Concentrations	Change	Equilibrium Concentrations
CO	0.052 M	-x	(0.052 - x) M
H_2O	0.052 M	-x	(0.052 - x) M
H_2	0.033 M	+x	(0.033 + x) M
CO_2	0.033 M	+x	(0.033 + x) M

Next, we substitute the equilibrium quantities into the mass action expression (see the last example),

$$0.62 = \frac{(0.033 + x)(0.033 + x)}{(0.052 - x)(0.052 - x)} = \frac{(0.033 + x)^2}{(0.052 - x)^2}$$

The simplest way to solve this problem is to take the square root of both sides of the equation; $\sqrt{0.62} = 0.79$

$$0.79 = \frac{0.033 + x}{0.052 - x}$$

Now multiply both sides by (0.052 - x).

$$0.79(0.052 - x) = 0.033 + x$$
$$0.041 - 0.79\,x = 0.033 + x$$
$$0.041 - 0.033 = x + 0.79x$$
$$0.008 = 1.79\,x$$
$$0.004 = x$$

The equilibrium concentrations become

$$[CO] = [H_2O] = 0.052 - 0.004 = 0.048 \text{ M}$$
$$[H_2] = [CO_2] = 0.033 + 0.004 = 0.037 \text{ M}$$

When K for a reaction is very small or very large, the position of equilibrium lies very close to either the reactants or products. Recognizing this fact can sometimes help us simplify the algebra involved in an equilibrium problem, as shown in Example 14.11.

Self-Test

12. At approximately 1700°C the equilibrium concentrations of the reactants and product in the equation,

$$N_2(g) + O_2(g) \rightleftharpoons 2NO(g)$$

are $[N_2] = 1.0 \times 10^{-4}$ M, $[O_2] = 2.5 \times 10^{-5}$ M
   $[NO] = 7.1 \times 10^{-7}$ M
What is K_c for this reaction?   _____

13. In a furnace operating at 1700°C the concentrations of N_2 and O_2 are 4.0×10^{-4} M and 1.0×10^{-5} M, respectively. At this temperature $K_c = 2.0 \times 10^{-4}$ (the answer to the last question!). What concentration of $NO(g)$ will be present in the gases escaping from the furnace? (Assume the N_2 and O_2 concentrations are equilibrium concentrations.)

   _____

14. At a certain temperature $K_c = 0.5$ for the reaction,

$$H_2(g) + I_2(g) \rightleftharpoons 2HI(g)$$

If 0.40 mol of H_2 and 0.40 mol of I_2 are placed into a 1.0-liter container at this temperature, what will be the equilibrium concentration of each gas?

   _____

15. At 25°C, the reaction, $2HCl(g) \rightleftharpoons H_2(g) + Cl_2(g)$ has $K_c = 3.2 \times 10^{-34}$. If 0.400 mol of HCl is placed in a 4.00-liter container at this temperature, what will be the concentrations of H_2 and Cl_2 after equilibrium has been reached?

   _____

New Terms

Answers to Self-Test Questions

1. (a)
$$K_c = \frac{[PCl_3][Cl_2]}{[PCl_5]} \qquad K_p = \frac{p_{PCl_3} \, p_{Cl_2}}{p_{PCl_5}}$$

(b)
$$K_c = \frac{[H_2SO_4][HBr]^2}{[Br_2][SO_2][H_2O]^2} \qquad K_p = \frac{p_{H_2SO_4} \, p_{HBr}^2}{p_{Br_2} \, p_{SO_2} \, p_{H_2O}^2}$$

(c)
$$K_c = \frac{[XeO_3]^2[Xe]^4[O_2][HF]^{24}}{[XeF_4]^6[H_2O]^{12}}$$

$$K_p = \frac{p_{XeO_3}^2 \, p_{Xe}^4 \, p_{O_2} \, p_{HF}^{24}}{p_{XeF_4}^6 \, p_{H_2O}^{12}}$$

(d)
$$K_c = \frac{[NO_2F]^2}{[NO_2]^2[F_2]} \qquad K_p = \frac{p_{NO_2F}^2}{p_{NO_2}^2 \, p_{F_2}}$$

2. K = 217 when values are substituted in the expression,
$$K = \frac{[NO_2]^2}{[N_2O_4]}$$

3. d < b < a < c   4. K = 0.35   5. zero, since log 1.0 = 0
6. +16.1 kcal (+67.5 kJ)   7. Δn_g = -2, K_c = 4.3 x 10^8
8. Δn_g = 0, K_c = K_p = 0.35
9. (a)
$$K_c = \frac{1}{[H_2]^2[O_2]} \qquad \text{(b)} \quad K_c = \frac{1}{[CO_2][H_2O]} \qquad \text{(c)} \quad K_c = \frac{[Br_2]}{[Cl_2]}$$

10. (a) D   (b) I   (c) D   (d) I   (e) I   (f) N   (g) N
11. only (d) will change K
12. K_c = 2.0 x 10^{-4}
13. 8.9 x 10^{-7} M
14. $[H_2]$ = $[I_2]$ = 0.30 M; $[HI]$ = 0.20 M
15. $[H_2]$ = $[Cl_2]$ = 1.8 x 10^{-18} M

15 ACID-BASE EQUILIBRIA IN AQUEOUS SOLUTIONS

This chapter deals quantitatively with the equilibria involving the autoionization of water and the dissociation of weak acids and bases. These are important in any aqueous system, particularly biological ones where many important molecules behave as weak acids or bases. Many of the numerical problems in this chapter and the next require the application of some simple algebra. Don't panic! Follow the procedures shown in the worked-out examples which explain how to approach these problems. The important thing is to try not to rush - don't skip steps in the reasoning. If you proceed slowly, you should be able to master the material in Chapters 15 and 16.

15.1 THE IONIZATION OF WATER AND THE pH CONCEPT

Objectives

To establish the quantitative criteria for equilibrium in the autoionization of water and to devise a system for expressing small concentrations of H_3O^+.

Review

In this section you saw that the equilibrium condition for the ionization of water reduces to

$$K_W = [H^+][OH^-] = 1.0 \times 10^{-14}$$

In any solution in which water is the solvent this condition holds. You are expected to know the value, $K_w = 1.0 \times 10^{-14}$.

In pure water, $[H^+] = [OH^-] = 1.0 \times 10^{-7}$ M. When H^+ or OH^- are present from another source (e.g., an acid or a base in the solution), $[H^+] \neq [OH^-]$. The product of their concentrations, however, must equal K_w.

In general, for any quantity X,

$$pX = -\log X$$

For the hydrogen ion concentration,

$$pH = -\log [H^+]$$

Similarly, for hydroxide ion,

$$pOH = -\log [OH^-]$$

Remember that the sum of pH and pOH equals pK_w.

$$pH + pOH = pK_w = 14.0$$

You should be able to calculate pH given $[H^+]$, and also $[H^+]$ given pH. Review Examples 15.2, 15.3 and 15.4 in the text. Note that common logarithms are used to compute pH, not natural logarithms!

Self-Test

1. Calculate the $[OH^-]$ in the following solutions:

   (a) $[H^+] = 1.0 \times 10^{-8}$ M _____

   (b) $[H^+] = 4.2 \times 10^{-12}$ M _____

   (c) $[H^+] = 8.4 \times 10^{-2}$ M _____

2. Calculate the $[H^+]$ in the following solutions:

   (a) $[OH^-] = 1.0 \times 10^{-4}$ M _____

   (b) $[OH^-] = 2.8 \times 10^{-9}$ M _____

   (c) $[OH^-] = 6.7 \times 10^{-12}$ M _____

3. Calculate the pH and pOH of solutions with the following concentrations:

   (a) $[H^+] = 2.0 \times 10^{-6}$ M _____

(b) $[H^+] = 8.5 \times 10^{-9}$ M   _____

(c) $[OH^-] = 3.4 \times 10^{-6}$ M   _____

4. Calculate the $[H^+]$ in the following solutions:

   (a) pH = 8.50   _____

   (b) pH = 13.34   _____

   (c) pOH = 13.34   _____

5. Calculate the $[OH^-]$ in the following solutions:

   (a) pH = 10.65   _____

   (b) pH = 4.26   _____

   (c) pOH = 9.26   _____

6. Calculate the pH of the following solutions:

   (a) 0.0200 M HNO_3 _____

   (b) 3.4×10^{-4} M KOH   _____

   (c) 6.2×10^{-3} M $Ba(OH)_2$ _____

   (d) 0.635 g NaOH dissolved in 850 mL of solution_____

New Terms

Ion product constant
   An equilibrium constant that is equal to an ion product, for example, $K_w = [H^+][OH^-]$.

Ionization constant (Dissociation constant)
   The equilibrium constant for the ionization of a weak electrolyte.

pH
   A logarithmic measure of acidity (pH = -log $[H^+]$). A solution is acidic if its pH < 7, neutral if pH = 7, and basic if pH > 7 (at 25°C).

pK_w
   -log $[K_w] = 14.00$ (at 25°C)

pOH
   -log $[OH^-]$

15.2   DISSOCIATION OF WEAK ACIDS AND BASES

Objectives

To deal quantitatively with equilibria involving the dissociation of weak acids and bases. You should be able to calculate K, given equilibrium concentrations. You should be able to calculate equilibrium concentrations from K and the concentration of the weak acid or base.

Review

You should learn the general equations for the ionization of weak acids and bases. For a weak acid,

$$HA \rightleftharpoons H^+ + A^-$$

we have

$$K_a = \frac{[H^+][A^-]}{[HA]}$$

For a weak base, B, that reacts with the solvent,

$$B + H_2O \rightleftharpoons HB^+ + OH^-$$

we have

$$K_b = \frac{[HB^+][OH^-]}{[B]}$$

Examples 15.5 and 15.6 in the text show you how to calculate the equilibrium constant if you have information that allows you to compute equilibrium concentrations. Remember the equation for percent dissociation (see the New Terms at the end of this section.)

To calculate equilibrium concentrations from K you must know the amount of weak acid or base placed in the solution. The following example is typical.

Example 15.1

What are the concentrations of H^+, OCl^- and HOCl in a solution labeled 0.10 M HOCl? For HOCl, $K_a = 3.1 \times 10^{-8}$.

Solution

    First, write the equation for the equilibrium.

$$HOCl \rightleftharpoons H^+ + OCl^-$$

The next step for problems of this type is to set up our table of concentrations as shown in the example problems in the text.

	initial concentration	change	equilibrium concentration
H^+	0.0	+x	x
OCl^-	0.0	+x	x
HOCl	0.10	-x	0.10 - x

      This column contains the concentrations of solutes placed into the solution.   This column represents the changes that occur because of reaction.   This column gives the equilibrium concentrations.

The entries in the table are obtained by the following reasoning. If no dissociation occurred, we would have [HOCl] = 0.10 M. HOCl does dissociate, however, and we want to calculate how much. The approach, then, is to let x equal the number of moles per liter of HOCl that have dissociated when equilibrium is reached. The concentrations at equilibrium, then, would be

    [HOCl] = 0.10 - x   (note that the concentration of HOCl is diminished by the quantity that is lost upon dissociation)

No H^+ or OCl^- were placed in the solution; they are there at equilibrium because of the dissociation of the HOCl.

    [OCl$^-$] = x   (note that [OCl$^-$] = [H$^+$] be-
    [H$^+$]   = x   cause they are formed in a 1:1 ratio. The amounts produced per liter are equal to the amount per liter of HOCl that has dissociated)

The equilibrium constant expression is

$$K_a = \frac{[H^+][OCl^-]}{[HOCl]} = 3.1 \times 10^{-8}$$

Substituting our expressions for the equilibrium concentrations from the last column of the table gives

$$\frac{(x)(x)}{(0.10 - x)} = 3.1 \times 10^{-8}$$

Expanding this out will give a quadratic equation. The problem can be simplified however. From the magnitude of K_a we know that very little HOCl will dissociate. What we do is assume that the amount that dissociates is negligible; that is,

$$0.10 - x \approx 0.10$$

This simplification gives

$$\frac{(x)(x)}{(0.10)} = 3.1 \times 10^{-8}$$

$$x^2 = (0.10)(3.1 \times 10^{-8}) = 3.1 \times 10^{-9}$$

$$x^2 = 31 \times 10^{-10}$$

$$x = \sqrt{31} \times 10^{-5}$$

$$x = 5.6 \times 10^{-5}$$

Finally, we have the equilibrium concentrations,

$$[HOCl] = 0.10 - 5.6 \times 10^{-5} = 0.10 \text{ M}$$

$$[H^+] = [OCl^-] = 5.6 \times 10^{-5} \text{ M}$$

Observe that x is indeed negligible compared to 0.10 when the difference is rounded to the proper number of significant figures. This justifies our assumption.

Sometimes you will have to deal with problems involving solutions containing a weak acid or base plus a salt of that acid or base. An example is $HC_2H_3O_2$ and $NaC_2H_3O_2$. In working problems of this type you should remember the following:

(1) Salts are completely dissociated. The concentration of the ion produced by the salt is entered in the "initial concentration" column.

(2) In the problems that you will encounter only one of the ions produced by the salt is important. The other is a spectator ion.

Review Examples 15.8 and 15.9 in the text.

314   Chapter 15

Self-Test

7. A 0.20 M solution of propionic acid, $HC_3H_5O_2$, has a hydro-
    gen ion concentration of 1.7×10^{-3} M. What is the value of
    K_a for propionic acid?

    _____

8. A 1.0 molar solution of the weak base methyl amine,
    CH_3NH_2, has a pH of 12.32. What is the value of K_b?

    _____

9. Aniline, $C_6H_5NH_2$, has an ionization constant, $K_b =$
    3.8×10^{-10}. Aniline reacts with water according to the
    equation, $C_6H_5NH_2 + H_2O \rightleftharpoons C_6H_5NH_3^+ + OH^-$. What are
    the OH^- and H^+ concentrations in a 0.01 M solution of
    $C_6H_5NH_2$?

    _____

10. Calculate the percent dissociation in a 0.25 M solution of
    HCN. $K_a = 4.9 \times 10^{-10}$

    _____

11. What is the value of pK_a for HCN? K_a is given in Question
    10.

    _____

12. What is the pH of a 0.20 M solution of lactic acid, $HC_3H_5O_3$,
    that also contains 0.30 M $NaC_3H_5O_3$? For lactic acid, $K_a =$
    1.38×10^{-4}.

    _____

New Terms

Acid ionization constant (Acid dissociation constant)
    The equilibrium constant for the ionization of a weak acid.

Base ionization constant, K_b
    The equilibrium constant for the ionization of a weak base.

Percent dissociation

$$\% \text{ dissociation} = \left(\frac{\text{amount dissociated}}{\text{total amount available}}\right) \times 100$$

$$= \left(\frac{\text{moles/liter dissociated}}{\text{moles/liter available}}\right) \times 100$$

15.3   DISSOCIATION OF POLYPROTIC ACIDS

Objectives

To consider equilibria for acids that dissociate in two or more steps. You should learn how to calculate the hydrogen ion concentration as well as the concentrations of other ions produced in the equilibria.

Review

For a diprotic acid there are two equilibria and two equilibrium constants. For H_2S, for example,

$$H_2S \rightleftharpoons H^+ + HS^- \qquad\qquad K_{a1} = \frac{[H^+][HS^-]}{[H_2S]}$$

$$HS^- \rightleftharpoons H^+ + S^{2-} \qquad\qquad K_{a2} = \frac{[H^+][S^{2-}]}{[HS^-]}$$

Remember, to calculate the hydrogen ion concentration in a solution of a polyprotic acid you always use K_{a1}. This is because the second and succeeding ionization steps almost always produce much less H^+ than the first (i.e., $K_{a1} \gg K_{a2} \gg K_{a3}\ldots$). You should also use K_{a1} to calculate the concentration of the anion produced in the first step.

For diprotic acids you should use K_{a2} to calculate the concentration of the anion produced in the second dissociation (e.g., S^{2-} in the second ionization of H_2S). If the diprotic acid is the only solute in the solution, the concentration of the anion, A^{2-} (e.g., S^{2-}) is equal to K_{a2}.

In a solution of a diprotic acid, H_2A, a combined expression

$$K_{a1}K_{a2} = \frac{[H^+]^2[A^{2-}]}{[H_2A]}$$

can be used <u>provided that</u> the values of any two of the three concentrations that appear in the expression are known. These are the <u>only</u> conditions under which this combined expression can be applied.

13. Calculate the concentrations of the ions, H^+, HA^- and A^{2-}, in a 0.10 M solution of the weak acid, H_2A. $K_{a1} = 2.0 \times 10^{-4}$, $K_{a2} = 5.0 \times 10^{-9}$

_____

14. In a solution of H_2SO_3 the sulfite concentration is 0.20 M and the pH is 6.50. What is the concentration of H_2SO_3 in the solution?

_____

New Terms

15.4   BUFFERS

Objectives

To learn how the pH of a solution can be controlled by a mixture of a weak acid or base and its salt. You should learn how to calculate the relative amounts of acid (or base) and salt needed to give a desired pH. You should also be able to calculate the effect on pH produced by addition of small amounts of strong acid or base to a buffer.

Review

Remember, a buffer is a mixture of a weak acid and a weak base. This can be obtained by mixing a weak acid with one of its salts, since the anion of the acid is a weak base. A buffer can also be made by mixing a weak base with one of its salts. The H^+ concentration in an acid buffer can be calculated from the equilibrium constant expression.

$$[H^+] = K_a \frac{[HA]}{[A^-]}$$

From this the Henderson-Hasselbalch equation, referred to often in biochemistry texts, can be derived.

$$pH = pK_a + \log \frac{[\text{anion, A}^-]}{[\text{acid, HA}]}$$

Similarly, the OH^- concentration in a basic buffer can be calculated by solving the equilibrium constant expression for $[OH^-]$,

$$[OH^-] = K_b \frac{[B]}{[HB^+]}$$

and

$$pOH = pK_b + \log \frac{[\text{cation, BH}^+]}{[\text{base, B}]}$$

There is really no need to memorize these equations, however, because the results can always be obtained by applying the principles learned in Section 15.2 (Example 15.8, for instance).

Review Example 15.12 (which shows you how to determine the acid-to-salt ratio needed to give a desired pH) and Example 15.13 (which shows you how to calculate the effect of additions of strong acid or base to a buffer).

Remember that when a salt like NH_4Cl or $NaC_2H_3O_2$ is dissolved in water it is completely dissociated. If the concentration of NH_4Cl in a solution is 0.10 M, the concentration of NH_4^+ (from this salt) is also 0.10 M. If the equilibrium involves NH_3 and NH_4^+, the Cl^- doesn't matter. It is there only to keep the solution electrically neutral; almost any anion would do. The Cl^- is a spectator ion.

Self-Test

15. Calculate the pH of the following solutions:

   (a)   0.25 M $HC_2H_3O_2$, 0.15 M $NaC_2H_3O_2$ _____

   (b)   0.25 M NH_3, 0.15 M NH_4Cl _____

16. What ratio of formate ion (CHO_2^-) to formic acid ($HCHO_2$) must be maintained to give a solution with a pH = 3.50 (for $HCHO_2$, $K_a = 1.8 \times 10^{-4}$)?

   _____

17. How much will the pH change if 0.2 mol of HCl is added to 1.0 L of a buffer composed of 1 M $HCHO_2$ and 1 M $NaCHO_2$ (the K_a is given in Question 16 above)?

   _____

New Terms

Buffer
    A mixture that contains both a weak acid and a weak base.
    It is capable of absorbing small additions of either a strong
    acid or strong base with little change in pH.

15.5   HYDROLYSIS OF SALTS

Objectives
    To learn what hydrolysis is, how to write equations for
    hydrolysis equilibria, and how to solve equilibrium prob-
    lems that deal with hydrolysis.

Review
    One of the first things you learn in this section is that
there is an inverse relationship between the strength of a
Brønsted acid and the strength of its conjugate base. Strong
acids have very weak conjugate bases; strong bases have very
weak conjugate acids.

    Solutions of salts contain two ions. The cation of the salt
can potentially serve as an acid; the anion as a base. Whether
a solution of a salt is acidic, basic, or neutral depends on the
strengths of these acids and bases.

    In determining what happens in a solution of a salt, we
have to examine the salt to determine what its "parents" are.
For example, sodium chloride, NaCl has as its "parents" the acid
HCl and the base NaOH. Each of these are strong, so we cate-
gorize NaCl as the salt of a strong acid and a strong base. On
the other hand, sodium nitrite, $NaNO_2$, is the salt of a weak
acid, HNO_2, and a strong base, NaOH.

Salts of strong acids and weak bases. Solutions of these salts
are neutral because the ions are very weak acids and bases.
Examples are NaCl and KNO_3.

Salts of weak acids and strong bases. Solutions of these salts
are basic because the anion of the weak acid is a moderately weak
base. Examples are $NaC_2H_3O_2$ and $NaNO_2$. In general, the

anion of the salt reacts as follows:

$$X^- + H_2O \rightleftharpoons HX + OH^-$$

Since a component of the salt is reacting with water, the phenomenon has come to be known as hydrolysis. As noted in the text, the values of K_a and K_b for the members of an acid-base conjugate pair are related as follows:

$$K_a \cdot K_b = K_w$$

In solving problems involving hydrolysis of salts of weak acids and strong bases, it is generally necessary to calculate K_b from the tabulated (or given) value of K_a. Other than this, such "hydrolysis" problems are really no different than other problems that you have already learned to solve that involve the ionization of weak bases.

Salts of strong acids and weak bases. Solutions of these salts are acidic because the cation of the weak base is a moderately strong acid. Examples are NH_4Cl and N_2H_5Cl. In general, the cation of a weak base, BH^+, reacts as follows:

$$BH^+ \rightleftharpoons H^+ + B$$

Usually you must calculate K_a for the cation from K_b for the weak base.

Salts of weak acids and weak bases. In these solutions there is both a weak acid (the cation of the weak base) and a weak base (the anion of the weak acid). Whether the solution of such a salt is acidic, basic, or neutral depends on the relative strengths of the acidic cation and basic anion, which can be determined by calculating K_a and K_b. If the acid is stronger than the base, the solution is acidic, and vice versa. If they are of equal strengths, the solution is neutral.

Salts of polyprotic acids. In these solutions, it is the anion that hydrolyzes. Although there are several steps in the hydrolysis, remember that only the first step is important. Also remember that the K_b for the anion is calculated using the K_a for the last step in the ionization of the acid. Thus, for the hydrolysis of the PO_4^{3-} ion, K_b is calculated using K_{a_3} for H_3PO_4.

Self-Test

18. Predict whether solutions of the following salts are acidic, basic, or neutral. (If you can't answer this question without looking elsewhere in the text, review the list of strong acids and bases given on Page 236. If you know the list of strong acids and bases, then you can recognize the weak ones, too, because they're not on the list.)

(a) NH_4ClO_3 _____

(b) $KCHO_2$ _____

(c) $KClO_4$ _____

(d) $N_2H_5NO_3$ _____

19. Write chemical equations for the hydrolysis of these ions.

(a) $CH_3NH_3^+$ _____

(b) OCl^- _____

(c) PO_4^{3-} _____

20. Calculate K_a or K_b for the following ions. (Refer to Tables 15.1 and 15.2 for necessary data.)

(a) $(C_2H_5)_2NH_2^+$ _____

(b) $C_3H_5O_2^-$ _____

(c) $C_6H_6O_6^{2-}$ _____

21. Calculate the H^+ concentration in 0.10 M NaF. For HF, $K_a = 6.5 \times 10^{-4}$.

_____

22. Calculate the H^+ concentration in 0.10 M CH_3NH_3Cl. For CH_3NH_2, $K_b = 3.7 \times 10^{-4}$.

_____

23. Will a solution of NH_4NO_2 be acidic or basic? $K_a = 4.5 \times 10^{-4}$ for HNO_2, $K_b = 1.8 \times 10^{-5}$ for NH_3.

_____

24. Calculate the H^+ concentration in a 0.050 M solution of K_2SO_3. For H_2SO_3, $K_{a_1} = 1.5 \times 10^{-2}$, $K_{a_2} = 1.0 \times 10^{-7}$

_____

(Notice that hydrolysis problems always ask about the acidity or basicity of a solution in which a salt is the only solute. Remembering this will help you recognize hydrolysis problems.)

New Terms

Hydrolysis
> The reaction of a substance with water. Hydrolysis of anions produces basic solutions and hydrolysis of cations produces acidic solutions.

15.6 ACID-BASE TITRATIONS: THE EQUIVALENCE POINT

Objectives

> To see how the pH at the equivalence point in an acid-base titration is influenced by hydrolysis. You should be able to calculate the pH at various points during a titration.

Review

> Three situations are discussed in this section:

(1) Titration of a strong acid with a strong base. When base is added to the acid, complete neutralization occurs and the H^+ concentration is decreased in direct proportion to the amount of OH^- added.

(2) Titration of a weak acid with a strong base. At the start of the titration the pH is controlled by the presence of the weak acid. Example 15.1 in the Study Guide illustrated how the H^+ concentration could be obtained for a solution of a weak acid.

> After some base has been added, the amount of weak acid has decreased and some of the anion of the acid is generated. In Section 15.4 you saw that a buffer can be prepared as a mixture of a weak acid and its anion. Therefore, between the start of the titration and the equivalence point the pH is calculated in the same way you would compute the pH of a buffer solution.

At the equivalence point the weak acid has been completely "neutralized"; that is, it has been converted to a salt of the acid. We have just seen in the last section that the anion of a weak acid hydrolyzes. As a result, calculation of the pH at the equivalence point is a hydrolysis problem.

(3) Titration of a weak base with a strong acid. The computations involved here are essentially identical to those for the weak acid-strong base titration.

Self-Test

25. Consider the neutralization of 0.10 M HOCl by the addition of solid NaOH (so that no volume change occurs). Calculate:

    (a) the pH before any NaOH is added   _____

    (b) the pH when half the HOCl has been
        neutralized   _____

    (c) the pH at the equivalence point   _____

        (For HOCl, $K_a = 3.1 \times 10^{-8}$ M)

New Terms

15.7   ACID-BASE INDICATORS

Objectives

To learn how an acid-base indicator functions.

Review

An acid-base indicator is itself a weak acid (or base). The molecular form of the indicator, HIn, has one color and the ionic form, In^-, has a different color. The color that is observed in a solution of the indicator is controlled by the ratio of [HIn] to [In^-], which is determined in turn by the H^+ concentration in the solution.

Self-Test

26. The indicator, methyl orange, has $pK_a = 3.5$. In acid, the indicator is red; in base, it is yellow-orange. What color will a solution of methyl orange be if the $[H^+] = 2.1 \times 10^{-3}$ M

New Terms

Indicator

A substance that changes color to signal the completion of a reaction during a titration. For acid-base reactions, an indicator is a weak acid or base whose molecular form differs in color from its ionic form.

Answers to Self-Test Questions

1.(a) 1.0×10^{-6} M (b) 2.4×10^{-3} M (c) 1.2×10^{-13}M

2.(a) 1.0×10^{-10} M (b) 3.6×10^{-6} M (c) 1.5×10^{-3} M

3.(a) pH = 5.70, pOH = 8.30 (b) pH = 8.07, pOH = 5.93 (c) pOH = 5.47, pH = 8.53 4.(a) 3.2×10^{-9} M (b) 4.6×10^{-14} M (c) 0.22 M 5.(a) 4.5×10^{-4} M (b) 1.8×10^{-10} M (c) 5.5×10^{-10} M 6.(a) 1.70 (b) 10.53 (c) 12.09 (In this soln, $[OH^-] = 1.24 \times 10^{-2}$ M) (d) 12.27 7. 1.4×10^{-5}

8. 4.4×10^{-4} (Did you remember to obtain $[OH^-]$ from pOH?)

9. $[OH^-] = 1.9 \times 10^{-6}$ M, $[H^+] = 5.3 \times 10^{-9}$ M 10. 4.4×10^{-3} %

11. $pK_a = 9.31$ 12. pH = 4.04 13. $[H^+] = [HA^-] = 4.5 \times 10^{-3}$ M, $[A^{2-}] = K_{a_2} = 5.0 \times 10^{-9}$ M 14. 1.3×10^{-5} M 15.(a) 4.52 (b) 9.48 16. $[CHO_2^-]/[HCHO_2] = 0.57$ 17. pH decreases by 0.17 18.(a) acidic (b) basic (c) neutral (d) acidic

19.(a) $CH_3NH_3^+ + H_2O \rightleftharpoons H_3O^+ + CH_3NH_2$

   (b) $OCl^- + H_2O \rightleftharpoons HOCl + OH^-$

   (c) $PO_4^{3-} + H_2O \rightleftharpoons HPO_4^{2-} + OH^-$

20.(a) $K_a = 1.0 \times 10^{-11}$ (b) $K_b = 7.1 \times 10^{-10}$ (c) $K_{b_1} = 1.3 \times 10^{-10}$

21. $[OH^-] = 1.2 \times 10^{-6}$ M, $[H^+] = 8.1 \times 10^{-9}$ M

22. $[H^+] = 1.6 \times 10^{-6}$ M

23. K_b for $NO_2^- = 2.2 \times 10^{-11}$, K_a for $NH_4^+ = 5.6 \times 10^{-10}$; the solution will be acidic.

24. $[OH^-] = 7.1 \times 10^{-5}$ M, $[H^+] = 1.4 \times 10^{-10}$ M

25.(a) 4.25 (b) pH = pK_a = 7.51 (c) 10.25

26. red, since [HIn] > [In$^-$]

16 SOLUBILITY AND COMPLEX ION EQUILIBRIA

This brief chapter concludes the discussion on the quantitative aspects of ionic equilibria by considering equilibria involving salts of low solubility. We will also examine equilibria of complex ions and the way that solubility is affected by complex ion formation.

16.1 SOLUBILITY PRODUCT

Objectives

To deal quantitatively with the solubility equilibria involving "insoluble" salts. You should learn how to write the equilibrium constant expression for the solubility equilibrium. You should be able to calculate K_{sp} from solubility, and solubility from K_{sp}. You should learn how to use the K_{sp} expression to predict whether or not a precipitate will form in a given solution.

Review

Remember that salts are completely dissociated when dissolved in water. The K_{sp} expression involves only the product of ion concentrations raised to exponents that are the coefficients in the chemical equation for the equilibrium.

Problems dealing with K_{sp} can be divided into three classes:

(1) Calculation of K_{sp} from solubility - This is shown in Examples 16.1 and 16.2 in the text. Calculate the ion concentrations from the molar solubility and the balanced equilibrium equation. For example, the molar solubility of Ag_2CrO_4 is 7.8×10^{-5} M. The equilibrium is

$$Ag_2CrO_4 \rightleftharpoons 2Ag^+ + CrO_4^{2-}$$

From the stoichiometry of the equation we would conclude that if 7.8×10^{-5} mol/L of Ag_2CrO_4 dissolves, then $[Ag^+] = 2(7.8 \times 10^{-5}$ M$) = 1.6 \times 10^{-4}$ M and $[CrO_4^{2-}] = 7.8 \times 10^{-5}$ M.

(2) Calculation of solubility from K_{sp} - This is illustrated in Examples 16.3 and 16.4. The important thing to remember with this kind of problem is to work through it methodically. Don't try to skip any of the reasoning steps. If you do, you are likely to make mistakes. Review the reasoning in these examples to be sure you understand it. Note that in constructing the concentration table for the problem the coefficient preceding the x's in the table are the same as the coefficients in the balanced equation for the equilibrium.

(3) Determining whether precipitation will occur - Determine the concentrations of the ions in the solution in question. Then remember the following:

$$\left. \begin{array}{l} \text{ion product} < K_{sp} \\ \text{ion product} = K_{sp} \end{array} \right\} \quad \text{no precipitate will form}$$

$$\text{ion product} > K_{sp} \qquad \text{precipitate will form}$$

Keep in mind that if the final solution is formed by mixing two solutions, you must consider dilution. Each solute is diluted when the other solution is added. Review Examples 16.5 and 16.6 in the text.

In Example 16.7 note that we can control the concentration of the precipitating ion (S^{2-} in this example), which comes from a weak acid, by properly adjusting the pH of the solution. This example is interesting because it demonstrates how ions can be separated by selective precipitation where the concentration of the precipitating agent (S^{2-} in this case) is controlled by the pH of the solution.

Self-Test

1. The molar solubility of CuCl is 5.7×10^{-4} M. What is the value of K_{sp} for CuCl?

    _____

2. The molar solubility of $PbBr_2$ is 1.05×10^{-1} M. What is the value of K_{sp}?

    _____

3. $K_{sp} = 7.0 \times 10^{-10}$ for $SrCO_3$. What is the molar solubility of $SrCO_3$?

    _____

4. $K_{sp} = 1.0 \times 10^{-22}$ for $Mn_3(PO_4)_2$. What is the Mn^{2+} concentration in a saturated solution of $Mn_3(PO_4)^2$?

    _____

5. A solution is prepared by mixing 100 mL of 0.10 M LiCl solution with 200 mL of 0.30 M NaF solution. LiF has $K_{sp} = 5 \times 10^{-3}$. Will a precipitate form in this solution?

    _____

6. A solution of 0.010 M Ca^{2+} also contains 0.10 M HF. The solution has had its acidity adjusted to a pH = 2.00 by addition of HCl. Given that for CaF_2, $K_{sp} = 1.7 \times 10^{-10}$ and for HF, $K_a = 6.5 \times 10^{-4}$, will a precipitate of CaF_2 form in this solution?

    _____

7. A solution contains 0.10 M Ca^{2+} and 0.10 M Ba^{2+}. HF is to be added until its concentration is 0.40 M to selectively precipitate CaF_2. What range of H^+ concentrations in the solution will permit CaF_2 to begin to precipitate without precipitating any BaF_2? For CaF_2, $K_{sp} = 1.7 \times 10^{-10}$; for BaF_2, $K_{sp} = 1.7 \times 10^{-6}$; for HF, $K_a = 6.5 \times 10^{-4}$.

    _____

New Terms

Ion product
    The product of ion concentrations. For a salt, the product of the concentrations of the ions, each raised to a power that is equal to the number of ions of that kind produced by one formula unit of the salt. (For example, the ion product for Ag_2S is $[Ag^+]^2[S^{2-}]$.)

Molar solubility
> The number of moles of solute dissolved in one liter of its saturated solution.

Solubility product constant, K_{sp}
> The equilibrium constant for the solubility of a salt. For a saturated solution, K_{sp} is equal to the product of the molar concentrations of the ions each raised to appropriate powers.

16.2   THE COMMON ION EFFECT AND SOLUBILITY

Objectives

> To see how the solubility of a substance is decreased by the presence of salts that provide a "common ion."

Review

The addition of a common ion to a solution containing a salt in equilibrium with its ions decreases the solubility of the salt. Review Examples 16.8, 16.9 and 16.10 in the text. Once again, approach this kind of problem in a deliberate, stepwise fashion; don't try to rush or skip steps in the reasoning.

Example 16.9 is typical of the kind of question that so often makes students ask, "When am I supposed to double something and when don't I double something?" Examine the concentration table constructed for this problem. Notice that in the column labeled "Initial concentration" the concentrations of the OH^- from the NaOH, which is already dissolved in the solution, is entered without reference to the equation for the equilibrium. If a solution contains 0.10 M NaOH, the OH^- concentration <u>from this source</u> is 0.10 M, not double that value. Now look at the column headed "Change." This is the column that contains x; the x's have coefficients corresponding to the coefficients of the ions in the balanced equation for the equilibrium. Remember, the only thing ever doubled (or tripled, etc.) are entries in the "Change" column.

Self-Test

8. $K_{sp} = 2 \times 10^{-8}$ for $PbSO_4$. What is the molar solubility of $PbSO_4$ in 0.010 M Na_2SO_4?

    _____

9. $K_{sp} = 2 \times 10^{-15}$ for $Fe(OH)_2$. What is the molar solubility of $Fe(OH)_2$ in a solution having a pH of 10.0?

    _____

10. $K_{sp} = 4.5 \times 10^{-17}$ for $Zn(OH)_2$. What is the molar solubility of $Zn(OH)_2$ in 1.0×10^{-3} M $Ba(OH)_2$?

    _____

11. What is the molar solubility of $Zn(OH)_2$ in 1.0×10^{-3} M $Zn(NO_3)_2$?

    _____

New Terms

Common ion
>   An ion that is common to more than one salt in a solution. Na^+ is the common ion between NaCl and $NaNO_3$.

Common ion effect
>   The solubility of a salt is less in a solution that already contains one of its ions than it is in pure water.

16.3   COMPLEX IONS AND THEIR EQUILIBRIA

Objectives

>   To learn what complex ions are and to examine their equilibria. You should learn how to write expressions for the formation constant and the instability constant for a complex ion.

Review

    The ions or molecules that attach themselves to the central atom in a complex ion are called ligands. The formation constant (or stability constant) is the K for the reaction in which the complex ion appears as a product (i.e., a formation reaction). For example,

$$Cu^{2+} + 4Cl^- \rightleftharpoons CuCl_4^{2-}$$

$$K_{form} = \frac{[CuCl_4^{2-}]}{[Cu^{2+}][Cl^-]^4}$$

The instability constant is the reciprocal of K_{form}.

Self-Test

12. Write expressions for K_{form} and K_{inst} for the complex ion $Zn(OH)_4^{2-}$.

New Terms

Complex ion (or simply a complex)
> A substance formed when one or more anions or neutral molecules become bonded to a metal ion.

Ligand
> A molecule or anion that can bind to a metal ion to form a complex.

Formation constant (also called Stability constant)
> The equilibrium constant for the formation of a complex ion.

Instability constant
> The equilibrium constant for the decomposition of a complex into its components.

16.4   COMPLEX IONS AND SOLUBILITY

Objectives

> To see how the formation of complex ions can affect solubility.

Review

> The formation of complex ions affects the solubility of some salts through a system of simultaneous equilibria, where shifting the position of one equilibrium affects the concentration of a species that is also involved in another equilibrium. This

then shifts the position of the second equilibrium. The overall equilibrium constant for the reaction, K_c, is the product of the K_{sp} for the insoluble salt and K_{form} of the complex ion.

$$K_c = K_{sp} \cdot K_{form}$$

Review the sample calculations in Examples 16.11 and 16.12.

Self-Test

13. How many moles of $Cu(OH)_2$ will dissolve in 1.0 liter of 1.0 M NH_3? $K_{sp} = 1.6 \times 10^{-19}$ for $Cu(OH)_2$; $K_{inst} = 2.1 \times 10^{-13}$ for $Cu(NH_3)_4{}^{2+}$. Ignore the ionization of NH_3 as a weak base.

New Terms

Answers to Self-Test Questions

1. 3.2×10^{-7} 2. 4.63×10^{-3} 3. 2.6×10^{-5} 4. 1.6×10^{-5} M

5. yes; $[Li^+][F^-] = (3.3 \times 10^{-2}$ M$)(2.0 \times 10^{-1}$ M$) = 6.6 \times 10^{-3} >$ K_{sp} 6. yes; $[F^-] = 6.5 \times 10^{-3}$, ion product $= 4.2 \times 10^{-7} > K_{sp}$

7. $[H^+]$ must be less than 6.3 M and greater than or equal to 0.063 M.

8. 2×10^{-6} M

9. 2×10^{-7} M

10. 1.1×10^{-11} M

11. 1.0×10^{-7} M

12.

$$K_{form} = \frac{[Zn(OH)_4{}^{2-}]}{[Zn^{2+}][OH^-]^4} \qquad K_{inst} = \frac{[Zn^{2+}][OH^-]^4}{[Zn(OH)_4{}^{2-}]}$$

13. 5.7×10^{-3} mol

17 ELECTROCHEMISTRY

This chapter examines the way redox reactions can be caused to occur by the action of electricity, and the way electricity can be obtained from redox reactions that occur spontaneously. The study of electrochemical properties has a wide-range of applications, from the construction of new and improved batteries and fuel cells to the study of the electrolyte balance in living cells.

Several new terms are introduced in the introduction to this chapter. They are: electrolytic cell, galvanic cell, voltaic cell, electrolysis. They will be discussed in detail later in the chapter.

17.1 METALLIC AND ELECTROLYTIC CONDUCTION

Objectives

To compare the way electrical charge is transported in metals and in solutions of electrolytes.

Review

In metals, conduction occurs by the movement of electrons; in solutions of electrolytes conduction takes place by the movement of ions. Remember that in every microscopic portion of the solution electrical neutrality is maintained, as illustrated in Figure 17.2.

New Terms

Electrochemistry
   The study of electrochemical changes.

Electrochemical change
   A chemical change that is caused by or that produces electricity.

Electrode
   An electrically conducting substance that carries an electrical charge, either given to it by an external voltage source or acquired as a result of a chemical reaction such as one that occurs in a battery.

Electrolytic cell
   An electrolysis apparatus.

Electrolytic conduction
   The transport of charge through a solution by the movement of ions.

Metallic conduction
   The transport of electrical charge through a metal by the movement of electrons.

17.2   ELECTROLYSIS

Objectives

   To examine the processes that take place at the cathode and anode in an electrolytic cell. You should learn from the examples given how the net reaction in the electrolysis of aqueous solutions is controlled by which redox reactions occur most easily.

Review

   In any electrochemical cell, we define the electrodes as:

      cathode - electrode where reduction occurs
      anode   - electrode where oxidation occurs

The net reaction in a cell is the sum of cathode (reduction) and anode (oxidation) half-reactions. The sum is taken so that an equal number of electrons are gained and lost. This is the same procedure you learned in the ion-electron method of balancing equations.

During the electrolysis of aqueous solutions there are usually competing reactions. The half-reactions that occur are those that take place most easily. Review the discussions on the electrolysis of aqueous NaBr, $CuSO_4$, $CuBr_2$, and Na_2SO_4.

Self-Test

1. What is the role of Na_2SO_4 in the electrolysis of aqueous Na_2SO_4 solutions?

    _____

2. Write the anode and cathode reactions for the electrolysis of H_2O.

    _____   _____

3. In the electrolysis of aqueous NaI, I_2 is produced at the anode rather than O_2. What does this imply about the relative ease of oxidation of H_2O and I^-?

    _____

New Terms

Electrolysis
   A chemical change caused by the passage of electricity through a molten ionic compound or through a solution that contains ions.

Electrolysis cell
   An apparatus for carrying out electrolysis.

Cell reaction
   The overall chemical change that takes place in a galvanic or electrolytic cell.

17.3   PRACTICAL APPLICATIONS OF ELECTROLYSIS

Objectives
   To see how electrolysis is applied in industrial processes

that affect the way we live.

Review

You should become familiar with the processes involved in the commercial electrolysis of sodium chloride (both molten and aqueous), the preparation of aluminum and magnesium, and the purification (refining) of copper.

Self-Test

4. What is the function of the cryolite in the Hall process?

   _____

5. Write chemical equations for the separation of magnesium from sea water.

   _____

   _____

   _____

6. What reaction occurs at the cathode in the electrolytic refining of copper?

   _____

7. Write equations for the electrode reactions in the electrolysis of aqueous NaCl using the mercury cell.

   anode: _____

   cathode: _____

8. Why is the mercury cell used in the electrolysis of aqueous NaCl?

   _____

   _____

9. If an object were to be electroplated with tin from a solution of $SnCl_2$, would the object be made the anode or the cathode? Why?

   _____

   _____

New Terms

Brine
   A concentrated aqueous solution of sodium chloride.

Diaphragm cell

An electrolysis cell for the electrolysis of brine in which the Cl_2 produced at the anode is kept from contacting the dilute NaOH solution formed at the cathode. So named because the electrolyte seeps slowly through a porous diaphragm before contacting the cathode.

Cryolite

Na_3AlF_6, the solvent used in the original Hall process for the production of aluminum by electrolysis.

Electroplating

The deposition of a thin layer of a metal on an object by electrolysis.

Hall process

The method for producing aluminum by electrolysis of Al_2O_3 dissolved in a cryolite, Na_3AlF_6.

17.4   QUANTITATIVE ASPECTS OF ELECTROLYSIS

Objectives

To examine, for electrolysis, the quantitative relationships between the amount of electricity consumed and the amount of chemical change produced. You should be able to perform calculations of the type illustrated in this section.

Review

The important relationships used in this section are:

$$1 \text{ faraday } (\mathcal{F}) = 1 \text{ mol of electrons}$$
$$1\mathcal{F} = 96,500 \text{ coulombs (C)}$$
$$1 \text{ coulomb} = 1 \text{ ampere x } 1 \text{ second}$$
or
$$1 \text{ C} = 1 \text{ A} \cdot \text{s}$$

Review Examples 17.1 and 17.2, which illustrate how these relationships are used. Remember that you must have a balanced half-reaction or know the number of electrons transferred in order to solve these problems.

A coulometer is a device in which the amount of chemical change produced in one cell is used to determine the number of faradays that have passed through another cell connected to it in series. Review Example 17.3.

Self-Test

10. How many (a) coulombs and (b) faradays are supplied by a current of 10.0 A for 8.00 hours?

(a) _____   (b) _____

11. How many grams of Cr will be produced by reduction of Cr^{3+} with a current of 1.50 A for 30.0 minutes?

_____

12. How many hours must a current of 14.0 A flow to reduce 1.00 mol of Al^{3+} to metallic aluminum in the Hall process?

_____

13. How many grams of Al are deposited on an electrode when 14.0 g of Ag are also produced when the two cells are connected in series?

_____

14. What current would be necessary to oxidize 1.00 g of water in 2.00 hours?

_____

New Terms

Coulomb
 The SI unit of electrical charge. It is the amount of charge that passes a given point in a wire when a current of 1 ampere flows for 1 second.

Coulometer
 An electrolysis cell in which the amount of chemical change that takes place is used to compute the number of coulombs that have passed through the cell.

Faraday
 One mole of electrons. 96,500 coulombs.

17.5   GALVANIC CELLS

Objectives

To see how electricity can be produced by a spontaneous redox reaction if the oxidation and reduction half-reactions can be physically separated.

Review

Remember that the redox reactions in a galvanic cell are separated into half-cells so that the electron transfer occurs through an external circuit. The cell compartments must be connected by a salt bridge or porous partition so that electrical neutrality can be maintained.

In a galvanic cell the anode (where oxidation occurs) is negative; the cathode is positive.

New Terms

Galvanic cell
> An electrochemical cell in which a spontaneous redox reaction produces electricity.

Half-cell
> One of the two electrode/electrolyte components of a galvanic cell.

Salt-bridge
> A tube containing an electrolyte that connects the two half-cells of a galvanic cell.

Voltaic cell
> Another term used to describe a galvanic cell.

17.6   CELL POTENTIALS

Objectives

To define a quantity that is a measure of the driving force of the redox reaction in a galvanic cell.

Review

The force with which a galvanic cell tends to push electrons through an external circuit is called its emf (electromotive force) and is measured in volts (V). It is also called the cell potential. Standard cell potentials, $\mathscr{E}°$, are used when all species are at a concentration of 1 M and the temperature is 25°C. Cell potentials should be measured with a potentiometer or other similar device that does not draw current from the cell while the measurement is being made.

Remember that the volt is a measure of the energy that is delivered by a flowing current.

$$1 \text{ volt} = 1 \text{ joule/coulomb}$$
$$1 \text{ V} = 1 \text{ J/C}$$

Self-Test

15. What three factors influence the cell potential for a redox reaction?

16. What is observed if one attempts to measure a cell potential with an ordinary voltmeter instead of a potentiometer?

17. How much work is done by the flow of 1.20 A for 5.00 min under a potential of 110 V?

New Terms

Cell potential, $\mathscr{E}_{cell}$
  The emf that can be produced by a galvanic cell when no current is drawn from the cell.

Electromotive force (emf)
  The voltage produced by a galvanic cell.

Potentiometer
  A device that permits the measurement of the emf of a galvanic cell without drawing current from the cell.

Standard cell potential, $\mathscr{E}°_{cell}$
  The potential of a galvanic cell at 25°C and 1 atm when all

ionic concentrations are 1 M and the partial pressures of all gases involved in the cell reaction are 1 atm.

Volt (V)

The SI unit of electrical potential or emf. $1 \text{ V} = 1 \text{ J C}^{-1}$.

17.7   REDUCTION POTENTIALS

Objectives

To treat the observed cell potential as the difference between the potentials of competing reduction reactions. Also, to devise a system for tabulating standard reduction potentials for a series of half-reactions. You should learn how to use standard reduction potentials to calculate the cell potential for an overall reaction. You should also learn how to predict the spontaneity of a reaction.

Review

In this section the idea is developed that the measured cell potential can be viewed as the difference between two reduction potentials. The reduction potential is a measure of the tendency of a reduction half-reaction to occur. When the reaction occurs at 25°C with all species at unit concentration, the term standard reduction potential is used.

The standard hydrogen electrode is assigned a reduction potential of exactly 0.000 volts. Other reduction potentials are compared to that of the hydrogen electrode. A positive $\mathscr{E}°$ means a half-reaction has a greater tendency to occur than the reaction,

$$2H^+ + 2e^- \rightleftharpoons H_2(g)$$

For a given overall reaction that can be divided into half-reactions, the standard cell potential is obtained as,

$$\mathscr{E}°_{cell} = (\mathscr{E}°_{substance\ reduced}) - (\mathscr{E}°_{substance\ oxidized})$$

Review the list of uses to which the table of reduction potentials (Table 17.1) can be put. Remember that a spontaneous reaction occurs only if the calculated $\mathscr{E}°_{cell}$ is positive. Learn the diagonal relationship described under 3 on Page 631.

Self-Test

18. Calculate the value of $\mathscr{E}^{\circ}_{cell}$ for the following reactions.

   (a) $Sn^{2+} + H_2 + 2OH^- \longrightarrow 2H_2O + Sn$ _____

   . (b) $4Fe + 3O_2 + 12H^+ \longrightarrow 6H_2O + 4Fe^{3+}$ _____

   (c) $2Al + 3Zn^{2+} \longrightarrow 2Al^{3+} + 3Zn$ _____

19. Determine whether the following are spontaneous reactions.

   (a) $Sn^{2+} + 2SO_4^{2-} \longrightarrow Sn + S_2O_8^{2-}$ _____

   (b) $Pb + PbO_2 + 4H^+ + 2SO_4^{2-} \longrightarrow 2PbSO_4 + 2H_2O$

   _____

   (c) $Mn^{2+} + 2Cl^- \longrightarrow Cl_2 + Mn$ _____

20. What is the cell potential and the spontaneous reaction that occurs between the following two half-reactions?

   $2NO + 2H^+ + 2e^- \rightleftharpoons H_2N_2O_2$ $\mathscr{E}^{\circ} = +0.71$ V

   $Rh^{3+} + 3e^- \rightleftharpoons Rh$ $\mathscr{E}^{\circ} = +0.80$ V

___

New Terms

Hydrogen electrode (standard hydrogen electrode)
   The standard of comparison for reduction potentials.

   $2H^+(aq) + 2e^- \rightleftharpoons H_2(g)$ $\mathscr{E}^{\circ}_{H^+} = 0.0$ V

   at 25°C, 1 atm, and 1 M H+.

Reduction potential
   A measure of the tendency of a given reduction half-reaction to occur, measured in units of volts.

Standard reduction potential
   The reduction potential of a half-reaction at 25°C when all ion concentrations are 1 M and all partial pressures of gases involved in the half-reaction are 1 atm.

17.8   SPONTANEITY OF OXIDATION-REDUCTION REACTIONS

Objectives

To relate the standard potential for a cell to $\Delta G°$ for the cell reaction.

Review

Remember the equations,

$$\Delta G = -n\mathscr{F}\mathscr{E}$$

and

$$\Delta G° = -n\mathscr{F}\mathscr{E}°$$

where n is the number of moles of electrons transferred and $\mathscr{F}$ is the faraday constant.

Self-Test

21. The standard cell potential for the reaction,

$$Mg + Ni^{2+} \longrightarrow Ni + Mg^{2+}$$

is 2.13 V.   Calculate $\Delta G°$ for the reaction. _____

22. What is $\Delta G°$ for the reaction in Self-Test Question 20?

_____

23. What would be the cell potential for a reaction that had reached a state of chemical equilibrium? Explain your answer? _____

New Terms

17.9   THERMODYNAMIC EQUILIBRIUM CONSTANTS FROM STANDARD CELL POTENTIALS

Objectives

To relate the standard cell potential to the thermodynamic equilibrium constant.

Review

Learn the equation,

$$\mathscr{E}^\circ = \frac{0.0592}{n} \log K_c$$

This equation can be used to evaluate K_c from measured standard cell potentials. Notice that it employs common logs (logarithms to the base 10), not natural logs. Review Example 17.5 in the text.

Self-Test

24. Using the data in Table 17.1, evaluate the thermodynamic equilibrium constant for the reaction,
$2Fe^{2+} + Br_2 \rightleftharpoons 2Fe^{3+} + 2Br^-$ _____

25. What is the equilibrium constant for the reaction in Self-Test Question 20?   _____

New Terms

17.10   THE EFFECTS OF CONCENTRATION ON CELL POTENTIALS: THE NERNST EQUATION

Objectives

To obtain a relationship between the cell potential and the concentrations of the species involved in the cell reaction.

Review

Learn the Nernst equation,

$$\mathscr{E} = \mathscr{E}^\circ - \frac{0.0592}{n} \log Q$$

where Q represents the mass action expression for the cell reaction (omitting the concentrations of any pure solids), and n is the total number of electrons transferred. Thus, the Nernst equation for the reaction

$$4Zn(s) + NO_3^-(aq) + 10\,H^+(aq) \longrightarrow NH_4^+(aq) + 4Zn^{2+}(aq) + 3H_2O$$

in which 8 electrons are transferred is

$$\mathscr{E} = \mathscr{E}^\circ - \frac{0.0592}{8} \log \frac{[NH_4^+][Zn^{2+}]^4}{[NO_3^-][H^+]^{10}}$$

Notice that common logs are used, not natural logs.

Self-Test

26. Calculate the potential generated by the cell reaction,

$$2Al + 3Fe^{2+}(0.0010\ M) \longrightarrow 2Al^{3+}(0.10\ M) + 3Fe \ \underline{\hspace{2cm}}$$

27. A cell is constructed in which one electrode consists of a Zn electrode dipping into 1.0 M $ZnSO_4$. The other electrode consists of a silver electrode in a solution containing Ag^+ of unknown concentration. The cell potential is observed to be 1.40 V with the Zn serving as the anode.

(a) What is the cell reaction? $\underline{\hspace{4cm}}$

(b) What is the Ag^+ concentration? $\underline{\hspace{3cm}}$

New Terms

Nernst equation
    See the definition above.

17.11   APPLICATIONS OF THE NERNST EQUATION

Objectives

To learn how the Nernst equation can be applied to electrochemical measurements of different kinds.

Review

For a concentration cell, which consists of two half-cells constructed of the same substances but with different concentrations of the electrolyte,

$$\mathscr{E}_{cell} = -\frac{0.0592}{n} \log \frac{[M^{n+}]_{dil}}{[M^{n+}]_{conc}}$$

Being able to use a measured cell potential to compute the concentration of an ion has a number of applications, including the computation of K_{sp} and the monitoring of the pH of a solution.

Self-Test

28. Calculate the potential of the concentration cell consisting of one iron electrode immersed in a 0.0010 M Fe^{3+} solution and another iron electrode immersed in a 0.10 M Fe^{3+} solution.

_____

29. Gaseous HCl was added to a solution of $AgNO_3$, causing AgCl to precipitate, until the Cl^- concentration in the solution was 0.10 M. A silver electrode was immersed in the solution and this half-cell was then connected to a zinc half-cell containing 1.00 M Zn^{2+}. The measured cell potential was 1.04 V with Zn serving as the anode.

    (a) What is the cell reaction? _____

    (b) What is the Ag^+ concentration in the solution containing the Ag electrode?

    _____

    (c) Compute K_{sp} for AgCl from these data.

    _____

New Terms

Concentration cell
>An electrochemical cell in which both electrodes are composed of the same substance, but the ion concentrations in the two half-cells are different.

Glass electrode
>A special electrode that is sensitive to the concentration of hydrogen ion in the solution that surrounds the electrode. It consists of a silver wire coated with AgCl immersed in an HCl solution, which is separated by a thin glass membrane from the bulk of the solution being tested.

17.12   PRACTICAL APPLICATIONS OF GALVANIC CELLS

Objectives

>To examine the chemistry of common (and not so common) practical galvanic cells that are used as sources of electricity.

Review

>Learn the chemical reactions that occur at the cathode and anode in the zinc-carbon dry cell, the alkaline battery, the silver oxide battery, the lead storage battery, and the nickel-cadmium cell. Review the principle of operation of the fuel cell as well as its potential advantages over conventional power sources.

Self-Test

30. After having reviewed this last section, write the chemical equations for the cathode and anode reactions in (a) the zinc-carbon dry cell, (b) the alkaline battery, (c) the silver oxide battery, (d) the lead storage battery, and (e) nickel-cadmium cell.

    (a) _____

    _____

    (b) _____

    _____

(c) _____

_____

(d) _____

_____

(e) _____

_____

New Terms

Zinc carbon dry cell

The ordinary dry cell in which zinc serves as the anode and MnO_2 serves as the cathode reactant.

Alkaline battery

A dry cell in which zinc serves as the anode and MnO_2 serves as the cathode in an alkaline KOH electrolyte.

Silver oxide battery

A battery in which zinc serves as the anode and Ag_2O serves as the cathode in an alkaline electrolyte.

Lead storage battery

The common automobile battery in which during discharge Pb serves as the anode and PbO_2 serves as the cathode in an H_2SO_4 electrolyte.

Nickel-cadmium cell

The nicad battery, in which during discharge Cd serves as the anode and NiO_2 serves as the cathode in an alkaline electrolyte. The nicad battery is rechargeable.

Fuel cell

A galvanic cell in which the anode and cathode reactants can be fed continuously, so power can be drawn from the cell continuously.

Answers to Self-Test Questions

1. It maintains electrical neutrality.
2. anode: $2H_2O \longrightarrow O_2 + 4H^+ + 4e^-$
   cathode: $2H_2O + 2e^- \longrightarrow H_2 + 2OH^-$ 3. H_2O is more difficult to oxidize than I^-.   4. It lowers the melting point of Al_2O_3.
5. $Mg^{2+} + 2OH^- \longrightarrow Mg(OH)_2(s)$
   $Mg(OH)_2 + 2HCl \longrightarrow MgCl_2 + 2H_2O$
   $MgCl_2(\ell) \longrightarrow Mg(\ell) + Cl_2(g)$
6. $Cu^{2+}(aq) + 2e^- \longrightarrow Cu(s)$
7. anode: $Na^+(aq) + e^- \longrightarrow Na$ (in Hg)
   cathode: $2Cl^-(aq) \longrightarrow Cl_2(g) + 2e^-$
8. The NaOH produced by the net overall process is not contaminated with NaCl.   9. Cathode, because Sn would have to be reduced from Sn^{2+} to Sn .   10.(a) 2.88×10^5 C   (b) $2.98 \mathscr{F}$
11. 0.485 g   12. 5.74 hr   13. 1.17 g Al   14. 1.49 A   15. nature of the species involved, their concentration, temperature
16. The voltage is lower when measured with a voltmeter that draws current.   17. 1.20 A x 5.00 min x 60 s/min = 360 C; 360 C x 110 J/C = 39.6 kJ   18.(a) 0.69 V   (b) 1.27 V
(c) 0.91 V   19.(a) not spontaneous   (b) spontaneous   (c) not spontaneous   20. $\mathscr{E}° = 0.09$ V;
$2Rh^{3+} + 3H_2N_2O_2 \longrightarrow 6NO + 6H^+ + 2Rh$ 21. -411 kJ (-98.2 kcal)
22. -52.1 kJ (-12.5 kcal)   23. $\mathscr{E} = 0$. At equilibrium $\Delta G = 0$. Since $\Delta G = -n\mathscr{F}\mathscr{E}$, $\mathscr{E}$ must also be zero.   24. 6.5×10^{10}
25. 1.3×10^9 26. 1.16 V
27.(a) $Zn + 2Ag^+ \longrightarrow Zn^{2+} + 2Ag$
   (b) $[Ag^+] = 2 \times 10^{-3}$ M
28. 0.039 V
29.(a) $Zn + 2Ag^+ \longrightarrow Zn^{2+} + 2Ag$
   (b) $[Ag^+] = 3 \times 10^{-9}$ M
   (c) $K_{sp} = 3 \times 10^{-10}$ M

30. See Pages 642-645 in the text.

18 METALS AND THEIR COMPOUNDS: THE REPRESENTATIVE METALS

As we discussed earlier, the chemical elements can be divided into three main types: metals, nonmetals, and metalloids. The metals themselves can be further divided into the representative metals (those found in the A-groups) and the transition metals (those in the B-groups and Group VIII). The properties of the A-group metals are determined by the electron population of the s and p orbitals of their outer shells; each of the inner subshells is either filled or empty. The transition metals, on the other hand, have a partially filled d subshell below the outer shell, and this gives them properties that differ in significant ways from the representative metals. For this reason, the transition metals and representative metals are discussed separately.

18.1 METALLURGY

Objectives

To learn how metals are extracted from their ores and purified to the point of being able to be put to practical use. You should learn the kinds of pretreatments given to ores, the way the metals are extracted from the ores, and the refining methods used to make them useful.

Review

The three principal steps in the commercial production of metals are: concentration, reduction and refining.

Concentration. Pretreatment procedures can be physical or chemical. Physical separations take advantage of differences in physical properties between the metal bearing component of the ore and the unwanted gangue (review flotation, amalgamation). Chemical separations rely on chemical properties to enrich the metal bearing component of the ore (review roasting, purification of Al_2O_3).

Reduction. Most metals are found in Nature in a combined state – that is, in compounds. Some occur in the oceans and on the ocean floor. On land they frequently occur in deposits of their carbonates, oxides, or sulfides.

Preparation of metals involves reducing the metal from a positive oxidation state to the free state. There are three methods described in this section:

(1) Thermal decomposition: This requires that the metal compound being decomposed have a small ΔH_f; otherwise excessively high temperatures must be reached to produce a measurable amount of the free metal. Be sure you understand the thermodynamic argument presented for this in the text. Review Examples 18.1 and 18.2 in the text.

(2) Reduction using a chemical reducing agent: This can only be used economically on metals of moderate activity. Two important chemical reducing agents are carbon and hydrogen. Be sure you know the chemistry of the blast furnace – which substances serve as raw materials and which reactions occur in the various stages.

(3) Electrolytic reduction: This must be used for very active metals. Halide salts are usually chosen for electrolysis because of their relatively low melting points. The production of aluminum is an exception.

Refining. This involves purification of the metal after reduction as well as the formation of alloys with desirable properties. Review the refining procedures used to produce steel from pig iron.

Self-Test

1. What property of Al_2O_3 is exploited in the purification of bauxite?

    _____

2. Write the chemical equation for the roasting of ZnS in air.

    _____

3. What is the active reducing agent in the blast furnace?

    _____

4. Write the chemical equation for the reaction between CaO and P_2O_5 during the formation of slag in the blast furnace.

    _____

5. What types of processes would probably be used to extract the metals from the following compounds?

    (a) PbO   _____

    (b) HgO   _____

    (c) NaCl   _____

6. Why would the reaction, $FeCl_3 + 3Na \longrightarrow Fe + 3NaCl$, be an uneconomical method for producing iron?

    _____

7. Why did the open hearth process replace the Bessemer process for the production of steel?

    _____

8. Why has the basic oxygen process largely replaced the open hearth process in the production of steel?

    _____

New Terms

Metallurgy
    The science and technology of metals. It is concerned with the procedures and chemical reactions that are used to separate metals from their ores and make them ready for practical uses.

Ore
> A substance that contains a desirable constituent in concentrations large enough to make its recovery economically worthwhile.

Manganese modules
> Lumps about the size of an orange that contain large concentrations of manganese and iron. They are found on the ocean floor.

Refining
> Purification and treatment of a metal to give it properties that are appropriate for specific applications.

Amalgam
> A solution of a metal in mercury.

Flotation
> A method for concentrating sulfide ores of copper and lead. Air is bubbled through a slurry of oil-coated ore particles, which stick to rising air bubbles and collect in a foam at the surface.

Gangue
> The unwanted rock and sand that is separated from an ore.

Roasting
> The heating of an ore in air, which converts sulfides to oxides.

Blast furnace
> An apparatus that is used to reduce metal ores such as iron oxides to the free metal. The reducing agent is carbon.

Slag
> A relatively low-melting mixture of impurities that forms in the blast furnace and other furnaces used in refining metals.

Pig iron
> The impure iron that comes from a blast furnace.

Cast iron
> Pig iron that has been cast into shapes by pouring the liquid metal into molds.

Coke
> Coal that has had its volatile components driven off at high temperature. It is mostly carbon.

Bessemer converter
: An outdated method for converting pig iron into steel, which involves blowing air through the molten pig iron to lower its carbon content.

Open hearth furnace
: A now obsolete furnace used to convert pig iron into steel.

Basic oxygen process
: A modern relatively fast method that is used to convert pig iron into steel. It involves blowing pure oxygen and powdered limestone through the molten pig iron, which lowers the carbon content and converts other impurities into slag.

18.2   TRENDS IN METALLIC BEHAVIOR

Objectives

To learn how the metallic character of the elements varies within the periodic table.

Review

Trends in metallic character parallel trends in the electronegativities of the elements - elements having high electronegativities are less metallic than those with low electronegativities. (Elements with low electronegativity are said to be electropositive.) Metallic character increases from top to bottom in a group and decreases from left to right across a period.

Acidic or basic properties of oxides serve as a measure of metallic character. Metal oxides are basic and nonmetal oxides are acidic. Some oxides (e.g., BeO and Al_2O_3) are amphoteric. Aluminum itself is amphoteric and dissolves in both acid and base with the liberation of hydrogen.

Self-Test

9. Choose the element with the more metallic character in each set below:
    (a) Mg or Sr   _____

    (b) Al or Mg   _____

(c) Ga, Cs, Tl, or Ba   _____

10. Which oxide is more basic, Al_2O_3 or In_2O_3?   _____

11. Which oxide is more acidic, Li_2O or BeO?   _____

12. Which is the most electropositive element among Mg, K, Sn, Cs?

    _____

13. Oven cleaners often contain NaOH. Why shouldn't they be used to clean aluminum oven pans?

    _____

    _____

14. Write an equation for the reaction of calcium oxide with hydrochloric acid.

    _____

15. Which group in the periodic table best illustrates the variation in metallic character within a group?

    _____

New Terms

Electropositive
    Having a low electronegativity.

18.3 IONIC-COVALENT CHARACTER OF METAL-NONMETAL BONDS

Objectives

    To learn how the relative degree of covalent character of metal-nonmetal bonds can be explained in terms of cation charge and size.

Review

    The degree to which a cation is able to polarize the electron cloud of an anion is related to the cation's ionic potential, ϕ. Ionic potential is the ratio of an ion's charge to its radius. Recalling from Chapter 3 the way in which atomic and ionic size varies within the periodic table, you can predict the relative degree of covalent character to metal-nonmetal bonds, as discussed on Page 663.

Self-Test

16. Arrange the following ions in order of increasing ionic potential:

	ion	radius (pm)
(a)	Er^{3+}	96
(b)	Be^{2+}	39
(c)	Ti^{4+}	68

_____

17. In each pair below, choose the substance with the greater degree of covalent character.

(a) $MgCl_2$ or $BeCl_2$ _____

(b) Al_2S_3 or Ga_2S_3 _____

(c) CrO_2^- or CrO_4^{2-} _____

(d) $FeCl_2$ or $FeCl_3$ _____

(e) SnS_2 or SnS _____

(f) CaS or Ga_2S_3 _____

New Terms

Ionic potential
    The ratio of an ion's charge (q) to its radius (r). $\phi = q/r$

18.4   COLORS OF METAL COMPOUNDS

Objectives

To learn what gives rise to the observed colors of compounds and to observe how color can be related to the degree of covalent character in certain metal-nonmetal compounds.

Review

The color that we observe for a particular compound is determined by the colors that the compound absorbs from white light. We see the colors that are not absorbed.

Absorption of light by typical ionic compounds is of the charge transfer type. As the metal-nonmetal bond becomes more covalent, less energy is needed to cause the charge transfer and the absorption band shifts from the UV region toward the blue end of the visible spectrum. This causes the compound to appear colored. The intensity of the observed color is proportional to the degree of covalent character.

The degree of covalent character of a metal-nonmetal bond increases with the size of the anion and with the charge on the anion. Both factors make the anion more polarizable.

Self-Test

18. Which is more covalent, Na_2S (Na—S distance = 283 pm) or NaCl (Na—Cl distance = 281 pm)?

_____

19. Choose the member of each pair that would be most deeply colored.
(a) Ag_2O or Ag_2S _____
(b) ZnS or ZnSe   _____

New Terms

Charge transfer process
    The transfer of an electron from one atom to another brought about by absorption of a photon that has the energy required for the process.

Charge transfer absorption band
    A band of wavelengths that a substance absorbs from the electromagnetic spectrum. The photons that are absorbed cause a charge transfer process to occur.

18.5   GROUP IA: THE ALKALI METALS

Objectives

To learn the chemical and physical properties of the Group IA metals and their important compounds.

Review

You should study this section (as well as others in this chapter) carefully in an effort to learn as much as possible. Pay particular attention to the following:

Occurrence and preparation. Sodium and potassium are the most important of the alkali metals. They are found in the ocean and in deposits on land. Recovery of sodium is accomplished by electrolysis of molten NaCl in the Downs cell. The other alkali metals are normally displaced from their halides by sodium at high temperatures.

Physical properties. Alkali metals are good conductors of heat and electricity. They are soft and low-melting because their metallic lattices contain only singly charged cations. The alkali metals and their salts produce characteristic emission colors. Learn the colors for the flame tests for Li, Na, and K.

Chemical properties and important compounds. All the alkali metals react vigorously with water (you should be able to write equations for the reactions). They have very negative reduction potentials. The reduction potential of Li is exceptionally negative because of the very large hydration energy of Li^+.

Alkali metals dissolve in liquid ammonia where they exist as M^+ ions and solvated electrons. These solutions are very powerful reducing agents.

Alkali metals react directly with most of the nonmetals. You should learn their reactions with O_2, and the uses for the various kinds of oxides that are formed. Of the alkali metals, only lithium reacts directly with nitrogen to form Li_3N.

The most important compound of the alkali metals is NaCl, which serves as the raw material for other sodium compounds. The raw material for potassium compounds is KCl. Sodium compounds such as NaOH, $NaHCO_3$, and Na_2CO_3 are made from NaCl. You should learn the chemical reactions involved in the Solvay process.

Self-Test

20. Write a molecular equation for the reaction of

    (a) Na with O_2 _____

    (b) Li with N_2 _____

    (c) KO_2 with H_2O _____

    (d) Cs with O_2 _____

    (e) Na with F_2 _____

    (f) K with S _____

    (g) Na with H_2O _____

21. What are the common names for

    (a) NaOH? _____

    (b) $Na_2CO_3 \cdot 10H_2O$? _____

    (c) $NaHCO_3$? _____

22. What is potash? _____

23. Write the ionic equation for the principal reaction that takes place in the Solvay process.

    _____

24. What color flame is produced by

    (a) potassium compounds? _____

    (b) lithium compounds? _____

    (c) sodium compounds? _____

25. Why are sodium vapor lamps so efficient? _____

    _____

26. Give the formula of an alkali metal compound that is used as

    (a) a bleaching agent _____

    (b) an ingredient in glass _____

    (c) a drug for treating manic depression _____

    (d) the most important commercial strong
        base _____

    (e)   an oxygen source in recirculating
          breathing apparatus

    (f)   a fertilizer

New Terms

The common names of many compounds are included in this section and others. These will not be listed separately under "New Terms," but they are generally given in italics in the text. You should ask your teacher which of them you are expected to know. The important new terms given in boldface type in this section are as follows:

Flame test
> Identification of an ion by the color produced when the ion is introduced into a flame. For example, sodium ion gives a flame a yellow color.

Solvay process
> A commercial process used to prepare Na_2CO_3 from NaCl and CO_2 in an aqueous solution made basic by ammonia.

18.6   GROUP IIA: THE ALKALINE EARTH METALS

Objectives

> To learn the chemical and physical properties of the Group IIA metals and their important compounds.

Review

Occurrence and preparation. The most important alkaline earth metals are calcium and magnesium. Learn the mineral sources of calcium. The chief source of magnesium is sea water. Beryl, an ore of beryllium, occurs sometimes as gem quality crystals.

Beryllium is obtained by electrolysis of $BeCl_2$ to which NaCl is added as an electrolyte. Learn how magnesium is separated from sea water to give the free metal. Beryllium and magnesium are the only alkaline earth metals that have practical uses as free metals. Learn why, and what some of these uses are.

Physical properties. The Group IIA metals are more dense, harder, and higher-melting than the metals of Group IA. Learn the colors of the flame tests for Ca, Sr, and Ba.

Chemical properties and important compounds. The alkaline earth metals are less reactive than the metals of Group IA. Only Ca, Sr, Ba, and Ra react with cold H_2O to liberate hydrogen. Magnesium is the only metal of this group that reacts with N_2.

Beryllium compounds are amphoteric and tend to be covalent. Learn the structure of $BeCl_2$. Study the reactions of Be and BeO with base.

Study the properties and uses of the oxides, hydroxides, sulfates, and carbonates of these metals. Especially important are: $CaCO_3$ and its thermal decomposition; MgO and $Mg(OH)_2$; $CaSO_4 \cdot 2H_2O$ (gypsum and plaster of paris); and barium sulfate.

Self-Test

27. Write equations for the reaction (if any) between

(a) Ca and H_2O _____

(b) Be and H_2O _____

(c) CaO and H_2O _____

(d) Ca and N_2 _____

28. Give formulas for the substances having the following common names:

(a) gypsum _____

(b) lime _____

(c) epsom salts _____

(d) milk of magnesia _____

(e) slaked lime _____

(f) limestone _____

29. What flame color is produced by compounds of

(a) calcium _____

(b) strontium _____

(c) barium _____

30. What is dolomite? _____

31. Write an equation for the thermal decomposition of limestone.

_____

32. Write equations for the recovery of magnesium from sea water. (Use a separate piece of paper.)

33. (a) Which metal is used in flashbulbs? _____

(b) What safety feature is provided by tools made of beryllium-copper alloy?

_____

(c) Why doesn't calcium have many practical uses as a free metal? _____

34. Which has a greater solubility in water

(a) $MgSO_4$ or $BaSO_4$? _____

(b) $Mg(OH)_2$ or $Ba(OH)_2$? _____

New Terms

In addition to many names for common chemicals, the following important terms were introduced in this section:

Calcining

Heating a substance strongly in air.

Slaking

Treating lime (CaO) with water, which produces $Ca(OH)_2$.

18.7   METALS OF GROUPS IIIA, IVA, AND VA

Objectives

To learn the properties of these metals and some of their compounds.

Review

Learn which elements in these groups are considered to be metals. Except for aluminum, they are post-transition elements and have a pseudonoble gas configuration beneath the outer shell.

The heavier metals exhibit two oxidation states. Learn what they are.

Occurrence and preparation. Aluminum is a very abundant metal, but its primary ore is bauxite. Learn how bauxite is purified so that it can be reduced in the Hall process.

Tin ore is SnO_2 and is reduced to the metal with carbon, and then purified by electrolysis. Learn the allotropes of tin. The principal ore of lead is PbS which is first converted to the oxide and then reduced with carbon.

Bismuth occurs as the oxide and sulfide. Bi_2S_3 is converted to Bi_2O_3 and then reduced with carbon. Wood's metal, an alloy of bismuth, has a very low melting point and is·used in the triggering mechanism of automatic sprinkler systems.

Chemical properties and compounds. Aluminum is very reactive. The metal is protected from oxidation by a tough Al_2O_3 coating. Al_2O_3 occurs in two forms, α-Al_2O_3 which is called corundum and γ-Al_2O_3. The α form is quite unreactive and several well-known gems consist of almost pure Al_2O_3.

Metallic aluminum is amphoteric (you should be able to write equations for its reaction with both acids and bases). The reaction of Al to form Al_2O_3 is very exothermic. Study the thermite reaction.

$AlCl_3$ is largely covalent. Know the structure of Al_2Cl_6 and be able to compare it to the structure of $BeCl_2$. When aluminum salts are dissolved in water, the aluminum ion exists as $Al(H_2O)_6^{3+}$. Study what happens as base is gradually added to a solution of $Al(H_2O)_6^{3+}$.

Aluminum sulfate forms double salts with Na_2SO_4, K_2SO_4, and $(NH_4)_2SO_4$. These salts are called alums and have the general formula $M^+M^{3+}(SO_4)_2 \cdot 12H_2O$. Alums are formed by Cr^{3+} and Fe^{3+} as well as Al^{3+}. Sodium alum, $NaAl(SO_4)_2 \cdot 12H_2O$, is used in baking powders.

Tin forms compounds of Sn^{2+} and Sn^{4+}. Both oxidation states are relatively stable. For lead, the 2+ state is much more stable than the 4+ state. Similarly, the 3+ state of bismuth is much more stable than the 5+ state.

Tin and lead are both amphoteric. You should be able to

write equations for their reaction with both acids and bases.
You should also study the applications of tin and lead compounds.

Bismuth(III) compounds tend to hydrolyze in water to give
the BiO^+ ion. Sodium bismuthate, $NaBIO_3$, is an extremely powerful oxidizing agent.

Self-Test

35. What is the pseudonoble gas configuration? _____

36. Which of these ions have a pseudonoble gas configuration:
    Sn^{2+}, Bi^{5+}, Al^{3+}, Sn^{4+}?

    _____

37. Which is a better oxidizing agent, SnO_2 or PbO_2?_____

38. Give the three principal chemical reactions in the purification
    of bauxite.

    _____

    _____

    _____

39. What is alnico? _____

40. What chemical reactions are involved in
    (a) the production of Sn from SnO_2?

    _____

    (b) the production of Pb from PbS?

    _____

41. What metals are found in the following alloys?

    (a) bronze _____

    (b) solder _____

42. What is Wood's metal? _____

    _____

43. Write chemical equations for the reaction of metallic aluminum
    with a strong acid and with a strong base.

    _____

    _____

44. On a separate sheet of paper, sketch the structures of molecular $AlCl_3$ and $BeCl_2$.

45. Write chemical equations showing how aluminum hydroxide dissolves in both acid and base.

_____

_____

46. Give the general formula for an alum. _____

47. Which alum is used in baking powders? _____

48. What is the reaction between plumbite ion and hypochlorite ion in basic solution?

_____

49. What is the name of the BiO^+ ion? _____

50. Balance the following equation which occurs in an acidic solution: $BiO_3^- + Mn^{2+} \longrightarrow MnO_4^- + Bi^{3+}$

_____

New Terms

Alum
    A double salt with the general formula $M^+M^{3+}(SO_4)_2 \cdot 12H_2O$, for example, $KAl(SO_4)_2 \cdot 12H_2O$.

Double salt
    Crystals that contain the components of two different salts in a definite ratio.

Thermite reaction
    The very exothermic reaction, $2Al + Fe_2O_3 \longrightarrow 2Fe + Al_2O_3$

Answers to Self-Test Questions

1. Its amphoteric nature. 2. $2ZnS + 3O_2 \longrightarrow 2ZnO + 2SO_2$
3. carbon monoxide 4. $3CaO + P_2O_5 \longrightarrow Ca_3(PO_4)_2$
5.(a) chemical reduction (b) thermal decomposition (c) electrolysis 6. Because Na would have to be produced by electrolysis, which is expensive. 7. Steel with more uniform properties

could be obtained.   8. It is much faster and therefore more economical.   9.(a) Sr   (b) Mg   (c) Cs   10. In_2O_3 11. BeO
12. Cs   13. Al reacts with base (see Page 662)
14. $CaO + 2HCl \longrightarrow CaCl_2 + H_2O$ 15. Group IVA
16. $Er^{3+} < Ti^{4+} < Be^{2+}$ 17.(a) $BeCl_2$ (b) Al_2S_3 (c) CrO_4^{2-}
(d) $FeCl_3$ (e) SnS_2 (f) Ga_2S_3 18. Na_2S 19.(a) Ag_2S
(b) SnSe

20.(a) $2Na + O_2 \longrightarrow Na_2O_2$

(b) $6Li + N_2 \longrightarrow 2Li_3N$

(c) $2KO_2 + 2H_2O \longrightarrow 2KOH + O_2 + H_2O_2$

(d) $Cs + O_2 \longrightarrow CsO_2$

(e) $2Na + F_2 \longrightarrow 2NaF$

(f) $2K + S \longrightarrow K_2S$

(g) $2Na + 2H_2O \longrightarrow 2NaOH + H_2$

21.(a) lye or caustic soda   (b) washing soda   (c) baking soda

22. K_2CO_3 23. $Na^+ + Cl^- + NH_4^+ + HCO_3^- \longrightarrow NaHCO_3 + NH_4^+ + Cl^-$ 24.(a) violet   (b) red   (c) yellow   25. Most of the light emitted appears in the visible region of the spectrum.
26.(a) Na_2O_2 (b) Na_2CO_3 (c) Li_2CO_3 (d) NaOH   (e) KO_2
(f) $KCl \cdot MgCl_2 \cdot 6H_2O$
27.(a) $Ca + 2H_2O \longrightarrow Ca(OH)_2 + H_2$

(b) $Be + H_2O \longrightarrow$ no reaction

(c) $CaO + H_2O \longrightarrow Ca(OH)_2$

(d) $Ca + N_2 \longrightarrow$ no reaction

28.(a) $CaSO_4 \cdot 2H_2O$ (b) CaO   (c) $MgSO_4 \cdot 7H_2O$ (d) $Mg(OH)_2$
(e) $Ca(OH)_2$ (f) $CaCO_3$ 29.(a) brick red   (b) crimson
(c) yellowish-green   30. $CaCO_3 \cdot MgCl_3$
31. $CaCO_3 \xrightarrow{\text{heat}} CaO + CO_2$
32. $CaCO_3 \xrightarrow{\text{heat}} CaO + CO_2$

$CaO + H_2O + Mg^{2+} \longrightarrow Ca^{2+} + Mg(OH)_2(s)$

$Mg(OH)_2(s) + 2HCl \longrightarrow MgCl_2(aq) + 2H_2O$

$MgCl_2(s) \xrightarrow{\text{electrolysis}} Mg + Cl_2$

33.(a) magnesium   (b) nonsparking   (c) It reacts with moisture and oxygen. (Its oxide coating does not protect the metal from further reaction.)   34. (a) $MgSO_4$ (b) $Ba(OH)_2$

35. $ns^2np^6nd^{10}$ (e.g., $3s^23p^63d^{10}$)   36. Bi^{5+} and Sn^{4+}

37. PbO_2

38. $Al_2O_3 + 2OH^- \longrightarrow 2AlO_2^- + H_2O$

$AlO_2^- + H_3O^+ \longrightarrow Al(OH)_3$

$2Al(OH)_3 \xrightarrow{heat} Al_2O_3 + 3H_2O$

39. a magnetic aluminum alloy containing iron (50%), nickel (20%), and cobalt (10%).

40.(a) $SnO_2 + C \longrightarrow Sn + CO_2$

(b) $2PbS + 3O_2 \longrightarrow 2PbO + 2SO_2$

$2PbO + C \longrightarrow Pb + CO_2$

41.(a) copper and tin   (b) tin and lead

42. a low-melting alloy of bismuth that also contains lead, tin, and cadmium.

43. $2Al + 6H^+ \longrightarrow 2Al^{3+} + 3H_2$

$2Al + 2OH^- + 2H_2O \longrightarrow 2AlO_2^- + 3H_2$

44. See Pages 679 and 685 of the text.

45. $Al(OH)_3(H_2O)_3 + H^+ \longrightarrow Al(OH)_2(H_2O)_4^+ + H_2O$

$Al(OH)_3(H_2O)_3 + OH^- \longrightarrow Al(OH)_4(H_2O)_2^- + H_2O$

46. $M^+M^{3+}(SO_4)_2 \cdot 12H_2O$

47. $NaAl(SO_4)_2 \cdot 12H_2O$

48. $Pb(OH)_4^{2-} + OCl^- \longrightarrow PbO_2 + H_2O + 2OH^- + Cl^-$

49. bismuthyl ion

50. $14H^+ + 5BiO_3^- + 2Mn^{2+} \longrightarrow 2MnO_4^- + 5Bi^{3+} + 7H_2O$

19 THE CHEMISTRY OF SELECTED NONMETALS, PART I: HYDROGEN, CARBON, OXYGEN, AND NITROGEN

Chapters 19 and 20 deal with the chemistry of the most important nonmetals. We begin here with four elements essential to living things, although this is certainly not the only place in Nature where they are found.

19.1   HYDROGEN

Objectives

To learn the chemical and physical properties of hydrogen and its compounds. You should learn the properties of hydrogen and its isotopes, its method of preparation and its uses, and how hydrogen compounds can be made.

Review

Hydrogen is the most abundant element in the universe, but little of it remains on Earth. Most of the hydrogen that is present on Earth is bound in water molecules. There are three isotopes of hydrogen: $_1^1H$, $_1^2H$ (deuterium), and $_1^3H$ (tritium).

367

Most naturally occurring hydrogen is ^1_1H.

Commercially, H_2 is generally obtained from natural gas, CH_4, by reaction with steam. It can also be made from coal by the water gas reaction. Electrolysis of brine is another commercial source of H_2. In the laboratory H_2 can be made by reaction of a nonoxidizing acid with a metal that has a negative reduction potential. You should study the commercial uses of hydrogen described on Pages 695 and 696.

Compounds of hydrogen. Binary compounds of hydrogen are called hydrides. Those formed with metals are ionic and contain the H^- ion. Reaction of H^- with water releases H_2. In covalent compounds, hydrogen only forms one bond. The simple covalent hydrides (Table 19.1) have formulas and structures that are easy to predict. More complex hydrides are formed by nonmetals that experience catenation - the linking of like-atoms together in chains.

Preparation of nonmetal hydrides. Two methods of preparation are discussed. One is the direct combination of hydrogen with the nonmetals. This is only successful if ΔG°_f for the compound is negative (Table 19.2). The second method of preparation is the addition of protons (H^+) to the conjugate base of the hydride.

$$X^{n-} + nH^+ \longrightarrow H_nX$$

In general, the weaker X^{n-} is as a base, the stronger must be the acid supplying the H^+. You should learn how the base strength of X^{n-} varies within the periodic table (across rows and down columns).

Hydrogen economy. The benefits of H_2 as a fuel are many, but the most significant problem is the difficulty of obtaining H_2 from its most abundant source, H_2O. Making H_2 from H_2O requires an input of energy. Among the possible sources of this energy are nuclear energy and solar energy.

Self-Test

1.   (a)   Give the symbols for the three isotopes of hydrogen.

_____

       (b)   Which one is radioactive?   _____

2.   What is heavy water? _____

3.   Give chemical equations for

(a)   the commercial preparation of H_2 from CH_4.

_____

(b)   the laboratory preparation of H_2.

_____

4.   Why can H_2 be collected by the displacement of water?

_____

5.   What is synthesis gas? _____

6.   What occurs during the hydrogenation of an unsaturated oil?

_____

7.   Complete the following equations. If there is no reaction, write N.R.

(a) $Li + H_2 \longrightarrow$

(b) $CaH_2 + H_2O \longrightarrow$

(c) $C + H_2O \xrightarrow{1000°C}$

(d) $AlP + H_2O \longrightarrow$

(e) $H_2 + Cl_2 \longrightarrow$

(f) $P + H_2 \longrightarrow$

(g) $NaCl + H_2SO_4(conc.) \longrightarrow$

8.   What is the major obstacle to the widespread use of H_2 as a fuel?

_____

9.   Why can't H_2Se be made by the direct combination of the elements?

_____

_____

New Terms

Protium
$_1^1H$, the most abundant isotope of hydrogen.

Deuterium
An isotope of hydrogen. $_1^2H$. Sometimes represented by the symbol D.

Tritium
The radioactive isotope of hydrogen, $_1^3H$, sometimes represented by the symbol T.

Heavy water
Water in which the hydrogen atoms are $_1^2H$ (deuterium, D). Also called deuterium oxide, D_2O.

Hydride ion
The ion, H^-.

Hydrides
Binary compounds that contain hydrogen.

Catenation
Linking together of atoms of the same element to give chains of atoms.

Hydrogenation
The addition of H_2 to organic molecules having double or triple bonds.

Synthesis gas
A mixture of CO and H_2.

Hydrogen economy
An economy built around the extensive use of hydrogen as a fuel.

19.2   CARBON

Objectives
To learn the chemical and physical properties of carbon and its compounds. You should know the allotropic forms of carbon and the important ionic and covalent compounds

of carbon.

Review

Carbon is a very common element. Besides being found in all living things, large deposits of carbon in the form of coal occur in many places. Coke is nearly pure carbon and is made by heating coal to high temperatures.

You should know the structures of diamond and graphite and how their physical properties are influenced by their structures. You should also know the properties and uses of activated carbon and carbon black.

Carbon forms two oxides, CO and CO_2. You should know their structures. Carbon monoxide is nearly nonpolar and has a low solubility in water. It can be made by burning carbon or a hydrocarbon in a limited supply of O_2, by the dehydration (removal of water from) of formic acid, and by the reaction of steam with C or CH_4. Carbon monoxide is an industrial fuel and an industrial reducing agent. It reacts with some metals to form metal carbonyl compounds in which the metal has an oxidation number of zero.

Carbon dioxide is nonpolar and moderately soluble in water. It can be made by combustion of a carbon-containing substance by the decomposition of limestone, and by the reaction of a carbonate or bicarbonate with an acid. Solid CO_2 is Dry ice, which sublimes at $-78°C$ at 1 atm. Learn the uses of CO_2 given on Page 704. Green plants consume CO_2 and produce carbohydrates during photosynthesis.

Aqueous solutions of CO_2 contain H_2CO_3, a weak diprotic acid. Carbonic acid forms two types of salts, carbonates and bicarbonates. Ground water containing dissolved CO_2 gradually dissolves limestone deposits and produces caverns. Learn how stalactites and stalagmites are formed. You should also learn what "hard water" is and how it can be "softened."

Other carbon compounds include the carbides - covalent carbides like carborundum, ionic carbides like Al_4C_3 and CaC_2, and interstitial carbides like tungsten carbide.

Hydrogen cyanide is made from ammonia and forms cyanide salts. The CN^- forms many stable complex ions. Carbon disulfide is made by combining sulfur and carbon. It is extremely flammable.

Self-Test

10. How do the structures of diamond and graphite differ?

_____

_____

11. What special property does activated carbon have? _____

_____

12. How can CO be made in small quantities in the laboratory? (Give a chemical equation.)

_____

13. What is the overall reaction for the reduction of Fe_2O_3 by CO?

_____

14. What is the oxidation number of Ni in $Ni(CO)_4$? _____

15. Give the equation for the thermal decomposition of limestone.

_____

16. What is Dry ice?   _____

17. Write an equation for the dissolving of limestone by water containing dissolved CO_2.

_____

18. (a) What ions are present in hard water? _____

    (b) Write an equation showing how washing soda is able to remove hardness ions.
    _____

19. (a) What is the Lewis formula of the anion in CaC_2?

    _____

    (b) What is the reaction of CaC_2 with water?

    _____

20. What is the formula for

    (a) carborundum   _____

(b) hydrogen cyanide   _____

(c) tungsten carbide   _____

New Terms

Carbide
    An inorganic compound of carbon (e.g., Mg_2C).

Carborundum
    Silicon carbide, SiC, which is a common abrasive.

Dry ice
    Solid CO_2.

Hard water
    Water containing the ions Ca^{2+}, Mg^{2+}, and Fe^{3+}, which
    interfere with the action of soap by forming insoluble pre-
    cipitates with the anions in the soap.

Hardness ions
    The ions found in hard water: Ca^{2+}, Mg^{2+}, and Fe^{3+}.

19.3   OXYGEN

Objectives

    To learn the properties of oxygen and its principal com-
    pounds.

Review

    Note the abundance of oxygen and its presence every-
where. Also note that O_2 molecules are paramagnetic, with two
unpaired electrons. Oxygen is normally recovered from liquefied
air. In the laboratory it can be prepared by the MnO_2-catalyzed
thermal decomposition of $KClO_3$. In nature, O_2 is a product of
photosynthesis.

    Oxygen exists in two allotropic forms, normal O_2 and
ozone, O_3. You should be able to draw the Lewis structures for
O_3 and explain its role in protecting the Earth from harmful UV
radiation from the sun. You should also know how nitrogen
oxides and chlorofluorocarbons can damage the Earth's ozone

shield.

Ionic oxides such as CaO are basic. In water, O^{2-} reacts to form OH^-. Insoluble oxides react with acids (as in the pickling of iron). Some metal oxides are amphoteric. Learn the reaction of Al_2O_3 with base.

Covalent oxides are normally formed by nonmetals and tend to be acidic. When they react with water they form oxoacids, which produce oxoanions upon neutralization. Oxygen usually forms one or two bonds; exceptions are CO and NO. Covalent oxides can be prepared by (a) direct union of the elements, (b) oxidation of a lower oxide, (c) combustion of a metal hydride, and (d) reduction of an oxoanion in a redox reaction.

Besides normal ionic oxides containing the O^{2-} ion, oxygen also forms peroxides and superoxides. Hydrolysis of peroxide ion gives H_2O_2 (you should know its structure). H_2O_2 decomposes easily to O_2 and H_2O, and is a strong oxidizing agent.

Self-Test

21. (a) What is the usual commercial source of oxygen?

_____

(b) Write an equation for the laboratory preparation of oxygen.

_____

22. Draw the Lewis structures for ozone.

23. How is ozone formed in the upper atmosphere?

_____

_____

24. Give chemical equations showing how traces of NO can remove relatively large amounts of O_3 from the stratosphere.

_____

_____

25. What is pickling? _____

_____

26. Complete and balance the following equations:

    (a) $Al_2O_3 + H^+ \longrightarrow$

    (b) $Li_2O + H_2O \longrightarrow$

    (c) $Na_2O_2 + H_2O \longrightarrow$

27. Write equations for two reactions that could be used to prepare SO_2.

    (a) _____

    (b) _____

28. Describe the structure of hydrogen peroxide.

New Terms

Ozone

   An allotrope of oxygen, O_3.

Pickling

   The removal of rust from iron or steel by reaction with acid.

19.4   NITROGEN

Objectives

   To learn the chemical and physical properties of nitrogen and its important compounds.

Review

   Most nitrogen on Earth exists as N_2 because of the great stability of this molecule, which results from the high $N \equiv N$ bond energy. Commercially, N_2 is obtained from liquefied air. In the laboratory, N_2 can be made by warming a solution containing NH_4^+ and NO_2^-. Most nitrogen is used to make NH_3. Other uses are based on the low reactivity of N_2 and the cold temperature of liquid N_2.

   Examples of ionic nitrides are Li_3N and Mg_3N_2. Learn what happens when they react with water. In the text, the covalent compounds of nitrogen are discussed in terms of the oxidation number of the nitrogen in the compounds. Pay particular attention to the following:

<u>-3 oxidation state</u>. The compound ammonia is discussed. Learn about the Haber process - the chemical reaction and the reaction conditions. By this time, you should know how NH_3 behaves as a base in water. The amide ion, NH_2^-, is the strong conjugate base of NH_3. The NH_4^+ ion is the weak conjugate acid of NH_3. Learn how NH_3 can be made in the laboratory. You should also learn the chemistry of the Ostwald process. (See the New Terms section.)

<u>-2 oxidation state</u>. Hydrazine is discussed. You should know its structure, how it is prepared, and how it behaves in water. Hydrazine is a powerful reducing agent.

<u>-1 oxidation state</u>. Know the structure of hydroxylamine and how this compound is prepared. Be able to write an equation for the functioning of hydroxylamine as a weak base.

<u>+1 oxidation state</u>. You should know how N_2O is prepared and be able to draw its Lewis structure. This and other nitrogen oxides have positive standard free energies of formation. They are stable at room temperature only because they decompose at an extremely slow rate. Learn the uses of N_2O.

<u>+2 oxidation state and +4 oxidation state</u>. Oxidation of NH_3 in the Ostwald process gives NO, which is easily oxidized to NO_2. In water, NO_2 reacts to give HNO_3 and NO.

Nitric oxide is a colorless, fairly reactive gas. Its bond order is 2.5 and rather easily forms the NO^+ ion, which has a bond order of 3.0. Nitrogen dioxide can be represented by two resonance structures, each of which places the unpaired electron on the nitrogen. Learn the equilibrium between NO_2 and N_2O_4, and the structure of both molecules.

You should learn the role of NO and NO_2 in photochemical smog, including (a) the formation of NO in auto engines, (b) oxidation of NO to NO_2, (c) photodecomposition of NO_2 to NO and O, (d) the formation of ozone, and (e) the oxidation of hydrocarbons to peroxyacylnitrates (PAN).

<u>+3 oxidation state</u>. Condensation of NO and NO_2 gives N_2O_3, the formal anhydride of HNO_2. Nitrous acid is a weak acid that can function as either an oxidizing agent or reducing agent. Nitrites are used as food preservatives. You should understand the rea-

sons why NO_2^- may be potentially harmful as well as why it is beneficial.

+5 oxidation state. Molecules of N_2O_5 exist in the vapor, but in the solid N_2O_5 produces the ions $NO_2^+NO_3^-$. N_2O_5 reacts with water to form HNO_3. Nitric acid is a strong acid and a powerful oxidizing agent. It is made by the Ostwald process. In concentrated form it is subject to photochemical decomposition, which is why concentrated HNO_3 is often slightly yellow. Aqua regia is one part HNO_3 and three parts HCl by volume. Learn why it is able to dissolve noble metals.

Self-Test

29. Write a chemical equation for the preparation of N_2 in the laboratory.

_____

30. Complete and balance the following equations. If no reaction occurs, write N.R.

(a) $Li_3N + H_2O \longrightarrow$

(b) $NO_2 + H_2O \longrightarrow$

(c) $NO + H_2O \longrightarrow$

(d) $NH_3 + H_2O \longrightarrow$

(e) $CaO + NH_4Cl \longrightarrow$

(f) $N_2O_5 + H_2O \longrightarrow$

(g) $O_3 + NO \longrightarrow$

(h) $Cu + HNO_3$ (dilute) $\longrightarrow$

(i) $HNO_2 + MnO_4^-$ (in acid solution) $\longrightarrow$

(j) $Zn + HNO_3 \longrightarrow$

(k) $NO + NO_2 + H_2O \longrightarrow$

31. What relationship exists between NO_2 and N_2O_4?

_____

32. (a) Write the chemical equation that occurs in the Haber process.

_____

(b) What is the first chemical reaction that takes place in the Ostwald process?

_____

33. Which is the only metal that reacts with N_2 at room temperature? _____

34. Why is N_2 so unreactive? _____
_____

35. Give the Lewis structure for

    (a) N_2H_4 (d) N_2O_3

    (b) NO_2 (e) N_2O_5 (in the gas phase)

    (c) N_2O_4

36. Why do O_2 and N_2 form stable mixtures? (That is, why don't O_2 and N_2 react with each other to a large degree in the atmosphere?) _____
_____

37. Write equations for

    (a) the formation of hydrazine.
    _____

    (b) the synthesis of hydroxylamine.
    _____

    (c) the laboratory preparation of pure HNO_3.
    _____

    (d) the synthesis of nitrous oxide.
    _____

38. Give equations for the sequence of chemical reactions that lead to the formation of ozone in photochemical smog.
    _____
    _____
    _____
    _____

New Terms

Disproportionation

A redox reaction in which a portion of a substance is oxidized while the rest is reduced. The same chemical substance undergoes both oxidation and reduction.

Haber process

The process used in the commercial preparation of ammonia.

Ostwald process

The commercial process for the manufacture of nitric acid from ammonia. The chemical reactions are:

$$4NH_3 + 5O_2 \longrightarrow 4NO + 6H_2O$$

$$2NO + O_2 \longrightarrow 2NO_2$$

$$3NO_2 + H_2O \longrightarrow 2HNO_3 + NO$$

Photochemical smog (usually just called Smog)

A type of urban air pollution caused by the interaction of sunlight and nitrogen oxides, which produces ozone and the unpleasant products of the reaction of ozone with airborn hydrocarbons.

Answers to Self-Test Questions

1.(a) $_1^1H$, $_1^2H$, $_1^3H$ (b) tritium   2. deuterium oxide, $_1^2H_2O$

3.(a) $CH_4(g) + H_2O(g) \xrightarrow[\text{catalyst}]{\text{heat}} CO(g) + 3H_2(g)$

  (b) $Zn + H_2SO_4 \longrightarrow ZnSO_4 + H_2$

4. Because it has a small solubility in water.   5. A mixture of CO and H_2.   6. Hydrogen is added to carbon-carbon double bonds, converting them to single bonds.

7.(a) $2Li + H_2 \longrightarrow 2LiH$

  (b) $CaH_2 + 2H_2O \longrightarrow Ca(OH)_2 + H_2$

  (c) $C + H_2O \xrightarrow{1000°C} CO + H_2$

  (d) $AlP + 3H_2O \longrightarrow Al(OH)_3 + PH_3$

(e) $H_2 + Cl_2 \longrightarrow 2HCl$

(f) $P + H_2 \longrightarrow N.R.$

(g) $NaCl + H_2SO_4 \longrightarrow HCl + NaHSO_4$

8. An economical way must be found to produce H_2 from H_2O.
9. Because H_2Se has a positive ΔG_f°. 10. Diamond has a three-dimensional network of C—C bonds; graphite consists of planar sheets of hexagonal rings. These sheets are stacked one on the other. 11. It has a very large ratio of surface area to mass and adsorbs large quantities of molecules on its surface.

12. $HCHO_2(\ell) \xrightarrow[\text{(conc.)}]{H_2SO_4} H_2O(\ell) + CO(g)$

13. $Fe_2O_3 + 3CO \longrightarrow 2Fe + 3CO_2$ 14. zero

15. $CaCO_3 \xrightarrow{\text{heat}} CaO + CO_2$ 16. Solid CO_2

17. $CaCO_3(s) + H_2CO_3(aq) \longrightarrow Ca(HCO_3)_2(aq)$

18.(a) Ca^{2+}, Mg^{2+}, Fe^{3+}

(b) Washing soda is $Na_2CO_3 \cdot 10H_2O$, which gives CO_3^{2-} in solution. $Ca^{2+} + CO_3^{2-} \longrightarrow CaCO_3(s)$

19.(a) $[:C \equiv C:]^{2-}$ (b) $CaC_2 + 2H_2O \longrightarrow Ca(OH)_2 + C_2H_2$

20.(a) SiC (b) HCN (c) WC

21.(a) the atmosphere (extraction from liquefied air)

(b) $2KClO_3(s) \xrightarrow[\text{heat}]{MnO_2} 2KCl(s) + 3O_2(g)$

22. See Page 708.

23. $O_2 \xrightarrow{h\nu} 2O$; $O + O_2 \longrightarrow O_3$

24. $NO + O_3 \longrightarrow NO_2 + O_2$; $NO_2 + O \longrightarrow NO + O_2$

25. Removal of an oxide coating from a metal by reaction of the oxide with an acid.

26.(a) $Al_2O_3 + 6H^+ \longrightarrow 2Al^{3+} + 3H_2O$

(b) $Li_2O + H_2O \longrightarrow 2LiOH$

(c) $Na_2O_2 + 2H_2O \longrightarrow 2NaOH + H_2O_2$

27.(a) $S + O_2 \longrightarrow SO_2$

(b) $2H_2S + 3O_2 \longrightarrow 2H_2O + 2SO_2$

28. See Pages 712 and 713.

29. $NH_4^+(aq) + NO_2^-(aq) \xrightarrow{\text{heat}} N_2(g) + 2H_2O$

30. (a) $Li_3N + 3H_2O \longrightarrow 3LiOH + NH_3$

   (b) $3NO_2 + H_2O \longrightarrow 2H^+ + 2NO_3^- + NO$

   (c) $NO + H_2O \longrightarrow$ no reaction

   (d) $NH_3 + H_2O \rightleftharpoons NH_4^+ + OH^-$

   (e) $CaO + 2NH_4Cl \longrightarrow CaCl_2 + 2NH_3 + H_2O$

   (f) $N_2O_5 + H_2O \longrightarrow 2HNO_3$

   (g) $O_3 + NO \longrightarrow NO_2 + O_2$

   (h) $3Cu + 8HNO_3 \longrightarrow 3Cu(NO_3)_2 + 2NO + 4H_2O$

   (i) $H^+ + 5HNO_2 + 2MnO_4^- \longrightarrow 5NO_3^- + 2Mn^{2+} + 3H_2O$

   (j) $4Zn + 10HNO_3 \longrightarrow 4Zn(NO_3)_2 + NH_4NO_3 + 3H_2O$

   (k) $NO + NO_2 + H_2O \longrightarrow 2HNO_2$

31. $2NO_2 \rightleftharpoons N_2O_4$

32. (a) $3H_2 + N_2 \rightleftharpoons 2NH_3$

   (b) $4NH_3 + 5O_2 \longrightarrow 4NO + 6H_2O$

33. Lithium

34. Because the triple bond in N_2 is so strong.

35. (a) see Page 717   (b) see Page 719   (c) see Page 719
    (d) see Page 721   (e) see Page 722

36. The ΔG_f° of the nitrogen oxides are positive, so virtually no reaction occurs.

37. (a) $2NH_3 + NaOCl \longrightarrow N_2H_4 + NaCl + H_2O$

   (b) $NaNO_2 + NaHSO_3 + SO_2 + 2H_2O \longrightarrow 2NaHSO_4 + NH_2OH$

   (c) $NaNO_3(s) + H_2SO_4(conc.) \xrightarrow{\text{heat}} NaHSO_4(s) + HNO_3(g)$

   (d) $NH_4NO_3 \xrightarrow{\text{heat}} N_2O + 2H_2O$

38. $N_2 + O_2 \longrightarrow 2NO$

   $2NO + O_2 \longrightarrow 2NO_2$

   $NO_2 \xrightarrow{h\nu} NO + O$

   $O + O_2 \longrightarrow O_3$

20 THE CHEMISTRY OF SELECTED NONMETALS, PART II: PHOSPHORUS, SULFUR, THE HALOGENS, THE NOBLE GASES, AND SILICON

In this chapter we conclude our discussion of the representative elements with an examination of the properties of a number of additional important nonmetals. As mentioned in the text, their properties cover a broad range, and as we will see, so do their uses.

20.1 PHOSPHORUS

Objectives

To learn the properties of phosphorus and its compounds, especially those containing oxygen.

Review

Phosphorus can exist in several allotropic forms. The most important are white phosphorus and red phosphorus. White phosphorus is very reactive because of the strained 60° bond angle in the P_4 tetrahedron. It is also very toxic. Red phosphorus is less reactive and relatively nontoxic. Its structure is unknown, but is probably polymeric.

Phosphorus is prepared from phosphate rock, which contains $Ca_3(PO_4)_2$, by reduction with carbon in an electric furnace.

Phosphides containing the P^{3-} ion hydrolyze to give PH_3. The most important phosphorus compounds are those with oxygen and the halogens. Two oxides are formed, P_4O_{10} and P_4O_6. You should know their structures, and how they relate to the structure of white phosphorus. P_4O_{10} is formed by burning phosphorus in an abundant supply of oxygen. It reacts with water to give H_3PO_4 and is a useful desiccant. In a limited supply of oxygen, combustion of phosphorus yields P_4O_6. This oxide reacts with water to give H_3PO_3. Phosphorous acid is a diprotic acid; be sure to learn its structure.

Phosphoric acid is made from phosphate rock by reaction with H_2SO_4, and by reaction of P_4O_{10} with H_2O. It is a triprotic acid and forms three types of salts. You should know how superphosphate fertilizer is made, how phosphate anions serve as buffers, and the uses of Na_3PO_4.

Dehydration of H_3PO_4 gives polymeric phosphates. You should know the structures of the pyrophosphate, metaphosphate, and tripolyphosphate ions, as well as their corresponding acids. Learn their uses, too. You should also know the effect that phosphate pollution has on lakes.

Phosphorus forms two series of halogen compounds, PX_3 and PX_5. You should be able to describe their structures. The most important of them are PCl_3 and PCl_5. Learn how they are made and how they react with water. PCl_5 exists as $PCl_4^+PCl_6^-$ in the solid state. It reacts with P_4O_{10} to give phosphoryl chloride, $POCl_3$.

Self-Test

1. What is the chief phosphorus-containing compound in phosphate rock?

2. Write a chemical equation showing how phosphorus is recovered from phosphate rock.

_____

3. On a separate sheet of paper, sketch the structures of P_4, P_4O_6, and P_4O_{10}.

4. Write an equation for the reaction of sodium phosphide with water.

_____

5. (a) Draw the Lewis structure for phosphine.

   (b) What would you predict the structure of phosphine to be?

   _____

6. Write equations for the reaction of water with

   (a) P_4O_6 _____

   (b) P_4O_{10} _____

   (c) PCl_3 _____

7. What is a desiccant? _____

_____

8. (a) Write the formulas of all the salts that can be formed by allowing KOH to react with H_3PO_3.

   _____

   (b) How is phosphorous acid usually made?

   _____

9. Draw the Lewis structure for the pyrophosphate ion. Be sure to indicate its charge.

10. (a) Which "phosphate" is used in liquid detergents?

    _____

(b) Which one is used in solid detergents? _____

11. Sketch the structures for PCl_3 and PCl_5 on a separate piece of paper.

12. What is the formula for phosphoryl chloride? _____

What is its principal use? _____

New Terms

Desiccant
A drying agent.

Electric furnace
A furnace in which heat is generated by the passage of a large electric current through the contents of the furnace.

Eutrophication
The natural aging process of a lake.

20.2 SULFUR

Objectives

To learn the properties of sulfur and its compounds. In particular, you should learn the properties of elemental sulfur and of the oxides, oxoacids, and oxoanions of sulfur.

Review

About half of the sulfur used by industry each year is mined by the Frasch process; the rest is recovered from natural gas and petroleum. Several allotropes of sulfur exist. The most stable is rhombic sulfur which contains S_8 rings. You should know the changes that occur as sulfur is heated gradually to its boiling point.

There are two important oxides of sulfur, SO_2 and SO_3. Burning sulfur or compounds that contain sulfur give SO_2. Sulfur dioxide dissolves in water to give H_2SO_3, a weak diprotic acid that is responsible for many of the harmful effects of acid rain. Sulfur dioxide is removed from industrial gases by reaction with moist limestone.

Oxidation of SO_2 to SO_3 is accomplished catalytically. When dissolved in water, SO_3 gives H_2SO_4, which is the world's most important industrial chemical. Usually the SO_3 is dissolved in H_2SO_4 to give $H_2S_2O_7$, which is then diluted with water to give H_2SO_4. Concentrated H_2SO_4 is a strong dehydrating agent and, when hot, is a reasonably strong oxidizing agent.

Sulfur forms binary sulfides with metals, many of which react with acids to give H_2S. In other "thio" compounds, sulfur replaces oxygen. Examples are thioacetamide and thiosulfate ion. Hydrolysis of thioacetamide gives H_2S. Thiosulfate ion is used in photography to dissolve undeveloped silver bromide. Oxidation of thiosulfate gives SO_4^{2-} with Cl_2 and $S_4O_6^{2-}$ with I_2.

Self-Test

13. Describe what happens when liquid sulfur is gradually heated to its boiling point.

_____

_____

_____

_____

14. How can SO_2 be conveniently prepared in the laboratory? (Write an equation.)

_____

15. (a) What is the formula for pyrosulfuric acid? _____

    (b) What is its reaction with water?

_____

16. Give Lewis structures for H_2SO_4 and H_2SO_3.

17. Write equations for the reaction of concentrated H_2SO_4 with iodide ion.

_____

18. Write equations for the following reactions.

(a) ZnS with HCl _____

(b) SO_2 with H_2O _____

(c) $S_2O_3{}^{2-}$ with AgBr _____

(d) $S_2O_3{}^{2-}$ with I_2 _____

(e) S with $SO_3{}^{2-}$ _____

New Terms

Acid rain
> Rain made acidic by dissolved sulfur oxides and nitrogen oxides, which come from burning high-sulfur fuels.

Contact process
> The commercial method of manufacturing sulfuric acid from sulfur.

$$S + O_2 \longrightarrow SO_2$$
$$2SO_2 + O_2 \longrightarrow 2SO_3$$
$$SO_3 + H_2SO_4 \longrightarrow H_2S_2O_7$$
$$H_2S_2O_7 + H_2O \longrightarrow 2H_2SO_4$$

Frasch process
> A method of mining sulfur from deep wells. Compressed air and superheated water are forced into a sulfur deposit where they melt the sulfur and bring it to the surface.

Thio
> In a chemical name, thio means sulfur in place of oxygen.

20.3 THE HALOGENS

Objectives
> To learn the properties of the halogens. You should learn their relative oxidizing strengths, how the elements are prepared, and the properties of the compounds described here.

Review

The halogens always occur in the combined state in nature, primarily as the halides. Learn the sources of the individual halogens.

As free elements the halogens are diatomic (e.g., F_2, Cl_2, Br_2, I_2). Learn the trends in their boiling points and in their electronegativities. The halogens decrease in oxidizing strength from F_2 to I_2, and a particular halogen will displace one below it (in the periodic table) from its compounds. For example, Cl_2 will displace Br^- and I^- from their compounds.

Fluorine is produced by electrolysis of KF, HF mixtures. Chlorine is produced by electrolysis of molten NaCl and by electrolysis of brine. In the laboratory, Cl_2 can be made by reacting HCl with a strong oxidizing agent such as MnO_2, $KMnO_4$, or $K_2Cr_2O_7$. Bromine is recovered from sea water by reacting Cl_2 with the Br^- that is present. Iodine is obtained from seaweed and from Chilean saltpeter, a source of $NaIO_3$.

Hydrogen halides can be made by direct combination of the elements. The vigor of the reaction decreases from fluorine to iodine. In the laboratory, HF is made from CaF_2 and concentrated H_2SO_4; HCl is prepared from NaCl and concentrated H_2SO_4. Hydrogen bromide and hydrogen iodide can be made from NaBr and NaI using concentrated H_3PO_4. (You should learn why H_2SO_4 cannot be used.) HF has a relatively high boiling point because of hydrogen bonding. Water solutions of the hydrogen halides are acidic. All except HF are strong acids. HF reacts with silica to produce SiF_4.

The halogens form four types of oxoacids: HOX, HXO_2, HXO_3, and HXO_4, which each produce a corresponding oxoanion when neutralized. These are summarized in Table 20.2. You should know their names and structures. The most important are the oxoacids and oxoanions of chlorine.

Chlorine disproportionates in water to give HOCl and HCl. In cold base, OCl^- and Cl^- are formed. In hot aqueous base ClO_3^- and Cl^- are formed. Perchlorate ion is formed by disproportionation of chlorate ion. The oxoacids and oxoanions of chlorine tend to be strong oxidizing agents. Exceptions are dilute solutions of $HClO_4$, which have poor oxidizing power.

The halogens form many compounds with the other non-metals. Their formulas are determined by (a) the number of halogen atoms that must be attached to give the nonmetal a complete octet and (b) the size of the halogen atoms that are attached. When the halogen atom is large (e.g., Br or I) the maximum number that can pack around the nonmetal is influenced by crowding, and the larger the central atom, the greater is the number of these large halogens that can be accommodated.

The tendency of the nonmetal halides to hydrolyze is influenced by their electronic and molecular structures. Carbon tetrachloride has little tendency to hydrolyze because carbon has no vacant orbitals to which an attacking water molecule can become attached. In SF_6, the sulfur is protected from attack by the surrounding "cage" of fluorine atoms.

Self-Test

19. (a) What are the principal sources of fluorine?

_____

(b) What is the principal source of chlorine?_____

20. In which substance are the London forces stronger, Br_2 or Cl_2?

_____

21. Complete and balance the following equations. If no reaction occurs, write N.R.

(a) $CaCl_2 + Br_2 \longrightarrow$

(b) $FeBr_3 + F_2 \longrightarrow$

(c) $PbI_2 + Cl_2 \longrightarrow$

22. Write an equation for the laboratory preparation of chlorine using MnO_2 as the oxidizing agent.

_____

23. What is the ionic equation for the electrolysis of brine?

_____

24. How can Br_2 be prepared in the laboratory?

_____

25. (a) At room temperature, which halogen is a deep red
        liquid?

        _____

    (b) Which is a dark metallic-looking solid?_____

26. Which metal halide is likely to be more ionic, $TiCl_2$ or $TiCl_4$?

        _____

27. Write an equation for the laboratory preparation of

    (a) HF   _____

    (b) HCl   _____

    (c) HBr   _____

28. Which hydrogen halide is found in muriatic acid?_____

29. Write an equation for

    (a) the reaction of chlorine with calcium oxide.

        _____

    (b) the reaction of chlorine with cold aqueous sodium
         hydroxide.

        _____

    (c) the disproportionation of potassium chlorate when
         heated.

        _____

    (d) the disproportionation of bromine in hot aqueous base.

        _____

    (e) the hydrolysis of silicon tetrachloride.

        _____

30. What is the formula of periodic acid?   _____

31. On a separate sheet of paper, draw the Lewis structures
    for chlorous acid and perchloric acid.

32. What molecular structure would be predicted for

    (a) BrF_3?   _____

    (b) TeI_4?   _____

(c) $GeCl_4$?   _____

33. What reaction would you predict if $GeCl_4$ were dissolved in water?

_____

34. What explanation is given for the ease of hydrolysis of $SiCl_4$? _____

_____

New Terms

20.4 NOBLE GAS COMPOUNDS

Objectives

To study which of the noble gases are able to form compounds and to examine the bonding in them.

Review

The noble gases are very unreactive, but the heavier ones – Kr, Xe, and Rn – have ionization energies that are sufficiently low to enable them to share electrons with other very electronegative elements. Compounds of xenon have been studied more extensively than those of either krypton or radon (which is radioactive, and therefore difficult to work with). One of the key points made in this section is that scientists must avoid blind spots in their chemical thinking. Study the way the bonding in XeF_2 and XeF_4 is explained.

Self-Test

35. What are the structures of

(a) XeO_2?   _____

(b) XeO_4?   _____

(c) XeF_4?   _____

New Terms

Clathrate
    A crystal in which noble gas atoms are trapped in a cagelike
    lattice.

20.5 SILICON

Objectives

    To learn the chemical and physical properties of silicon
    and the silicates.

Review

    Silicon is the second most abundant element on Earth.   It
is a metalloid and a semiconductor.   Silicon is recovered from
silica by reduction with carbon in an electric furnace.   Very
pure silicon is prepared by reduction of $SiCl_4$ with H_2, followed
by zone refining.   The element is relatively unreactive, but dissolves in base with the evolution of hydrogen.

    The most important compounds of silicon are the silicates.
The principal structural element common to all of them is the
SiO_4 tetrahedron.   By sharing corners with other SiO_4 tetrahedra, structures of varying degrees of complexity result.
These can be summarized as follows:

    (a)   Simple SiO_4 tetrahedron

           SiO_4^{4-} (orthosilicate ion)

    (b)   Sharing of a corner between two SiO_4 tetrahedra

           $Si_2O_7^{6-}$ (pyrosilicate ion)

    (c)   Sharing of two corners by each SiO_4 tetrahedron

           $(SiO_3)_n^{2n-}$ (metasilicate ion)

    This produces long strands.   Double strands are
    also formed, as shown in Figure 20.19.

(d) Sharing of three corners by each SiO_4 tetrahedron

$$(Si_2O_5)_n^{2n-}$$

This produces planar sheets.

(e) Sharing all four corners by each SiO_4 tetrahedron

SiO_2 (silica; quartz)

This gives a three-dimensional network of covalent bonds in which the SiO_4 tetrahedra are stacked in coils. Two types of crystals are found, depending on the direction of rotation of these coils.

Silicones are inorganic polymers in which the "backbone" of the polymer is a long chain of alternating silicon and oxygen atoms. They are formed by hydrolysis of compounds such as $(CH_3)_2SiCl_2$, which is accompanied by the elimination of H_2O from pairs of Si—O—H units and the linking together of silicon atoms by oxygen bridges.

Self-Test

36. Write the chemical equation for the production of silicon in an electric furnace.

_____

37. On a separate sheet of paper, draw the Lewis structure of (a) the orthosilicate ion, (b) the pyrosilicate ion, and (c) a portion of a metasilicate ion.

38. Name a mineral that contains

(a) simple SiO_4^{4-} ions   _____

(b) long double-chains of SiO_4 tetrahedra _____

(c) sheets of SiO_4 tetrahedra   _____

(d) the cyclic $Si_6O_{18}^{12-}$ ion   _____

39. What product would you expect from the hydrolysis of $(CH_3)_3SiCl$? Draw its expected structure.

New Terms

Silicone
A type of polymer in which the "backbone" consists of alternating silicon and oxygen atoms.

Zone refining
A method for producing very high purity solids. A thin cross section of a bar of the solid is melted and the molten zone is moved slowly from one end to the other. Impurities collect in the molten zone.

Answers to Self-Test Questions

1. $Ca_3(PO_4)_2$

2. $2Ca_3(PO_4)_2 + 6SiO_2 + 10C \longrightarrow 6CaSiO_3 + 10CO + P_4$

3. Compare your answers to the structures shown on Pages 728 and 730.

4. $Na_3P + 3H_2O \longrightarrow 3NaOH + PH_3$

5. (a) $H-\overset{\cdot\cdot}{P}-H$ (b) pyramidal
           $\overset{|}{H}$

6. (a) $P_4O_6 + 6H_2O \longrightarrow 4H_3PO_3$

   (b) $P_4O_{10} + 6H_2O \longrightarrow 4H_3PO_4$

   (c) $PCl_3 + 3H_2O \longrightarrow H_3PO_3 + 3HCl$

7. A substance that is able to remove water from a gas or liquid.

8. (a) K_2HPO_3 and KH_2PO_3

   (b) By the hydrolysis of PCl_3 (see answer 6c above)

9. $\left[\begin{array}{c} :\overset{\cdot\cdot}{O}: \quad :\overset{\cdot\cdot}{O}: \\ \overset{|}{\underset{|}{:\overset{\cdot\cdot}{O}-\overset{\cdot\cdot}{P}-\overset{\cdot\cdot}{O}-\overset{\cdot\cdot}{P}-\overset{\cdot\cdot}{O}:}} \\ :\overset{\cdot}{O}: \quad :\overset{\cdot}{O}: \end{array}\right]^{4-}$

10. (a) $Na_4P_2O_7$ (b) $Na_5P_3O_{10}$

11. Compare your answers to the structures shown on Page 733.

12. $POCl_3$; the manufacture of flame retardants.

13. The pale yellow nonviscous liquid thickens and darkens as S_8 rings break into S_8 chains that link to form long S_x chains. At still higher temperatures the chains break into smaller pieces and the dark red liquid becomes thin and nonviscous again.

14. $Na_2SO_3 + 2HCl \longrightarrow 2NaCl + H_2O + SO_2$

15.(a) $H_2S_2O_7$ (b) $H_2S_2O_7 + H_2O \longrightarrow 2H_2SO_4$

16.

$$H-\ddot{\underset{|}{\overset{\overset{\displaystyle :\ddot{O}:}{|}}{O}}-S-\ddot{\underset{|}{\overset{|}{O}}-H} \qquad H-\ddot{O}-\overset{..}{\underset{..}{S}}-\ddot{O}-H$$

17. $2I^- + 3H_2SO_4 \longrightarrow I_2 + SO_2 + H_2O + 2HSO_4^-$

18.(a) $ZnS + 2HCl \longrightarrow ZnCl_2 + H_2S$

(b) $SO_2 + H_2O \longrightarrow H_2SO_3$

(c) $2S_2O_3^{2-} + AgBr \longrightarrow Ag(S_2O_3)_2^{3-} + Br^-$

(d) $2S_2O_3^{2-} + I_2 \longrightarrow 2I^- + S_4O_6^{2-}$

(e) $S + SO_3^{2-} \longrightarrow S_2O_3^{2-}$

19.(a) CaF_2, Na_3AlF_6, $Ca_5(PO_4)_3F$ (b) $NaCl$

20. Br_2, as evidenced by its higher m.p. and b.p.

21.(a) N.R.

(b) $2FeBr_3 + 3F_2 \longrightarrow 2FeF_3 + 3Br_2$

(c) $PbI_2 + Cl_2 \longrightarrow PbCl_2 + I_2$

22. $4HCl + MnO_2 \longrightarrow MnCl_2 + Cl_2 + 2H_2O$

23. $2Na^+ + 2Cl^- + 2H_2O \longrightarrow 2Na^+ + 2OH^- + H_2 + Cl_2$

24. $MnO_2 + 2Br^- + 4H^+ \longrightarrow Mn^{2+} + Br_2 + 2H_2O$

25.(a) bromine (b) iodine   26. $TiCl_2$

27.(a) $CaF_2 + H_2SO_4 \longrightarrow CaSO_4 + 2HF(g)$

(b) $NaCl + H_2SO_4 \longrightarrow NaHSO_4 + HCl(g)$

(c) $NaBr + H_3PO_4 \overset{heat}{\longrightarrow} NaH_2PO_4 + HBr(g)$

28. HCl

29.(a) $CaO + Cl_2 \longrightarrow CaCl(OCl)$

(b) $Cl_2 + 2OH^- \longrightarrow Cl^- + OCl^- + H_2O$

(c) $4KClO_3 \longrightarrow 3KClO_4 + KCl$

(d) $3Br_2 + 6OH^- \longrightarrow BrO_3^- + 5Br^- + 3H_2O$

(e) $SiCl_4 + 2H_2O \longrightarrow SiO_2 + 4HCl$

30. HIO_4

31. See Table 20.2 on Page 748.

32. (a) T-shaped (b) distorted tetrahedral (c) tetrahedral

33. $GeCl_4 + 2H_2O \longrightarrow GeO_2 + 4HCl$

34. The availability of low-energy d orbitals in the valence shell of silicon allows attachment of H_2O as one step in the mechanism for the hydrolysis.

35. (a) nonlinear (AX_2E_2 type molecule)

    (b) tetrahedral (AX_4 type molecule)

    (c) square planar (AX_4E_2 type molecule)

36. $SiO_2 + 2C \longrightarrow Si + 2CO$

37. (a) see Page 757 (b) see Page 757 (c) see Page 758

38. (a) zircon (b) asbestos (c) mica, soapstone (d) beryl

39. $(CH_3)_3Si-O-Si(CH_3)_3$

$$\begin{array}{ccc} & CH_3 & CH_3 \\ & | & | \\ H_3C-Si & -O-Si & -CH_3 \\ & | & | \\ & CH_3 & CH_3 \end{array}$$

21 THE TRANSITION ELEMENTS

This chapter deals with the chemistry of the elements in the center of the periodic table and those in the two rows that are placed just below the main body of the table.

21.1   GENERAL PROPERTIES

Objectives

To examine some general trends and relationships among the physical and chemical properties of the transition elements.

Review

Learn the nomenclature used to refer to the different types and classes of transition elements. Review the properties that most transition metals have in common:

      (a)   multiple oxidation states
      (b)   many compounds are paramagnetic
      (c)   many compounds are colored
      (d)   strong tendency to form complex ions

New Terms

d-block elements (Main transition elements)
   The transition elements found in the main part of the periodic table between Groups IIA and IIIA.

Inner transition elements
   The two long rows of elements (at. no. 58-71 and 90-103)
   that are written just below the main body of the periodic
   table.

Triad
   Any one of the three horizontal sets of elements in
   Group VIII (e.g., Fe, Co, and Ni).

21.2   ELECTRONIC STRUCTURE AND OXIDATION STATES

Objectives

   To review the electronic structures of the transition elements and to examine trends in the stabilities of oxidation
   states. You should learn the maximum oxidation states
   observed in the various B-groups and the relative stabilities of high and low oxidation states.

Review

   The electronic structures of the transition elements are
given in Tables 21.2 to 21.4. Note the irregularities at Cr and
Cu in the first transition series. This is accounted for on the
basis of the added stability possessed by a half-filled or filled
subshell.

   The oxidation states for the d-block elements are summarized in Figure 21.2. There are several points you should know.

(1) All elements in the first transition series (except Sc) show
    a +2 oxidation state.

(2) For Groups IIIB to VIIB the maximum positive oxidation
    state is equal to the group number. This also applies to
    the Group IIB elements and, to some extent, to the Group
    IB elements.

(3) In a given period, the higher oxidation states become less stable (relative to the lower ones), moving from left to right.

(4) In a given group, the higher oxidation states become relatively more stable, moving from top to bottom.

Self-Test

1. Predict the electron configurations of the following elements:

(a) Ti _____   (d) Co _____

(b) Cr _____   (e) Cu _____

(c) Mn _____

2. Why do nearly all first transition series elements show a +2 oxidation state? _____

3. Choose the compound in each pair that is expected to be the better oxidizing agent.

(a) V_2O_5 or Ta_2O_5 _____

(b) MnO_2 or TiO_2 _____

(c) Sc_2O_3 or Mn_2O_3 _____

New Terms

21.3   ATOMIC AND IONIC RADII

Objectives

To investigate trends in these two properties. Learn what is meant by "lanthanide contraction" and how it affects the chemistry of the elements of the third transition series.

Review

Only small horizontal changes in size occur among the transition elements because of the effectiveness of the d electrons at shielding the outer s electrons from the nucleus.

Large size increases occur from the first to the second series, but little or no changes occur from the second to the third series. This is due to the lanthanide contraction.

Self-Test

4. Molybdenum and tungsten have the same atomic radii, but their atoms differ greatly in atomic mass. The density of molybdenum is 10.2 g/cm^3. Compute the expected density of tungsten.

   _____

5. In each pair, which has the higher ionization energy?

   (a) Fe or Ru _____   (b) Ru or Os _____

New Terms

21.4   MAGNETISM

Objectives

To account for the magnetic properties of the transition metals and their compounds. You should learn the origin of ferromagnetism and how it differs from paramagnetism.

Review

Paramagnetism arises from the presence of unpaired electrons in atoms, molecules, or ions. Ferromagnetism appears to result from the alignment of many paramagnetic ions in domains in the solid state only. Alignment of domains produces a "permanent magnet." The formation of ferromagnetic domains seems to depend on interionic spacings.

Self-Test

6. Which three pure metals are ferromagnetic?

   _____

7. Why does melting a ferromagnetic solid produce a paramag-
    netic liquid?

_____

_____

New Terms

Ferromagnetism

> The strong magnetism associated with iron, cobalt, and
> nickel, which results from the alignment of the magnetic
> poles (in the solid state) of large numbers of paramagnetic
> atoms.

Domain

> A region in a ferromagnetic substance in which the individual
> paramagnetic atoms are all aligned in the same direction.

21.5   PROPERTIES OF SOME IMPORTANT TRANSITION METALS

Objectives

> To learn some of the physical and chemical properties of
> the important transition metals.

Review

Chromium. This hard, brittle, lustrous metal is familiar to every-
one. One of its principal uses is in stainless steel. Chromium's
major oxidation states are +2, +3, and +6; the most stable with
respect to redox is the +3 state, which exists as $Cr(H_2O)_6^{3+}$ in
water. Chromium(III) hydroxide is amphoteric. The CrO_4^{2-} and
$Cr_2O_7^{2-}$ ions are strong oxidizing agents. You should know the
structures of these ions and the equilibrium that exists between
them.

Manganese. This metal is more easily oxidized than chromium.
Its major uses are in alloys. The principal oxidation states of
Mn are: +2 (the pale pink $Mn(H_2O)_6^{2+}$ ion), +4 (MnO_2), +6 (the
green manganate ion, MnO_4^{2-}), and +7 (deep violet permanganate
ion, MnO_4^-). The most stable state is +2. You should know why
MnO_4^- is a useful titrant for redox reactions in acidic solution,

and why it is seldom used for titrations in basic solution.

Iron. This is the most-used transition metal because of its desirable physical properties and its relative ease of extraction from its compounds. Iron has two principal oxidation states, +2 and +3. The +2 state is generally easily oxidized to the +3 state. You should know the three oxides of iron and their properties. Study the mechanism believed to be responsible for the rusting of iron.

Cobalt. This metal is useful in alloys. It has two oxidation states, +2 and +3. In water, the pink $Co(H_2O)_6^{2+}$ ion is most stable. In the presence of complex ion-forming substances, the +3 state is often preferred.

Nickel. This metal is very corrosion resistant and is used in stainless steels. Iron-nickel alloys are impact resistant. The most stable oxidation state of nickel is +2. In water it exists as the emerald green $Ni(H_2O)_6^{2+}$ ion. NiO_2 is important as the cathode material in nickel-cadmium batteries.

The Coinage Metals - copper, silver, and gold. The reactivities of these metals are low, and decrease from copper to silver to gold. They do not dissolve in nonoxidizing acids. Copper and silver dissolve in HNO_3, but gold will only dissolve in aqua regia. Principal oxidation states are: copper (+1, +2), silver (+1), gold (+1, +3). Copper(I) disproportionates in water to give Cu and Cu^{2+}. You should learn the qualitative tests for Cu^{2+} and Ag^+.

Zinc, Cadmium, and Mercury. Both Zn and Cd are reactive metals that dissolve in acids such as HCl. Mercury, the only liquid metal at room temperature, does not react with HCl, but does dissolve in HNO_3. Each of these elements has a +2 oxidation state. Mercury also has a +1 state where it exists as the ion Hg_2^{2+}. Zinc and cadmium are used to protect steel from corrosion. Coating steel with zinc is called galvanizing. Zinc prevents iron from rusting by providing cathodic protection. Zinc is amphoteric, but cadmium is not, so cadmium is used to protect steel when the environment will be basic. Zinc has a relatively low toxicity, but both cadmium and mercury are quite poisonous. You should learn the qualitative test for mercury(I) salts.

Self-Test

8. Which metals, besides iron, are used to make stainless steel?

_____

9. (a) What equilibrium exists between chromate ion and dichromate ion?

_____

   (b) Sketch the structures of these two ions.

10. Write an equation showing how $Cr(H_2O)_6^{3+}$ behaves like a weak acid.

_____

11. What is the formula for chromic acid?   _____

12. (a) Why is MnO_4^- a useful titrant for redox reactions in acidic solution?

_____

_____

   (b) Why is it less useful when the reaction is to be carried out in basic solution?

_____

_____

13. Under what conditions is the manganate ion stable?

_____

14. (a) Give the formulas for the three oxides of iron.

_____

   (b) Which one is magnetic?   _____

15. (a) What substances must be present in order for iron to rust?

_____

   (b) What is the formula for rust?   _____

16. What are the principal oxidation states of

   (a) iron?   _____

   (b) cobalt?   _____

(c) chromium?   _____

(d) manganese?   _____

17. Which of the coinage metals dissolve in HCl? _____

18. When a clear colorless aqueous solution was acidified with HCl, a white precipitate was formed. This was separated from the remainder of the solution and treated with aqueous ammonia, which caused the precipitate to turn black. The solution of ammonia was then separated from the black precipitate and acidified with HNO_3. This caused a white precipitate to form. On the basis of these observations, which metal ions were present in the original aqueous solution?

_____

19. Complete and balance the following equations. If no reaction occurs, write N.R.

(a) $Mn + HCl \longrightarrow$

(b) $Fe + H_2SO_4 \longrightarrow$

(c) $Zn + OH^- \longrightarrow$

(d) $Cd + OH^- \longrightarrow$

(e) $Ag + HNO_3 \longrightarrow$

20. What color are the following?

(a) $Cu(H_2O)_4^{2+}$ _____

(b) $Mn(H_2O)_6^{2+}$ _____

(c) $Co(H_2O)_6^{2+}$ _____

(d) MnO_4^- _____

(e) $Cu(NH_3)_4^{2+}$ _____

(f) $HgNH_2Cl$ _____

(g) $Ni(H_2O)_6^{2+}$ _____

(h) CrO_4^{2-} _____

(i) $AgCl$ _____

(j) $Cr(H_2O)_6^{3+}$ _____

New Terms

Cathodic protection
Protecting a metal from corrosion by coating it with another metal that is more easily oxidized, and which thereby causes the protected metal to be the cathode in a galvanic cell.

Coinage metals
Copper, silver, and gold.

Galvanizing
Coating a steel object with zinc to protect it from corrosion.

Rust
Hydrated iron(III) oxide, $Fe_2O_3 \cdot xH_2O$.

Stainless steel
A type of steel alloy that is resistant to corrosion. It generally contains chromium and nickel alloyed with iron.

21.6 COORDINATION COMPOUNDS

Objectives

To define what is meant by "coordination compound," to examine the kinds of compounds that are formed, and to review the terminology used to describe them.

Review

Complex ions formed from a metal ion and one or more ligands are called coordination compounds. Ligands are nearly always neutral molecules or negatively charged ions which have a pair of electrons that can be donated in a coordinate covalent bond. The metal and all ligands in the first coordination sphere are generally enclosed within brackets (e.g., $[Co(NH_3)_6]^{3+}$). Monodentate ligands provide one coordinating atom; bidentate ligands provide two and form ring structures. These complexes are called chelates. A polydentate ligand is able to provide more than one donor atom. Important bidentate ligands are:

oxalate ion, $C_2O_4^{2-}$

ethylenediamine (en), $H_2N-CH_2-CH_2-NH_2$

An important polydentate ligand is EDTA.

Self-Test

21. What is the charge on the metal ion in each of the complex ions below?

   (a) $[Mn(C_2O_4)_3]^{3-}$ _____

   (b) $[FeCl_6]^{4-}$ _____

   (c) $[Cr(en)_2Cl_2]^+$ _____

   (d) $[Ni(CN)_4]^{2-}$ _____

   (e) $[PtCl_6]^{2-}$ _____

New Terms

Complex ion (or simply a complex)
    A substance formed when one or more anions or neutral molecules become bonded to a metal ion.

Coordination compound
    A compound that contains a metal ion bonded to one or more neutral molecules or anions (ligands).

Chelate
    A complex that contains rings formed by polydentate ligands.

First coordination sphere
    The set of ligands that surround a metal ion in a complex.

Ligand
    An atom or a group of atoms bonded to a central atom in a molecule or polyatomic ion. A molecule or anion that can bind to a metal ion to form a complex.

Monodentate ligand
    A ligand that can attach itself to a metal atom by only one of its atoms. Examples are ammonia and water.

Bidentate ligand
    A ligand that has two atoms that can become simultaneously attached to the same metal ion in a complex.

Polydentate ligand
    A ligand that has two or more donor atoms that can become simultaneously attached to a metal ion.

21.7   COORDINATION NUMBER AND STRUCTURE

Objectives

To examine the kinds of structures formed when different numbers of atoms are coordinated to the central metal ion.

Review

Learn the definition of coordination number. Review the structures that are found for C.N. = 2, 4 and 6. Learn to draw the 2-dimensional representation of octahedral coordination described in Figure 21.10.

Self-Test

22.   Practice drawing, on a separate piece of paper, the geometries observed most commonly for C.N. = 2, 4 and 6. Check yourself by referring to Figure 21.9 and 21.10 in the text.

New Terms

Coordination number
The number of donor atoms that surround a metal ion in a complex.

21.8   NAMING COORDINATION COMPOUNDS

Objectives

To learn how to name coordination compounds. You should be able to write the name, given the formula of a complex; you should be able to write the formula, given the name of a complex.

Review

Learn the nomenclature rules given on Pages 788 and 789 in the text. After you feel you know them, practice on the following Self-Test.

<u>Self-Test</u>

23. Name the following:

    (a) $[Co(NH_3)_6]^{3+}$ _____

    (b) $[CoBr_6]^{3-}$ _____

    (c) $[Mn(en)_2Cl_2]^+$ _____

    (d) $[Ni(H_2O)_6]^{2+}$ _____

    (e) $[Fe(H_2O)_4(NH_3)_2]^{2+}$ _____

    (f) $[Ag(CN)_2]^-$ _____

24. Write the formulas for the following:

    (a) tetraamminedichloronickel(II) _____

    (b) sodium bis(carbonato)dichlorocobaltate(III)

    _____

    (c) dithiosulfatoargentate(I) ion _____

    (d) hexaaquachromium(III) hexacyanochromate(III)

    _____

    (e) diaquabis(oxalato)chromate(III) ion _____

    (f) diammineaquachlorodithiocyanatomanganate(II) ion

    _____

    (g) dicyanobis(ethylenediamine)cobalt(III) chloride

    _____

<u>New Terms</u>

21.9   ISOMERISM AND COORDINATION COMPOUNDS

Objectives

To learn the meaning of the term "isomerism" and to see how it is applied to coordination compounds. You should learn the different types of isomerism described in this section.

Review

Compounds having the same formula but different structures are called isomers. Review the following types of isomerism: ionization isomerism, stereoisomerism, geometrical isomerism, optical isomerism. Be sure you know the difference between cis- and trans- isomers. Remember that optical isomers are nonsuperimposable mirror images of each other and are said to be chiral. Optically active compounds have the ability to rotate plane polarized light. An equal mixture of optical isomers is said to be racemic.

Self-Test

25. Sketch the cis-trans isomers for (a) $[Co(H_2O)_4Cl_2]^+$ and (b) $[Co(C_2O_4)_2Cl_2]$.

26. Which of the following are expected to exhibit optical isomerism?

    (a) $[Co(NH_3)_6]^{3+}$

    (b)   trans-$[Co(C_2O_4)_2Cl_2]^{3-}$

    (c) $[Co(en)_3]^{3+}$

    (d)   cis-$[Co(en)_2(NH_3)_2]^{3+}$

    (e)   cis-$[Co(NH_3)_4Cl_2]^+$ _____

New Terms

Isomers
Compounds that have the same formula but differ in the way their atoms are arranged.

Stereoisomers
Isomers that have the same atoms bonded to each other but differ in the way the atoms are arranged in space.

Geometrical isomers
Isomers that differ in the relative orientations of the atoms.

Ionization isomers
Coordination compounds that have the same molecular formulas, but in which different anions serve as ligands.

Cis-
A term applied to a geometrical isomer in which two groups are located on the same side of some central reference line in the molecule or ion.

Trans-
A term applied to a geometrical isomer in which two groups are located on opposite sides of some central imaginary line in the molecule or ion.

Chiral
Possessing a "handedness." A term applied to optical isomers, which are not superimposable on their mirror images.

Optical activity
The rotation of the plane of polarized light as it passes through a chiral substance, either in its pure state or in a solution.

Optical isomers (Enantiomers)
Isomers that are nonsuperimposable mirror images of each other.

Polarized light
Light in which the oscillations of the light waves are all in the same plane.

Racemic
A mixture that contains equal numbers of the two optical isomers of a substance, and which does not rotate the plane of polarized light in either direction.

Dextrorotatory

An optical isomer that causes a rotation of plane polarized
light in a clockwise direction, when looking toward the
source, as the light passes through a solution of the isomer.

Levorotatory

An optical isomer that causes a rotation of plane polarized
light in a counterclockwise direction, when looking toward
the source, as the light passes through a solution of the
isomer.

21.10 BONDING IN COORDINATION COMPOUNDS: VALENCE BOND THEORY

Objectives

To account for the structure and magnetic properties of
complex ions using the valence bond theory.

Review

To form coordinate covalent bonds, the metal ion must
provide one empty hybrid orbital for each coordinating ligand
atom.   An inner orbital complex is formed if the d subshell below
the metal atom's outer shell is used.   For C.N. = 6 the hybrids
are specified as d^2sp^3.   An outer orbital complex is formed if the
d orbitals are from the metal atom's outer shell.   For C.N. = 6,
these hybrids are specified as sp^3d^2.

When the metal ion has four, five or six d electrons, it is
necessary to choose between inner and outer orbital complexes
because they lead to different magnetic properties.   As a general
rule, for d^4 or d^6 ions of the first transition series, inner orbital
complexes are preferred except when the ligands are F^- or H_2O.
For d^5 ions, outer orbital complexes are preferred except when
the ligand is NO_2^- (nitro) or CN^-.

Tetrahedral complexes use sp^3 hybrid orbitals; square
planar complexes use dsp^2 hybrids.

Self-Test

27.   Give the orbital diagrams for the following octahedral com-

plex ions.

(a) $[MnCl_6]^{2-}$

(b) $[FeCl_6]^{3-}$

(c) $[Co(CN)_6]^{3-}$

New Terms

Inner orbital complex
> A complex in which the metal ion uses d orbitals below its outer shell in forming hybrid orbitals used for bonding to the ligands.

Outer orbital complex
> A complex in which the metal ion uses d orbitals in its outer shell to form the hybrid orbitals that are used in bonding to the ligands.

21.11   CRYSTAL FIELD THEORY

Objectives

To describe a bonding theory that can explain the colors of complex ions as well as their magnetic properties.

Review

Crystal field theory considers the effect of the ligand ions (or dipoles) on the energies of the d orbitals of the metal ion. In an octahedral complex the ligands split the d orbitals into a low energy set of three orbitals (the t_{2g} level) and a high energy set of two orbitals (the e_g level).   The energy difference between them is called Δ. When a complex absorbs light, an electron is raised in energy from the t_{2g} to the e_g level.   The color of the light absorbed depends on the magnitude of Δ.   The size of Δ is influenced by the nature of the ligands.   Learn the shapes of the d orbitals (Figure 21.20) and the spectrochemical series given on Page 800.

For metal ions with d^4, d^5, d^6 or d^7 configurations the magnetic properties are determined by the magnitude of Δ in relationship to the **pairing** energy P.   Review the discussion of the factors that determine whether a low spin or high spin complex is formed.

Review the splitting patterns of the d orbitals for tetrahedral and square planar complexes. Remember that Δ_{tetr} is always much less than Δ_{oct}.

Self-Test

28. On a separate sheet of paper, sketch the CFT splitting pattern for d orbitals in octahedral, square planar, and tetrahedral complex ions. Check your answers by referring to Figures 21.27 and 21.29 in the text.

29. On a separate sheet of paper, indicate the electron population of the t_{2g} and e_g orbitals in low and high spin complexes for a d^7 metal ion.

30. Which complex in each pair below should absorb light of higher frequency (shorter wavelength)?

    (a) $[CrCl_6]^{3-}$ or $[CrBr_6]^{3-}$ _____

    (b) $[CrCl_6]^{3-}$ or $[Cr(NH_3)_6]^{3+}$ _____

    (c) $[NiCl_6]^{4-}$ or $[Ni(NO_2)_6]^{4-}$ _____

    (d) $[Fe(NH_3)_6]^{3+}$ or $[Fe(CN)_6]^{3-}$ _____

31. In a certain complex containing a metal ion with a d^6 configuration, the pairing energy is greater than Δ. Will this complex be low spin or high spin?

    _____

New Terms

Crystal field theory
  A theory that considers the effects of the polar or ionic ligands of a complex on the energies of the d orbitals of the central metal ion.

Crystal field splitting, Δ
  The energy difference between sets of d orbitals in a complex.

High spin complex
  A complex in which there is minimum pairing of electrons in the d orbitals of the central metal ion.

Low spin complex
    A complex in which there is a maximum pairing of electrons
    in the orbitals of the central metal atom.

Pairing energy
    The amount of energy that must be absorbed to cause two
    electrons to occupy the same orbital with their spins paired.

Spectrochemical series
    A list of ligands arranged in order of their ability to pro-
    duce a large crystal field splitting.

Answers to Self-Test Questions

1. See Table 21.2 in the text.   2. From the loss of two 4s electrons   3.(a) V_2O_5 (b) MnO_2 (c) Mn_2O_3 4. d = 19.5 g/cm^3
(calculated). The atomic weight of W (183.85) is 1.92 times
larger than that of Mo (93.94), so 1.92 times as much mass is
packed into the same volume. Therefore, the density of W
should be 1.92 times larger than that of Mo. The actual measured density of tungsten is 19.3 g/cm^3.   5.(a) Fe (b) Os
6. iron, cobalt, and nickel   7. Melting destroys the domains,
which are necessary for ferromagnetism.   8. chromium and nickel

9.(a) $CrO_4^{2-} + 2H^+ \rightleftharpoons Cr_2O_7^{2-} + H_2O$ (b) See Page 776.

10. $Cr(H_2O)_6^{3+} + H_2O \rightleftharpoons Cr(H_2O)_5OH^{2+} + H_3O^+$ 11. H_2CrO_4

12.(a) MnO_4^- is deep violet, Mn^{2+} is very pale pink; MnO_4^-
    serves as its own indicator.

  (b) MnO_4^- gives solid MnO_2 in basic solution, which obscures
    the endpoint.

13. Very basic conditions

14.(a) FeO, Fe_2O_3, Fe_3O_4 (b) Fe_3O_4, magnetite

15.(a) oxygen <u>and</u> moisture   (b) $Fe_2O_3 \cdot xH_2O$

16.(a) +2, +3 (b) +2, +3 (c) +2, +3, +6 (d) +2, +4, +6, +7

17. none of them   18. Hg_2^{2+} and Ag^+

19.(a) $Mn + 2HCl \longrightarrow MnCl_2 + H_2$

  (b) $Fe + H_2SO_4 \longrightarrow FeSO_4 + H_2$

(c) $Zn + 2OH^- + 2H_2O \longrightarrow Zn(OH)_4^{2-} + H_2$

(d) N.R.

(e) $3Ag + 4HNO_3 \longrightarrow 3AgNO_3 + NO + 2H_2O$

20.(a) pale blue (b) pale pink (c) pink (d) deep violet
(e) deep blue (f) white (g) green (h) yellow (i) white
(j) violet   21.(a) +3 (b) +2 (c) +3 (d) +2 (e) +4

22. See Figure 21.9.   23.(a) hexaamminecobalt(III) ion
(b) hexabromocobaltate(III) ion
(c) dichlorobis(ethylenediamine)manganese(III) ion
(d) hexaaquanickel(II) ion   (e) diamminetetraaquairon(II) ion
(f) dicyanoargentate(I) ion

24.(a) $[Ni(NH_3)_4Cl_2]$ (b) $Na_3[Co(CO_3)_2Cl_2]$ (c) $[Ag(S_2O_3)_2]^{3-}$
(d) $[Cr(H_2O)_6][Cr(CN)_6]$ (e) $[Cr(C_2O_4)_2(H_2O)_2]^+$
(f) $[Mn(NH_3)_2(SCN)_2(H_2O)Cl]^-$ (g) $[Co(en)_2(CN)_2]Cl$

25. (a)

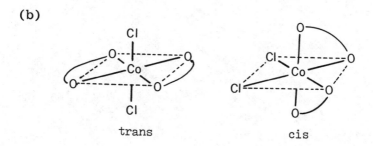

trans   cis

(b)

trans   cis

26. c and d

27. (a) ↑ ↑ ↑ XX XX   XX   XX XX XX   _ _ _ _ _
           3d   4s   4p   4d

(b) ↑ ↑ ↑ ↑ ↑   XX   XX XX XX   XX XX   _ _ _ _ _

(c) ↑↓ ↑↓ ↑↓ XX XX   XX   XX XX XX   _ _ _ _ _

28. See Figures 21.27 and 21.29.

29. $\underline{\uparrow}$ $\underline{\uparrow}$ e_g $\underline{\uparrow}$ $\underline{}$

$\underline{\uparrow\downarrow}$ $\underline{\uparrow\downarrow}$ $\underline{\uparrow}$ t_{2g} $\underline{\uparrow\downarrow}$ $\underline{\uparrow\downarrow}$ $\underline{\uparrow\downarrow}$

high spin   low spin

30.(a) $[CrCl_6]^{3-}$ (b) $[Cr(NH_3)_6]^{3+}$ (c) $[Ni(NO_2)_6]^{3-}$

(d) $[Fe(CN)_6]^{3-}$

31. high spin

22 NUCLEAR CHEMISTRY

In this chapter we will examine nuclear changes, what their implications are in chemistry, and how they can be harnessed in energy production. This latter topic, of course, has become an important issue lately because of growing demands for energy and the increasing price of energy-rich fuels.

22.1 SPONTANEOUS RADIOACTIVE DECAY

Objectives

> To review the types of nuclear decay processes that occur and to learn how to write nuclear equations.

Review

> You should be sure you know the mass, charge and symbol for each of the particles in Table 22.1. If necessary, review the method of indicating mass number and atomic number for isotopes in Section 3.10, Page 98 of the text.

> In balancing a nuclear equation, remember that mass and charge must both be balanced. This requires that the sum of mass numbers (left superscript) on both sides of the arrow must be equal. Also, the algebraic sum of charges (left subscripts) on both sides of the arrow must be the same. Review Example 22.1 in the text.

Kinetically, radioactive decay is a first-order process. The relative rate of decay of radioisotopes are usually expressed in terms of the half-life, $t_{\frac{1}{2}}$, which is the time required for half of the sample to decay. Learn to apply Equations 22.1 and 22.2 (review Examples 22.2 and 22.3).

Learn the various units used to express intensities and amounts of radiation, as well as how nuclear radiation is detected.

Self-Test

1. Without referring to the text, write the symbols for the following. Afterward, check your answer by referring to Table 22.1 in the text.

   (a) proton _____   (d) alpha particle _____

   (b) neutron _____   (e) positron _____

   (c) beta particle _____

2. Fill in the missing symbol in each of the following:

   (a) $^{27}_{13}Al + ^{4}_{2}He \longrightarrow$ _____ $+ ^{1}_{0}n$

   (b) $^{63}_{29}Cu + ^{1}_{1}H \longrightarrow$ _____

   (c) $^{133}_{56}Ba + ^{0}_{-1}e \longrightarrow$ _____

   (d) $^{213}_{83}Bi \longrightarrow ^{209}_{81}Tl +$ _____

   (e) $^{209}_{82}Pb \longrightarrow ^{209}_{83}Bi +$ _____

   (f) $^{238}_{92}U +$ _____ $\longrightarrow ^{247}_{99}Es + 5 ^{1}_{0}n$

   (g) $^{235}_{92}U + ^{1}_{0}n \longrightarrow ^{139}_{36}Ba +$ _____ $+ 3 ^{1}_{0}n$

3. The half-life of $^{90}_{38}Sr$ is 19.9 years. What is the rate constant for the decay process? _____

4. What do the letters stand for in the unit rad? _____

_____

5. If a person weighing 73.0 kg received a dose of radiation equal to 0.500 Gy, how many joules were absorbed?

What is the dose in rad? _____

New Terms

Radioactive decay
   The gradual transformation of a collection of unstable nuclei into a collection of stable nuclei by the emission of various forms of radiation (α, β, or γ).

Radioactive series (Decay series)
   The series of radioactive isotopes produced one after another during the decay of some particular radioactive element. The series terminates when a stable nonradioactive nucleus is formed.

Radioactivity
   The spontaneous emission of radiation by certain unstable atomic nuclei.

Radioisotope
   A radioactive isotope.

Nuclide
   A general term used to describe the nucleus of a particular isotope.

Radionuclide
   The nucleus of a radioactive isotope.

Alpha particle (α-particle)
   The nucleus of a helium atom, $_2^4\text{He}$. One of the types of radiation given off by radioactive substances.

Beta particle (β-particle)
   A particle given off by a radioactive nucleus. It is actually an electron. Its symbol is $_{-1}^0\text{e}$.

Gamma rays (γ-rays)
   High energy, short wavelength (high frequency) radiation similar to X rays that is given off by radioactive substances.

Geiger–Müller counter
   A device used to detect radioactive emissions.

Parent isotope
   The isotope that changes into some other isotope in a radioactive decay.

Daughter isotope
   An isotope produced in a radioactive decay.

Becquerel (Bk)
   A unit of radioactive activity: 1 Bk = 1 disintegration/sec-
   ond.

Specific activity
   The number of nuclear disintegrations per second per gram
   of sample.   In the SI, its units are Bk g^{-1}.

Curie (Ci)
   A measure of radioactive activity related to radium as a
   standard.   1 Ci = 3.7 x 10^{10} Bk.

Gray (Gy)
   A unit used to express the absorbed dose of radiation.   One
   gray (1 Gy) is a dose of 1 joule per kilogram of absorbing
   material.

Rad
   A unit of radiation absorbed dose: 1 rad = 10^{-5} J/g =
   10^{-2} Gy.

Rem
   Radiation equivalent in man.   A unit of absorbed dose that
   takes into account the kind of radiation and the degree to
   which it is absorbed by animal tissue.

22.2   APPLICATIONS OF NUCLEAR REACTIONS

Objectives

   To learn how nuclear reactions and radioactivity are used.

Review

Archaeological dating makes use of the known half-lives of certain isotopes. Review Example 22.4 on Page 815.

Chemical applications of radioisotopes rely primarily on their ability to be detected and counted. This section illustrates several examples of applications to chemical analysis, the study of descriptive chemistry, and the study of reaction mechanisms.

Review the reasoning involved in the isotope dilution method. Apply this reasoning to Question 7 in the Self-Test. Also review the principles of neutron activation analysis.

Self-Test

6. A piece of wood taken from a burial mound of ancient civilization was found to contain only 1/3 as much carbon-14 as in a live tree. Estimate the age of the wood (and the burial mound).

_____

7. A 1.00-g portion of KCl labeled with ^{40}K and having a specific activity of 100 Bk per gram was added to a 112-g sample of a mixture of KCl and other salts. By fractional crystallization, some pure KCl was recovered from the mixture. This KCl had a specific activity of 1.2 Bk per gram. What weight of KCl was in the original 112-g sample? What percent of the sample was KCl?

_____

8. A student proposed the following structure for the thiosulfate, $S_2O_3{}^{2-}$, ion: $[O-S-O-S-O]^{2-}$. Thiosulfate is formed from $SO_3{}^{2-}$ by reaction with elemental sulfur.

$$S + SO_3{}^{2-} \longrightarrow S_2O_3{}^{2-}$$

If radioactive sulfur is used in this reaction, the $S_2O_3{}^{2-}$ becomes labeled. When treated with H^+, the $S_2O_3{}^{2-}$ decomposes and SO_2 is evolved. None of the radioactivity occurs in this SO_2. How does this argue against the structure proposed by the student?

New Terms

Isotope dilution
> An analytical method in which a small amount of a radioactive
> isotope is added to a sample and in which the extent of
> dilution is used to compute the amount of nonradioactive
> isotope originally present in the sample.

Neutron activation analysis
> An analytical procedure in which nonradioactive isotopes are
> bombarded by neutrons, making some of their atoms radio-
> active. From the frequencies of the γ rays emitted by the
> bombarded sample, the concentrations of the various elements
> in the sample can be determined.

Tracer study
> The use of radioisotopes to follow the fate of certain atoms
> during chemical reactions.

22.3   NUCLEAR STABILITY

Objectives

> To look at the characteristics exhibited by both stable and
> unstable nuclei. You should learn the kinds of reactions
> unstable nuclei undergo to become stable.

Review

Stable nuclei lie in a "band of stability." With the exception of hydrogen, stable nuclei always possess at least as many
neutrons as protons; at high atomic number, neutrons outnumber
protons. The band of stability ends at Z = 83.

Elements having an n/p ratio that is too high generally
decay by beta emission or neutron emission. Elements with low
n/p ratios tend to emit positrons or undergo electron capture.
Elements with Z > 83 undergo alpha emission or nuclear fission.

Stable nuclei with odd numbers of both protons and neutrons are rare. Conversely, stable nuclei with even numbers of
protons and neutrons are much more common. Some nuclei are
very stable and possess "magic numbers" of both protons and

neutrons. This supports the nuclear shell theory.

<u>Self-Test</u>

9. The isotope $^{107}_{48}$Cd decays by electron capture. Write the nuclear equation for the reaction.

_____

10. The isotope $^{107}_{49}$In lies below the band of stability. Which of the following is a likely decay mode for this isotope?

(a) $^{107}_{49}$In $\longrightarrow$ $^{107}_{50}$Sn + $^{0}_{-1}$e   (c) $^{107}_{49}$In $\longrightarrow$ $^{103}_{47}$Ag + $^{4}_{2}$He

(b) $^{107}_{49}$In $\longrightarrow$ $^{106}_{49}$In + $^{1}_{0}$n   (d) $^{107}_{49}$In $\longrightarrow$ $^{107}_{48}$Cd + $^{0}_{1}$e

_____

<u>New Terms</u>

Band of stability
    The collection of stable nuclei with various numbers of protons and neutrons that fall within a narrow band on a plot of numbers of neutrons versus numbers of protons.

Electron capture (K-capture)
    Capture of an electron from an atom's 1s orbital (K shell) by an unstable nucleus. It converts a proton to a neutron in the nucleus.

Fission
    Splitting of a heavy unstable nucleus into several pieces, usually with the emission of large amounts of energy.

Magic numbers
    Numbers of protons and neutrons found in especially stable nuclei.

22.4   NUCLEAR TRANSFORMATIONS

Objectives

> To briefly examine how nuclear reactions can be brought
> about by bombarding nuclei with various particles.

Review

> Nuclear transformations occur when target nuclei are bom-
barded with various particles.   Learn the shorthand notation used
to describe these reactions (e.g., $^{27}_{13}Al\,(\alpha,n)\,^{30}_{15}P$).

New Terms

Nuclear transformations
> Changes in nuclei brought about by bombarding them with
> high energy particles such as neutrons.

Particle accelerator
> A device that accelerates charged particles to very high
> speeds (high energies) before allowing them to bombard
> target nuclei.

Cyclotron
> A type of particle accelerator that is used to study nuclear
> reactions.

Transuranium elements
> All the elements after uranium ($Z = 92$) in the periodic table.
> They are not naturally occurring.

22.5   EXTENSION OF THE PERIODIC TABLE

Objectives

> To consider the possibility of stable superheavy elements
> beyond the current range of the periodic table.

Review

The possibility of very heavy stable nuclei is predicted on the basis of magic numbers of 114 for protons and 184 for neutrons.

Self-Test

11. How many electrons could be accommodated in a g subshell?

_____

12. Which element (currently known) would be expected to have chemical properties most similar to element Z = 114?

_____

13. If element 115 were isolated, what would you expect the formula of its oxide to be?

_____

New Terms

22.6 NUCLEAR BINDING ENERGY

Objectives

To examine the energy that is associated with nuclear stability and the strong attractive forces that bind nuclear particles together.

Review

The mass of a given nucleus is always <u>less</u> than the sum of the masses of the individual protons and neutrons that go toward forming the nucleus. The difference between the calculated and actual masses is called the mass defect. Its energy equivalent is called the binding energy and can be calculated from the mass defect by applying Einstein's equation, $E = mc^2$. In these calculations, illustrated on Page 826, use the value,

$$c = 2.99792 \times 10^8 \text{ m/s}$$

The binding energy can be expressed in MeV, in which case,

$$1 \text{ amu} = 931 \text{ MeV}$$

The highest binding energy per nucleon occurs in the vicinity of iron in the periodic table.

Self-Test

14. (a) Compute the binding energy for $^{32}_{16}S$ which has an atomic mass of 31.97207 amu.

    _____

    (b) What is the binding energy per nucleon for $^{32}_{16}S$?

    _____

New Terms

Binding energy
　　The energy equivalent of the mass defect of a nuclide. This energy would have been released on formation of the nuclide from its protons and neutrons.

Mass defect
　　The difference between the actual mass of a nuclide and the mass computed by adding the weights of the corresponding number of protons and neutrons.

MeV (million electron volts)
　　An energy unit used to express binding energies and energy changes that accompany nuclear reactions. 1 MeV per nuclide corresponds to an energy of 9.65×10^7 kJ/mol.

Nucleon
　　An individual particle found in an atomic nucleus.

22.7   FISSION, FUSION, AND NUCLEAR ENERGY

Objectives

To examine nuclear fission and fusion processes and to consider them as potential sources of energy.

Review

Fission chain reactions occur because more neutrons are

produced during fission than are consumed. The minimum amount of fissionable material required to sustain a chain reaction is called the critical mass.

Review the operation of a nuclear reactor. A breeder reactor produces more fuel than it consumes.

Nuclear fusion involves the creation of a heavier nucleus from two lighter ones. Fusion liberates a large amount of energy but requires extremely high temperatures to occur.

Fission releases energy because the lighter particles produced have greater binding energy. Fusion releases energy because the heavier particles formed have much larger binding energies.

New Terms

Critical mass
   The minimum amount of fissionable material that must be present to sustain a nuclear chain reaction.

Fusion
   Melting. In nuclear reactions, it is the joining of light-weight nuclei to produce heavier nuclei with the simultaneous emission of large amounts of energy.

Plasma
   A very hot, high energy gas composed of ions.

Breeder reactor
   A nuclear reactor that produces plutonium from ^{238}U. The amount of fissionable Pu produced is greater than the amount of nuclear fuel consumed.

Answers to Self-Test Questions

1. See Table 22.1.

2.(a) $^{30}_{15}P$ (b) $^{64}_{30}Zn$ (c) $^{133}_{55}Cs$ (d) $^{4}_{2}He$ (e) $^{0}_{-1}e$ (f) $^{14}_{7}N$

   (g) $^{139}_{36}Kr$

3. $k = 3.48 \times 10^{-2} \text{ yr}^{-1}$
4. Radiation absorbed dose
5. 36.5 J, 50 rad
6. 9000 years
7. 83.3 g KCl, 74.4%
8. Since either bond 1 or 2 in $O-S\overset{1}{-}O\overset{2}{-}S-O$ would be expected to break with equal ease, there is no reason to expect that this structure would <u>never</u> give the labeled sulfur in the SO_2. An unsymmetrical structure is required to explain the results of this experiment. The actual structure of $S_2O_3^{2-}$ is

$$\left[\begin{array}{c} O \\ | \\ S-S-O \\ | \\ O \end{array} \right]^{2-}$$

9. $^{107}_{48}Cd + ^{0}_{-1}e \longrightarrow ^{107}_{47}Ag$
10. d
11. 18
12. Pb
13. X_2O_3
14. (a) 272 MeV   (b) 8.50 MeV/nucleon

23 ORGANIC CHEMISTRY

In this chapter we deal with the chemistry of carbon compounds. These range from simple molecules such as methane, CH_4, to extremely large polymer molecules such as polystyrene or polyethylene. The purpose of the chapter is to acquaint you with the breadth of the subject, rather than to delve too deeply into specific areas, and to illustrate some of the many practical uses to which organic compounds are applied.

23.1 HYDROCARBONS

Objectives

To examine the class of organic compounds called hydrocarbons. You should learn the nomenclature for the first ten members of the alkane, alkene and alkyne series. You should also become familiar with the bonding and structure of these compounds.

Review

Saturated hydrocarbons (the alkanes) contain only single bonds; unsaturated hydrocarbons contain either carbon–carbon double bonds (alkenes) or triple bonds (alkynes). In the alkanes the carbon is sp^3 hybridized and lies at the center of a tetrahedron. When doubly bonded, carbon employs sp^2 hybrid orbitals; when triply bonded, carbon utilizes sp hybrids.

Review the names of the alkanes in Table 23.1. You

should be able to identify the number of carbon atoms in the chain by the stem of the name; for example, pentane signifies a five carbon atom chain.

Self-Test

1. Indicate the number of carbon atoms in each of the following:

   (a) butene _____   (e) ethene _____

   (b) hexyne _____   (f) nonene _____

   (c) octane _____   (g) propyne _____

   (d) methane _____   (h) heptene _____

2. Write the molecular formulas for the following:

   (a) propene _____   (c) decyne _____

   (b) butane _____   (d) pentane _____

3. How many π-bonds would be found in:

   (a) hexene _____   (d) C_5H_8 _____

   (b) butylene _____   (e) C_8H_{18} _____

   (c) C_6H_{12} _____

New Terms

Aliphatic hydrocarbons
    Hydrocarbons that lack the benzene ring structure.

Alkane
    A saturated hydrocarbon of general formula C_nH_{2n+2}.

Alkene
    A hydrocarbon with one carbon–carbon double bond and having the general formula C_nH_{2n}.

Alkyne
    A hydrocarbon with one carbon–carbon triple bond and having the general formula C_nH_{2n-2}.

Homologous series
    A series of hydrocarbons in which each member differs from the preceding member by the same grouping of atoms.

Hydrocarbon
    A compound composed of only carbon and hydrogen.

Olefin
    An alkene.

Paraffin
    The general name given to the alkane series of hydrocarbons.
    Also, high molecular weight hydrocarbons such as $C_{20}H_{42}$
    that exist as waxes at room temperature.

Saturated hydrocarbon
    A hydrocarbon in which all the carbon-carbon bonds are
    single bonds.

Unsaturated hydrocarbon
    A hydrocarbon having one or more carbon-carbon double or
    triple bonds in its structure.

23.2 ISOMERS OF ORGANIC COMPOUNDS

Objectives

    To examine the types of isomerism that occur among organ-
    ic compounds.

Review

    Structural isomers occur with the alkanes by branching of
chains. Among alkenes and alkynes there are also different possible positions of the double or triple bond. Stereoisomerism includes cis-trans isomerism (geometrical isomers) and optical isomerism. Cis-trans isomers occur in alkenes, where free rotation
about the carbon-carbon double bond cannot occur. Optical isomers exist when a molecule contains one or more asymmetric carbon atoms (carbon atoms attached to four different groups).

Self-Test

4. On a separate sheet of paper draw the cis and trans isomers
    of butene. Check your answer by turning to Page 844 of
    the text.

5. Which of the following can exist as optical isomers?

(a)
$$Cl-\underset{\underset{F}{|}}{\overset{\overset{H}{|}}{C}}-CH_3$$

(b)
$$CH_3-\underset{\underset{CH_3}{|}}{CH}-CH_3$$

(c)
$$CH_3-CH_2-\underset{\underset{CH_3}{|}}{CH}-CH_2-CH_2-CH_3$$

New Terms

Assymmetric carbon atom
A carbon atom that is bonded to four different groups and which is a center of chirality.

Structural isomers
Isomers that differ in the sequence in which their atoms are bonded together.

23.3 NAMING ORGANIC COMPOUNDS

Objectives

To describe the nomenclature system that has been devised to name organic compounds. You should be able to name straight and branched-chain alkanes, alkenes, and alkynes.

Review

Review the nomenclature rules and examples on Pages 847 to 850 of the text. When you feel confident that you have learned the rules, try the Self-Test for this section.

Self-Test

6. Name the compounds in Table 23.2 in your text.

7. Name the following:

(a)
$$CH_3-CH=\underset{\underset{CH_3}{|}}{C}-CH_2-CH_3$$

_____

(b) CH$_3$-C=C-CH$_2$-CH$_3$
           CH$_3$ C=CH$_2$
                    CH$_3$

New Terms

Alkyl group

A group of atoms, derived from an alkane by loss of a hydrogen, that replaces a hydrogen in another molecule.

Trivial name

The common name for a compound.

23.4   CYCLIC HYDROCARBONS

Objectives

To examine a class of hydrocarbons composed of ring structures.

Review

Learn the nomenclature that is applied to these cyclic compounds. Note that their stability and structure can be related to the C—C—C angle within the ring structure.

Self-Test

8. Write structural formulas for the cyclic hydrocarbons represented by

    (a) ⬜ _____

    (b) ⬠ _____

    (c) ⬡ _____

9. Name the compounds in Question 8.

(a) _____

(b) _____

(c) _____

New Terms

Cyclo-
   A prefix that means that the carbon chain in an organic
   molecule exists in the form of a ring.

23.5 AROMATIC HYDROCARBONS

Objectives

   To study the structure, bonding and nomenclature of
   benzene related compounds.

Review

   Remember that benzene has a planar ring structure that
can be viewed as a resonance hybrid of two structures with alternating single and double bonds. Molecular orbital theory
views the bonding in terms of a delocalized π-electron cloud.

   Review the nomenclature system for benzene derivatives.

Self-Test

10. What is the C—C—C bond angle in benzene?_____

11. Name the following:

(a)

_____

(b) [benzene ring]$CH_2-CH=CH_2$

(c) [benzene ring]$\overset{\displaystyle CH_3}{\underset{\displaystyle }{CH}}-\overset{\displaystyle CH_3}{\underset{\displaystyle CH_3}{C}}$[benzene ring]

New Terms

Aromatic hydrocarbon

A hydrocarbon that contains a benzene ring structure.

Meta–

In a benzene ring, positions separated by one intervening carbon atom.

Ortho–

In the benzene ring, positions that are adjacent to each other.

Para–

In the benzene ring, positions separated by two intervening carbon atoms.

Phenyl group

Benzene, with one hydrogen removed, that becomes attached to some other organic molecule in place of a hydrogen.

23.6   HYDROCARBON DERIVATIVES

Objectives

To see how most organic compounds can be considered to be derived from hydrocarbons by substituting certain groups of atoms (called functional groups) for hydrogen in the parent hydrocarbon molecule.

Review

A functional group is some group of atoms that imparts a characteristic property to an organic molecule. Review the functional groups in Table 23.5 on Page 861 of the text.

Typical reactions discussed in this section include addition reactions, which are characteristic of unsaturated hydrocarbons. Markovnikov's rule states that when HX is added across a double bond, the H goes to the carbon atom already containing the most H's. Remember that saturated hydrocarbons primarily undergo substitution reactions.

Self-Test

12. Without referring to Table 23.5, identify the following functional groups:

   (a) $\overset{\displaystyle O}{\overset{\displaystyle \|}{-C-H}}$ _____

   (b) $-OH$ _____

   (c) $-C\overset{\displaystyle O}{\underset{\displaystyle OH}{}}$ _____

   (d) $-\overset{|}{C}-O-\overset{|}{\underset{|}{C}}-$ _____

   (e) $-\overset{\displaystyle O}{\overset{\displaystyle \|}{C}}-O-\overset{|}{\underset{|}{C}}-$ _____

13. Write chemical equations for the following, showing the structures of the main product:

   (a) $CH_3-CH{=}CH_2 + Br_2 \longrightarrow$ _____

   (b) $CH_3-CH_3 + Cl_2 \longrightarrow$ _____

   (c) $CH_3-\underset{\underset{\displaystyle CH_3}{|}}{C}{=}CH_2 + HCN \longrightarrow$ _____

   (This is an addition reaction, too.)

New Terms

Addition reaction
A reaction in which a molecule such as H_2 is added across a double or triple bond in an organic molecule.

Functional group
A group of atoms in an organic molecule that gives the molecule certain characteristic properties.

Markovnikov's rule
During an addition reaction, the hydrogen of the molecule being added becomes attached to the carbon that is already bonded to the larger number of hydrogen atoms.

Substitution reaction
A reaction in which one atom replaces another in a molecule.

23.7 HALOGEN DERIVATIVES

Objectives

To learn about some methods of preparation and characteristic reactions of halogenated hydrocarbons. You should also become aware of some of the many uses of these compounds.

Review

Many common chemicals contain halogens. Examine some of these examples on Page 862. Halogenated compounds can be prepared by substitution reactions of halogens with alkanes, and by halogen addition to alkenes. The most important methods involve reactions in which the OH group of an alcohol is displaced by a halogen.

Self-Test

14. List some uses of halogen-containing compounds._____

_____

_____

15. Give an example of a reaction that might be used to prepare $CH_3-CHCl-CH_3$ from $CH_3-CHOH-CH_3$.

New Terms

23.8   ORGANIC COMPOUNDS THAT CONTAIN OXYGEN

Objectives

To examine some properties and chemical reactions involving a number of interrelated oxygen-containing functional groups. You should also learn some applications of the various kinds of compounds discussed in this section.

Review

Six major functional groups are discussed in this section: alcohols, aldehydes, ketones, acids, esters, and ethers. Be sure you can distinguish among them.

Some important relationships in this section are:

(1) Alcohols can be oxidized to give aldehydes or ketones; aldehydes can be oxidized to give acids.

(2) The products of oxidation of an alcohol depend on whether the alcohol is primary, secondary, or tertiary.

(3) Acids react (reversibly) with alcohols to produce esters by a condensation reaction involving elimination of water. The base-catalyzed hydrolysis of an ester is called saponification.

(4) Aldehydes and ketones contain the carbonyl group, $>C=O$.

(5) The acidity of organic acids arises from the carboxyl group, $-COOH$.

(6) Condensation of two alcohols produces an ether.

Self-Test

16. Give some uses for:

   (a) alcohols _____

   (b) ketones _____

   (c) esters _____

   (d) ethers _____

17. Give the major organic product in each of the following:

(a)
$$CH_3-\overset{\displaystyle O}{\overset{\|}{C}}-O-C_2H_5 + H_2O \xrightarrow{H^+}$$ _____

(b) $CH_3-\underset{\underset{OH}{|}}{CH}-CH_3 \xrightarrow{\text{oxidation}}$ _____

(c) $CH_3OH + CH_3COOH \longrightarrow$ _____

(d)
$$CH_3-\overset{\displaystyle O}{\overset{\|}{C}}-CH_3 + NaBH_4 \longrightarrow$$ _____

New Terms

Alcohol

   An organic compound with an —OH group attached to a hydrocarbon in place of a hydrogen, for example, CH_3OH.

Aldehyde

   An organic molecule with the structure $R-\overset{O}{\overset{\|}{C}}-H$

Carbinol group

   The group of atoms, C—OH, in an organic molecule.

Carbonyl group

   The group $-\overset{O}{\overset{\|}{C}}-$

Carboxyl group

   The group $-\overset{O}{\overset{\|}{C}}-OH$

Condensation reaction
    A reaction that joins together two molecules with the simultaneous elimination of a small molecule such as water.

Ester
    An organic molecule with the structure

$$R-\overset{\displaystyle O}{\overset{\|}{C}}-O-R$$

Esterification
    The reaction of an organic acid with an alcohol to form an ester.

Saponification
    The base-catalyzed hydrolysis of an ester.

Ether
    An organic molecule with the structure $R-O-R$.

Ketone
    An organic compound with the structure

$$R-\overset{\displaystyle O}{\overset{\|}{C}}-R$$

Organic acid
    An organic molecule with the structure

$$R-\overset{\displaystyle O}{\overset{\|}{C}}-O-H$$

Primary alcohol
    An alcohol with the formula, $R-CH_2OH$.

Secondary alcohol
    An alcohol with the structure

$$R-\overset{\displaystyle R}{\underset{\displaystyle H}{\overset{|}{\underset{|}{C}}}}-OH$$

Tertiary alcohol
    An alcohol with the structure

$$R-\overset{\displaystyle R}{\underset{\displaystyle R}{\overset{|}{\underset{|}{C}}}}-OH$$

23.9   AMINES AND AMIDES: ORGANIC DERIVATIVES OF AMMONIA

Objectives

To examine this class of organic compounds that can be considered to be derivatives of ammonia.

Review

Remember the functional groups for amines and amides. Learn to distinguish between primary, secondary, and tertiary amines. Amines give basic aqueous solutions for the same reasons that solutions of ammonia are basic (the lone pair of electrons on the nitrogen atom of the amine is capable of accepting a proton from water).

Self-Test

18. Draw structural formulas for

(a) dimethyl amine   (c) urea

(b) pyridine

19. Write a chemical equation showing how dimethyl amine behaves as a base in water.

New Terms

Amide

An organic molecule with the structure $R-\overset{\overset{\displaystyle O}{\|}}{C}-NH_2$

Amine

An organic molecule derived from ammonia by replacing hydrogen atoms in NH_3 with organic groups.

Heterocycle
An organic ring structure in which one or more atoms in the ring is an element other than carbon.

23.10 POLYMERS

Objectives

To learn the general types of polymers that are formed and how their properties are related to their structure.

Review

Polymers are built by linking many small units (monomers) together to give long chains. Two polymer types exist. Addition polymers are formed by adding one monomer unit to another. Polyvinyl chloride is an example (you've probably read that vinyl chloride monomer has been linked to cancer). Condensation polymers are formed by elimination of a small molecule (e.g., H_2O) from between two monomer units. The polymeric oxoacids in Chapter 20 are condensation polymers.

Structural strength in polymers is improved by cross-linking between polymer chains (e.g., in Bakelite and rubber).

Self-Test

20. Which of the following polymers are addition polymers: polystyrene, dacron, nylon, polyvinyl chloride, teflon?

_____

New Terms

Monomer
A small molecule that combines with others to form polymers.

Polymer
A large molecule formed by linking together many smaller molecules.

Addition polymer
A polymer formed simply by the joining together, or addi-

tion, of monomer units.

Condensation polymer
A polymer formed by linking together monomers, with the simultaneous elimination of small molecules such as water.

Copolymer
A polymer formed from two or more different monomer units.

Cross linking
The joining of adjacent polymer strands to give a three-dimensional rigid structure.

Polyester
A copolymer of a difunctional alcohol with a difunctional organic acid.

Vulcanization
Treatment of natural rubber with sulfur, which forms sulfur bridges between adjacent polymer strands.

Answers to Self-Test Questions

1.(a) 4 (b) 6 (c) 8 (d) 1 (e) 2 (f) 9 (g) 3 (h) 7
2.(a) C_3H_6 (b) C_4H_{10} (c) $C_{10}H_{18}$ (d) C_5H_{12} 3.(a) one
(b) one (c) one (d) two (e) none 4. See Page 844.
5. optical isomers found for (a) and (c) 6.(a) hexane
(b) 2-methylpentane (c) 3-methylpentane
(d) 2,3-dimethylbutane (e) 2,2-dimethylbutane
7.(a) 3-methyl-2-pentene (b) 2,4-dimethyl-3-ethyl-2,4-pentadiene
8.(a) (b) (c)

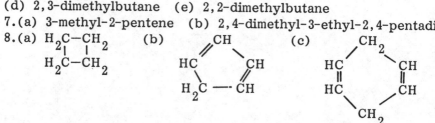

9.(a) cyclobutane (b) 1,3-cyclopentadiene
(c) 1,4-cyclohexadiene 10. 120° 11.(a) 1,2,4-trimethylbenzene
(b) 3-phenyl-1-propene (c) 2-methyl-2,3-diphenylbutane (Did you name it as a derivative of ethane?) 12. Check your answer in Table 23.5. 13.(a) $CH_3-CHBr-CH_2Br$ (b) CH_3CH_2Cl + HCl plus other substituted ethanes (c) $CH_3-C(CH_3)CN-CH_3$

14. See Page 863.   15. $CH_3-CHOH-CH_3$ + HCl $\longrightarrow$
$CH_3-CHCl-CH_3$ + H_2O 16.(a) See Pages 863-866.   (b) See
Pages 866-867.   (c) See Pages 868-870.   (d) See Page 870.
17.(a) CH_3COOH + C_2H_5OH (b) $CH_3-CO-CH_3$
(c) $CH_3-COO-CH_3$ (d) $CH_3-CHOH-CH_3$
18.(a)   (b)   (c)

$$\underset{H-N-CH_3}{\overset{CH_3}{|}}$$

$$\overset{O}{\overset{\|}{H_2N-C-NH_2}}$$

19. $(CH_3)_2NH$ + H_2O $\rightleftharpoons$ $(CH_3)_2NH_2^+$ + OH^-

20. polystyrene, polyvinyl chloride, teflon

24 BIOCHEMISTRY

Biochemistry is the study of the chemical reactions that take place in living systems, and it is one of the most important areas of chemical research today. The remarkable breakthroughs that have occurred over the past 20 years or so have produced an impressive list of Nobel Prize winners. In this chapter we examine four important kinds of biomolecules. Read the chapter with an eye toward understanding how these substances are usually composed of simple building blocks and how the structures of biomolecules control their properties and biochemical activity.

24.1 PROTEINS

Objectives

To learn how proteins are constructed from amino acids and how protein molecules twist and bend to assume shapes that control their biological functions.

Review

The important ideas developed in this section are the following:

(1) The nature of an α-amino acid. What are the main features of an α-amino acid?

(2) The peptide bond. What is it? How is it formed?

(3) The primary structure of a protein. This is the sequence of amino acids in the peptide chain.

(4) The secondary structure of a protein. The α-helix is an example. How is the structure held in place?

(5) The tertiary structure of a protein. This is found in globular proteins and is controlled by hydrogen bonding, ionic interactions, interactions of nonpolar groups with the polar solvent (water), and the formation of disulfide bridges between cysteine molecules at different places along the chain.

(6) The quaternary structure of some proteins. This concerns the packing of globular proteins into more complex structures.

In addition, the structure of heme is described. The main thing to remember is that the heme group contains an iron atom held in a square planar ligand called a porphyrin. A similar structure is found for chlorophyll.

Self-Test (Use a separate sheet of paper to answer the following three questions.)

1. Sketch the general structure of an α-amino acid.

2. Draw the backbone for the primary structure of a tripeptide.

3. What is a disulfide bridge?

New Terms

Alpha amino acid
    A molecule with the structure

$$R-\underset{\underset{NH_2}{|}}{CH}-\overset{\overset{O}{\|}}{C}-OH$$

Alpha helix (α-helix)
    The coil structure assumed by a polypeptide chain.

Difunctional molecule
    A molecule having two functional groups.

Peptide
    A polymer of α-amino acids. Proteins are composed of peptides.

Peptide bond (Peptide linkage)
    The structure

$$
\cdots -\overset{\displaystyle \overset{\textstyle O}{\|}}{C}-\underset{\displaystyle \underset{\textstyle H}{|}}{N}- \cdots
$$

Polypeptide
    A peptide composed of many α-amino acid units. Proteins are polypeptides.

Protein
    A polymer of α-amino acids that has a specific biological function.

Primary structure
    The sequence of the various amino acids in a polypeptide or protein.

Secondary structure
    The coiling that takes place in a polypeptide chain.

Tertiary structure
    The way a coiled polypeptide chain folds to give a globular protein.

Quaternary structure
    The way certain folded polypeptide chains pack together in a complex protein.

Disulfide bridge
    A bridge between portions of polypeptide chains. It is created by the formation of $-S-S-$ between adjacent chains, and this holds the polypeptide chains in a particular configuration.

Porphyrin
    A square planar ligand structure that is found in a number of biologically important molecules such as heme and chlorophyll.

Heme group
    A porphyrin structure having an Fe^{2+} ion in the center. It is responsible for hemoglobin's ability to carry oxygen and for myoglobin's ability to hold oxygen until needed for metabolism.

24.2 ENENZYMES

Objectives

To see how proteins serve as catalysts to promote very specific biochemical reactions.

Review

The most important idea developed here is the "lock and key" relationship between the enzyme and the molecule upon which it acts (the substrate). This is illustrated for chymotrypsin, but holds for other enzyme-substrate interactions as well.

Review the mechanism of enzyme inhibition.

Self-Test

4. How is an enzyme irreversibly poisoned?

_____

5. What is competitive inhibition?

_____

New Terms

Coenzyme
A substance needed by an enzyme in order to function.

Enzyme
A biological catalyst that is very effective and highly specific for a particular reaction.

Inhibition
The blocking of enzyme activity by blockage of the active enzyme site.

Substrate
The substance acted upon by an enzyme.

24.3 CARBOHYDRATES

Objectives

To examine the structure and properties of the class of compounds called carbohydrates.

Review

These substances are called carbohydrates because their formulas are often of the form, $C_n(H_2O)_m$. They are in fact condensation polymers of monosaccharides (polyhydroxy alcohols also containing an aldehyde or ketone functional group). You should know that the monosaccharides usually exist in cyclic structures. Glucose, one of the most important monosaccharides, can exist in two forms (α-D-glucose and β-D-glucose).

Sucrose is a disaccharide. You should know the general features of the glycoside linkage.

Starch and cellulose are polymers of glucose units. Starch is formed from α-D-glucose units; cellulose from β-D-glucose units.

Self-Test

6. What are the molecular formulas for the following?

    (a) sucrose _____   (b) glucose _____

7. What is the empirical formula for amylose (starch)?_____

8. On a separate sheet of paper, sketch the formation of a glycoside linkage. Compare your answer to Figure 24.15 on Page 891.

9. What characterizes the names of carbohydrates?

New Terms

Carbohydrate

An organic compound that contains carbon, hydrogen, and oxygen and in which the ratio of hydrogen to oxygen is 2 to 1. This gives it a general formula $C_n(H_2O)_m$, although there are no intact water molecules in the structure. An example is sucrose (table sugar) $C_{12}H_{22}O_{11}$.

Deoxyribose
A five-carbon sugar that is one of the building blocks of DNA.

Glycoside linkage
The $-C-O-C-$ linkage that holds sugar molecules together in a polysaccharide.

Monosaccharide (Simple sugar)
A simple sugar unit that combines with others to form polysaccharide chains in more complex sugars such as sucrose, starch, and cellulose.

Polysaccharide
A polymer formed from simple, monomeric sugar molecules.

Ribose
A five-carbon sugar that is one of the building blocks of RNA.

24.4   LIPIDS

Objectives

To study the nature of this class of compounds and to see how lipids are employed by organisms.

Review

Lipids are water insoluble substances found in fats and in cell membranes. Neutral lipids are esters of glycerol and fatty acids (long hydrocarbon chains with a carboxyl group on one end). Saponification of a triglyceride gives glycerol and the anions of the fatty acids. The latter constitute a soap. Review micelle formation in solutions of soap.

Phospholipids contain two fatty acid molecules plus phosphoric acid esterified to glycerol. The phosphoric acid is also esterified to another alcohol. Phospholipids are an important component of cell membranes, forming a bilayer structure.

Another class of lipids are steroids which possess a fused ring system and display very high biological activity.

Self-Test (Use a separate sheet of paper to answer the next four questions.)

10. Draw the general structure of a nonpolar lipid. Write a reaction to show what happens when the lipid molecule is saponified. Check your answer on Pages 893 and 894 of the text.

11. Sketch a micelle formed from anions of fatty acids. You can check your answer on Page 895 of the text.

12. Sketch a bilayer structure typically formed by phospholipids. Check your answer on Page 896.

13. Draw the fused ring structure characteristic of steroids. Check your answer on Page 896.

New Terms

Lipid
    A water-insoluble substance that can be extracted from cells by nonpolar solvents.

Fatty acid
    An organic acid having a long hydrocarbon-chain tail.

Phospholipid
    An ester of glycerol, two fatty acids, and phosphoric acid, which in turn is esterified to another alcohol. Phospholipids are found in cell membranes.

Bilayer structure
    The structure of a cell membrane in which the nonpolar tails of two layers of phospholipids face each other while the polar heads face the aqueous environment on either side of the bilayer.

Steroid
    A lipid with a complex ring structure that possesses very high biological activity.

Triglyceride
    An ester of glycerol and three fatty acid molecules.

24.5 NUCLEIC ACIDS

Objectives

To study the composition of nucleic acids (DNA and RNA) and to see how the double helix structure of DNA can account for the transmission of genetic information from one generation to another.

Review

Key points to learn from this section are that nucleic acids are composed of three parts: a nitrogenous base, a five-carbon sugar (ribose or deoxyribose), and phosphoric acid. You should familiarize yourself with the structures of ribose and deoxyribose.

A nucleoside is formed from the nitrogenous base and the sugar. Addition of the phosphoric acid gives a nucleotide - the monomer unit in the DNA or RNA chain. Nucleotides are linked to give the nucleic acid.

In DNA two nucleic acid strands intertwine to give the double helix. These are matched and held together by base-pairing through hydrogen bond formation. Replication involves untwining the two strands and building new complementary strands against each of them, in which the original nuclei acid strands serve as templates.

Self-Test (Use a separate sheet of paper to answer the next two questions. Check your answers by referring to the text.)

14. Sketch the structure of ribose and deoxyribose.

15. Sketch the structure of (a) a nucleoside; (b) a nucleotide.

16. Which bases are able to pair in DNA? _____

_____

New Terms

Nucleotide

The units that form the building blocks of nucleic acids. They are composed of even simpler units - a five-carbon sugar, phosphoric acid, and a nitrogenous base.

Nucleic acid
    A polymer of nucleotide units. Varieties include DNA and
    RNA.

DNA
    Deoxyribonucleic acid, the carrier of genetic information to
    a cell nucleus.

RNA
    Ribonucleic acid. A type of nucleic acid involved in protein
    synthesis.

Double helix
    The intertwining of complementary DNA strands.

24.6 PROTEIN SYNTHESIS

Objectives

    To learn how DNA in the nucleus of a cell serves to pro-
    vide the key to determining the primary structure of
    proteins.

Review

    Study the functions of DNA, mRNA, and tRNA as well as
the pairing of bases between DNA and RNA. Notice that uracil
is found in RNA instead of thymine.

Self-Test

17. Use the DNA/mRNA base pairing scheme to deduce the base
    sequence that would occur in mRNA if the following base
    sequence occurred in DNA.

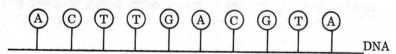

DNA

18. Use the genetic code in Table 24.3 to identify the amino acid sequence that could be constructed from mRNA with the following base sequence.

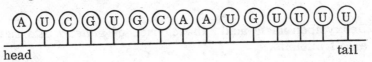

head   tail

_____

19. What amino acid sequence would occur if the fourth base were removed from the mRNA in Question 18?

_____

New Terms

Codon
    A sequence of three bases along an m-RNA strand that serves as a code for a particular amino acid in a growing polypeptide chain.

Genetic code
    The base sequences found in m-RNA that specify the various amino acids used in building protein molecules.

Genetic disease
    A "disease" or malfunction of cells that is caused by a fault in the DNA.

Messenger RNA (m-RNA)
    A form of RNA that carries the code for the sequence of amino acids in proteins from the DNA inside the cell nucleus to locations outside the nucleus where protein synthesis takes place.

Transfer RNA (t-RNA)
    A small RNA unit that carries amino acids to their proper location along m-RNA during protein synthesis.

Answers to Self-Test Questions

1. R—CH—COOH
       |
       NH$_2$

2. H$_2$N—CH—C—NH—CH—C—NH—CH—C—OH
          | || | || | ||
          R$_1$ O   R$_2$ O   R$_3$ O

3. R$_1$—S—S—R$_2$ where R$_1$ and R$_2$ belong to different parts of the protein backbone

4. When the inhibitor becomes permanently bound to the enzyme active site, the enzyme molecule becomes inoperative.

5. There is a competition between the substrate and inhibitor for the active site on the enzyme.

6. (a) $C_{12}H_{22}O_{11}$, or $C_{12}(H_2O)_{11}$ (b) $C_6H_{12}O_6$ or $C_6(H_2O)_6$

7. $C_6H_{10}O_5$ or $C_6(H_2O)_5$

8. See Figure 24.15.

9. They end in <u>ose</u> (e.g., suc<u>rose</u>).

10. See Pages 893 and 894.

11. See Page 895.

12. See Page 896.

13. See Page 896.

14. See Page 891.

15. See Page 898.

16. cytosine and quanine (C and G); thymine and adenine (T and A)

17.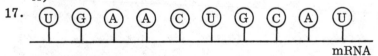

    mRNA

18. ile-val-gln-cys-phe

19. ile-cys-asn-val